35/58

2/57

MICROBIOLOGY

General and Applied

MICROBIOLOGY

GENERAL AND APPLIED

By WILLIAM BOWEN SARLES
WILLIAM CARROLL FRAZIER
JOE BRANSFORD WILSON
STANLEY GLENN KNIGHT

DEPARTMENT OF BACTERIOLOGY
UNIVERSITY OF WISCONSIN

HARPER & BROTHERS, PUBLISHERS
NEW YORK

MICROBIOLOGY, General and Applied

CONTENTS

v

PART II.   THE PHYSIOLOGY OF MICROORGANISMS

PART III.   CULTIVATION, OBSERVATION AND CLASSIFICATION OF MICROORGANISMS

PREFACE

THIS book is for the use of students who are beginning a study of microbiology or bacteriology. It is realized that the majority of the students enrolled in their first course in this field of study will not become microbiologists or bacteriologists. For this reason an attempt is made to emphasize the application of microbiology to agriculture, to industry, and to the home. Some consideration is given to the disease-producing activities of microorganisms and to the general subject of immunity, but, unlike most books on general microbiology, this book deals mainly with the nondisease-producing microorganisms and the relation of their activities to the lives of plants, animals, and human beings.

For the benefit of those students who wish to obtain more information on any of the subjects considered in this book, a list of references is given at the end of each chapter to books, review articles, and papers which may be used as a starting point for a more thorough study of each subject.

This first printed edition has been prepared on the basis of knowledge gained through the use of five mimeographed editions, which were published in 1939, 1940, 1947, 1948, and 1949, respectively. Dr. Janet McCarter Woolley was a co-author of the first two editions; much of the material in PART VIII, Infectious Diseases of Animals and Plants, represents a revision of material prepared originally by Mrs. Woolley.

The help of Dr. G. A. Rohlich, Professor of Hydraulic and Sanitary Engineering, in the preparation of Chapters 22 and 23, is gratefully acknowledged. We also wish to acknowledge with thanks the aid of Professor A. J. Riker, Department of Plant Pathology, in the preparation of Chapter 33.

The authors also wish to thank their fellow members of the Department of Bacteriology for helpful criticisms and suggestions.

WILLIAM B. SARLES
WILLIAM C. FRAZIER
JOE B. WILSON
STANLEY G. KNIGHT

Madison, Wisconsin
November, 1950

PART I

An Introduction
to the Microorganisms

Microorganisms are living things so small that they can be seen only with the aid of a microscope. They are widely distributed in nature and are responsible for many physical and chemical changes of importance to the life of plants, of animals, and of human beings. Altogether too many students believe that all "microbes" or "germs" are harmful, and that they are an entirely undesirable group of living things. While it is true that some microorganisms produce disease, the great majority of them do not. In fact, the activities of these hosts of nondisease-producing microorganisms make possible the continued existence of plants and animals on the earth. In addition, many kinds of microorganisms are used in industries to manufacture products of great value to man. But the activities of nondisease-producing microorganisms are not always desirable. Foods may be spoiled as a result of their attack, fabrics and fibers may be rotted, and fermentation processes may be upset by undesirable organisms. From a practical point of view we are interested in the microorganisms because of the things that they do, the physical and chemical changes which they produce. Also, we are interested in ways and means to control undesirable organisms and to put the useful ones to work; but a study of the activities and the means for control of microorganisms must be based upon knowledge of their nature and life processes.

Microbiology or bacteriology is a branch of biological science which deals with the bacteria and related forms of life. Most of these related living organisms are not similar to the bacteria in form or structure, but they are included in a study of microbiology because often they are found living in association with the bacteria, and because their activities frequently are closely related to those of the bacteria.

It is not possible in a book of this size to describe in detail all of the different kinds of bacteria, rickettsiae, viruses, yeasts, molds, algae, and protozoa; nor is it considered necessary for a student interested in the practical applications of microbiology to memorize detailed classifications of these forms of life. A brief outline of the classification of these forms is given in Appendix A, and it is suggested that this outline be studied in order to gain some knowledge of the general taxonomic relationships of these organisms. It is the purpose of the first seven chapters of this book to describe briefly the distinctive characteristics of the bacteria and of the related forms of life that have been mentioned.

1. TRUE BACTERIA

WHERE BACTERIA ARE FOUND, AND WHAT THEY ARE

Bacteria are probably the most widely distributed of all living organisms. They have been found in the atmosphere up to four miles above the earth, and in mud three miles beneath the surface of the sea. Some kinds of bacteria have been isolated from the water of hot springs at a temperature of 75° C., others from antarctic ice. A fertile soil often contains as many as 100,000,000 bacteria per gram. With the facts in mind that an acre-foot of soil weighs approximately 2,000,000 pounds and that there are 453.6 grams in a pound, some idea can be obtained of the truly tremendous numbers of bacteria in the soil.

Actually, there are comparatively few places in nature where bacteria cannot be found. The blood of normal animals, tissues in the physiological interior of healthy animals and plants, deep layers of soil and rocks, and the pits of active volcanoes are about the only places in nature where bacteria are not commonly found.

Before studying the agencies that affect the life of bacteria and the chemical and physical changes caused by these microorganisms, it is necessary to become acquainted with their general nature, to get some idea of what they are.

Bacteria are microscopic, unicellular fungi of the class *Schizomycetes;* they contain no chlorophyll, and reproduce asexually by fission. At present, the "true" bacteria are believed to be the smallest and least complex in structure of all living things that can be seen with the ordinary compound microscope and induced to grow on artificial culture media. The very fact that

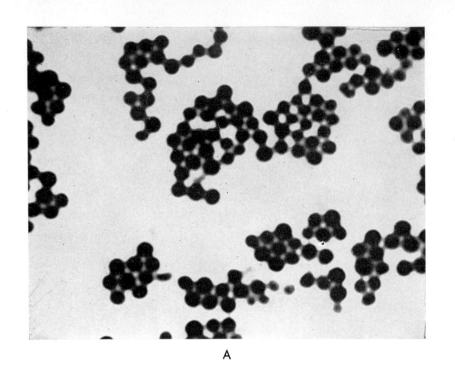

A

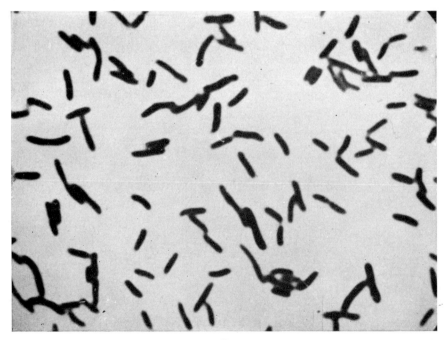

B

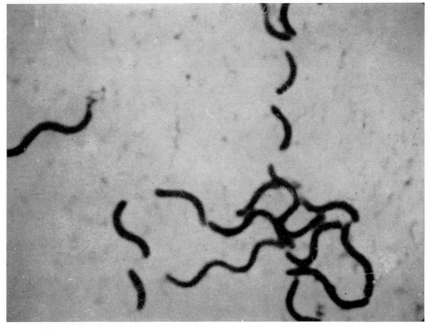

C

FIGURE 1. Light microscope pictures showing the three common shapes of true bacteria. **A,** Coccus. **B,** Bacillus. **C,** Spirillum. The cells were made more visible by staining with a dye. Since the bacteria were growing when stained, some of the cells are loosely joined to other cells to form short chains or clumps. Enlarged 2000X. (From J. Nowak.)

they are so minute in size and so simple in structure makes it difficult to classify them, but they are placed in the Plant Kingdom because as a group they exhibit closer relationships to the blue-green algae and to the fungi than to the protozoa.

Bacteria are divided into two main groups, "true" bacteria and "higher" bacteria, on the basis of their structure and manner of growth. Some bacteria, although they exhibit the main characteristics of the class *Schizomycetes,* possess certain structures or develop in manners similar to other forms of life. Thus, some bacteria resemble certain of the protozoa, some are alga-like, some exhibit a few of the characteristics of the slime molds, and others are definitely mold-like. These forms are referred to as "higher" bacteria because of their relationships to more highly developed living things. The "true" bacteria, which have been studied most extensively, and which are apparently of greatest importance, are the most primitive members of the class and show no well-defined relationships to any of the so-called "higher"

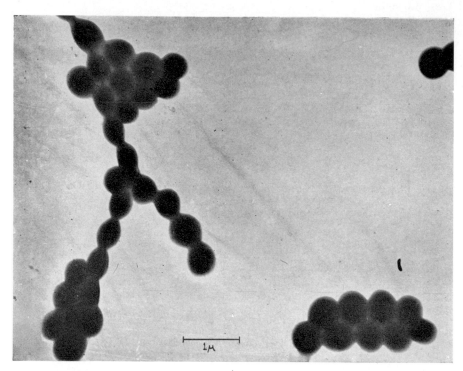

A

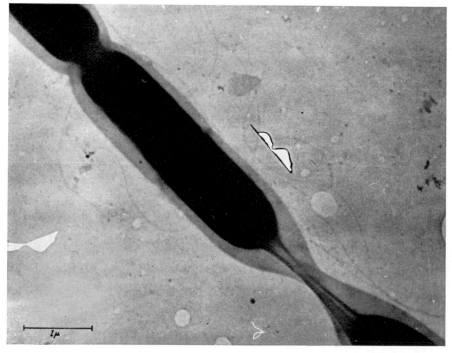

B

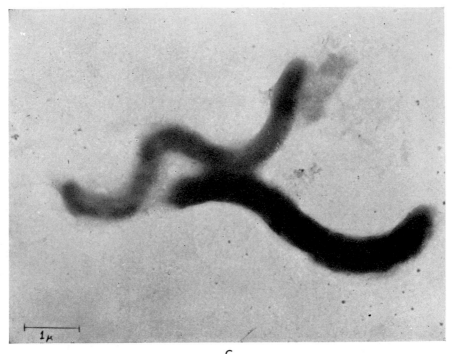

C

FIGURE 2. Electron microscope pictures showing the three common forms of true bacteria. **A,** Coccus. **B,** Bacillus. **C,** Spirillum. Note that some of the cocci and bacilli are in the process of dividing and thin strands of protoplasm connect incompletely divided cells. Enlarged about 18,750X, 21,000X, and 18,750X respectively. (A. Mudd and Anderson, S.A.B. No. 87; B. Johnson, S.A.B. No. 58; C. Polevitsky and Picard, S.A.B. No. 117.)

forms of life. The "true" bacteria, or *Eubacteriales,* are our first, and main concern.[1] The "higher" bacteria are described in Chapter 7.

THE SHAPES OF TRUE BACTERIA

The cells of true bacteria exist in any one of three common forms: the spheroidal, or **coccus;** the cylindrical, or **bacillus;** and the spirillar, or **spirillum.**

The coccus form of bacterial cell is not truly spherical, but as a rule the cells are spheroidal. Under certain conditions, some of the cocci may become elongated so as to appear almost cylindrical, but when returned to their original environment they again become spheroidal. Bean-shaped and cone-shaped cocci are fairly common.

Bacilli are cylindrical, or rod-shaped, cells. In some bacillus forms the

[1] An outline of the classification of bacteria may be found in Appendix B.

transverse is almost as long as the longitudinal axis, but in others the cell may be from three to ten times as long as its diameter. The ends of bacilli may be square-cut, rounded, or even club-shaped. Many bacilli are quite uniform in diameter throughout their entire length, while others are boat-shaped or show irregularities of one sort or another. Some bacilli are straight rods, but others have a tendency to bend.

The cells of spirillar forms are characteristically bent or coiled in a spiral form. Some are comma-shaped; others are long and coiled like a corkscrew. The cell walls of the comma-shaped cells, which are known as vibrios, and of the spirillar forms, which are called spirilla, are rigid and do not allow much bending of the cells.

The young, active cells of true bacteria are remarkably constant in shape when cultivated in a constant, uniform environment. For example, cultures of certain lactic acid-producing bacilli have been kept alive through transfers to fresh media every month for more than twenty years. Young cells of these cultures look the same today as cells of similar age at the time the cultures were first isolated. Of course variations in the form of these bacteria can be induced by changing the environment; also, old cells in a culture do not have the same appearance as young ones, but young cells under constant environmental conditions are quite constant in morphology.

Figure 1[2] shows the three common forms of "true" bacteria as they appear when photographed through a compound microscope employing transmitted, visible light. Figure 2[3] illustrates the three common forms of "true" bacteria as shown by the electron microscope.

Figure 3 presents a diagrammatic comparison between the working principles of the compound light microscope and the electron microscope.

Since bacteria are much too small to be seen with the unaided eye, the microscope is one of the most important tools of the bacteriologist. The science of bacteriology owes much to the physicists who have worked to perfect the modern compound microscope. All compound microscopes operate on the same basic principles: the object to be magnified is illuminated by a beam of light that has been intensified by condensing lenses; an enlarged image of the illuminated object is formed by objective lenses, and this enlarged image is further magnified by an ocular lens that works with the eye much as a very strong magnifying glass or jeweler's lens. The usual compound microscope can be used effectively to magnify objects 1000 to

[2] The photomicrographs in Figure 1 are taken from J. Nowak. *Documenta Microbiologica.* Jena, Gustav Fischer, 1927; and are reproduced with the permission of the publishers. Photomicrographs in all subsequent figures credited to Nowak are reproduced from this same book.

[3] Illustrations which have an **S.A.B.** number were obtained from the Committee on Materials for Visual Instruction in Microbiology, Society of American Bacteriologists.

2000 times, but because of limitations of the lens systems, and of the length of visible light waves, it is not possible to obtain greater powers of magnification. To some extent the limitations of magnification of the light microscope have been overcome by the electron microscope. The electron microscope is based on the same principles as the light microscope but the mechanics of magnification are different. The electron microscope "illuminates" the object with a beam of electrons instead of a beam of light and the electron beam is focused by magnets instead of lenses because the electrons cannot pass through glass. Electron beams have smaller wave lengths than visible light rays hence they can "illuminate" smaller objects, and the images produced can be magnified to a greater extent. Since an electron beam is not visible, the image formed is projected on a fluorescent screen. The electron microscope magnifies objects 10,000 to 80,000 times and has contributed much to bacteriology.

The Size and Weight of Bacterial Cells

Bacteria are almost inconceivably small. Their size is expressed in terms of microns. One micron, designated by the symbol μ, is equal to 1/1,000,000 of a meter, or 1/1000 millimeter, which is about 1/25,400 inch. Within the group of true bacteria there exists a tremendous difference in size between the smallest and the largest forms. One of the smallest bacteria, *Dialister pneumosintes*, is rod-shaped and is from 0.15 to 0.3 μ in length. One of the largest of the true bacteria, *Spirillum volutans*, is 1.5 μ in diameter and from 13 to 15 μ in length. These species represent extremes in size. The cocci average about 0.5 to 1.0 μ in diameter; the bacilli average approximately 0.5 μ in diameter and 1.5 μ in length. Different species of the spirilla vary so much in size that averages of their dimensions would mean little.

Perhaps it may be easier to visualize the minuteness of bacteria by making a few comparisons. If 50,000 cocci having an average diameter of 0.5 μ were arranged in a straight chain, it would be found that the length of this chain would be only one inch; a chain containing 100 cocci of this size would stretch 50 microns—approximately the thickness of this page. An average coccus magnified 500 times becomes not much larger than the period at the end of this sentence. An average man magnified to the same degree would be over one-half of a mile tall and a sixth of a mile broad across his shoulders.

The weight of a bacterial cell is extremely small. On the average, bacteria contain from 70 to 85 per cent of water. Their specific gravity ranges from 1.04 to 1.10. The weight of an individual bacillus of average size is approximately 2×10^{-12} grams, which means that about 500,000,000,000 cells

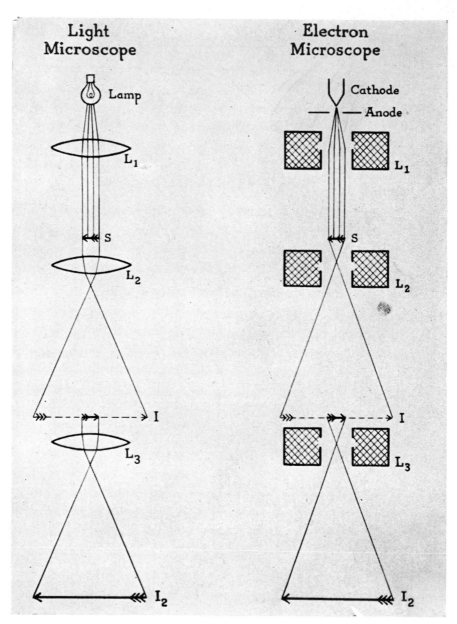

FIGURE 3. A comparison of the optical system of the compound light microscope and that of the RCA electron microscope. A system of magnets in the electron microscope serve the same function as the glass lenses in the light microscope. In the diagrams, L_1 is the condensing lens, L_2 is the objective lens, and L_3 is the ocular or projector lens. S is the object, I the primary image, and I_2 is the final highly magnified image. (Courtesy of Radio Corporation of America; S.A.B. No. 31.)

would be needed to yield one gram of moist, undried cell substance. The number of bacteria necessary to make up the 300 to 500 pounds of bacterial cells that exist in an acre-foot of fertile soil is therefore truly tremendous.

CELL SURFACE OF BACTERIA

The surface area of living cells such as bacteria is of great importance in determining how rapidly a given number or mass of cells can absorb food and cause chemical changes. In general, the greater the surface area in proportion to the weight of the cell, the greater will be the rapidity with which food may be absorbed per unit mass of cells. This relation of surface area to cell mass is so important that it must be thoroughly understood in order to comprehend the reasons for the tremendous quantities of foods utilized and the amazing chemical changes caused by bacteria. Perhaps the following development of the concept will help.

Consider a cube of metal which measures exactly one centimeter on each edge. Such a cube would have a surface area of 6 square centimeters. If this cube were cut up into 1,000 cubes, each 0.1 centimeter on each edge, the total surface area of the 1,000 cubes would be $6 \times (0.1)^2 \times 1,000$, or 60 square centimeters. Continuing this subdivision of the cubes would give the results recorded in Table 1.

TABLE 1.   Relation of Size to Surface Area of Cubes[4]

Length of Each Edge of Cube	Number of Cubes	Total Surface of Cubes
1 cm.	1	6 cm.^{2}
0.1 cm.	1,000	60 cm.^{2}
0.01 cm.	1,000,000	600 cm.^{2}
0.001 cm.	1,000,000,000	6,000 cm.^{2}
0.0001 cm. (1 micron)	1,000,000,000,000	60,000 cm.^{2}

Thus, by dividing the original cube, which had a surface area of 6 square centimeters, and, for purposes of description, a weight of 6 grams, into 1,000,000,000,000 cubes, each with a surface area of 6 square microns, the ratio of surface area to weight has been increased tremendously.

1. With one cube, 1 cm. on each edge:

$$\frac{\text{Ratio of surface}}{\text{area to weight}} = \frac{\text{Surface area}}{\text{Weight}} = \frac{6 \text{ cm.}^2}{6 \text{ gm.}} = 1$$

2. With 1,000,000,000,000 cubes, each 1 μ on each edge:

$$\frac{\text{Ratio of surface}}{\text{area to weight}} = \frac{\text{Surface area}}{\text{Weight}} = \frac{60,000 \text{ cm.}^2}{6 \text{ gm.}} = 10,000$$

[4] From C. S. Mudge and F. R. Smith, *A fundamental approach to bacteriology.* San Francisco, J. W. Stacey, Inc., 1939, pp. 11–13.

From these simple calculations it is evident that the total surface area of the cubes, as well as the ratio of surface area to weight, has been increased 10,000 times by dividing the original cube into 1,000,000,000,000 cubes of equal size.

These calculations may be applied to living things with the following results:

1. For a 220-pound man:

$$\text{Ratio of surface area to weight} = \frac{\text{Surface area}}{\text{Weight}} = \frac{24,000 \text{ cm.}^2}{100,000 \text{ gm.}} = 0.24$$

2. For *Escherichia coli*, a common bacterium that grows in the intestinal tract of all warm-blooded animals:

$$\text{Ratio of surface area to weight} = \frac{\text{Surface area}}{\text{Weight}} = \frac{1 \times 10^{-7} \text{ cm.}^2}{2 \times 10^{-12} \text{ gm.}} = 50,000$$

From these figures it may be seen that the ratio of the surface area to weight is about 200,000 times greater for the bacterial cell than for the body of a 220-pound man. This relationship must be kept in mind when considering the activities of bacteria. The smaller the cell, the greater will be its surface area in proportion to its weight, and the greater will be the rapidity with which it can absorb food and produce chemical changes.

THE CELL STRUCTURE OF BACTERIA

It has been pointed out that the true bacteria are some of the smallest and perhaps the simplest forms of life, but this statement is not entirely accurate. The extremely small size and the absence of recognized sexual reproduction in the true bacteria create an illusion of simplicity. It is known that the chemical composition of the protoplasm of bacterial cells is as complex as that of other living cells. Furthermore, recent work indicates that the biochemistry of the life processes of true bacteria is in many ways similar to or even more complex than that of other living cells. Failure of bacteriologists to recognize and describe a multiplicity of structures in bacterial cells may be regarded as an indication of the deficiency of the methods which have been employed in studies of bacterial cell structure. The development and proper use of new techniques may reveal structures in bacterial cells that previously employed methods have failed to demonstrate. Any description of the structure of the cells of true bacteria may have to be altered markedly as the results of studies now underway in many laboratories become known.

The Outer Coverings of the Cell

Carefully performed experiments have shown that true bacterial cells possess well-defined outer coverings, at least one of which is a fairly rigid structure which holds the cell in shape. Although much remains to be done in order to determine more definitely the structure of the cell's outer coverings, they appear to be made up of three layers. The inner layer, or **cytoplasmic membrane,** consists largely of lipoids and lipoproteins. Probably this layer is built up gradually by the cytoplasm as the cell matures; it is quite flexible, and has the property of differential permeability. This means that it will allow water and substances in true solution to diffuse through it at varying rates, but will not allow the passage of substances which are not in true solution. The middle layer, or **cell wall,** is the rigid part of the outer

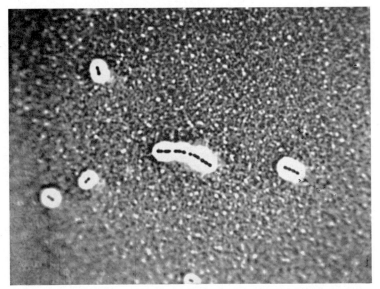

FIGURE 4. Photomicrograph showing capsules around streptococci. The capsules around the cells are clear; the cells and background are stained. Enlarged 1000X. (Courtesy of W. D. Frost.)

coverings of the cell. Its chemical composition may vary in different species of bacteria since cellulose, hemicelluloses, and chitin have all been reported as the main constituents of the cell wall. Possibly the cell wall is also differentially permeable. The third, or outside layer of the cell's outer coverings is known as the **slime layer.** The thickness of this layer varies with different species and with the conditions of cultivation.

Capsules

If the slime layer surrounding a bacterial cell is thick, gummy, and mucilaginous it is called a **capsule.** In most cases the capsule is composed of complex carbohydrates and uronic acids, but in some species it consists of proteins. The capsule protects the cell against adverse conditions and serves to hold groups of cells together. The possession of a capsule is frequently of great practical importance. Some species of bacteria form capsules more commonly than others. Figure 4 is a photomicrograph of encapsulated streptococci.

Bacterial Protoplasm

In general, the structure and composition of the protoplasm of bacterial cells is similar to that of other living cells. However, in the bacteria it is

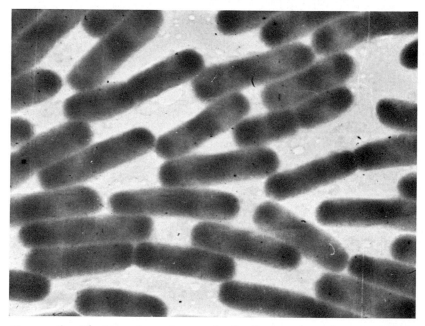

FIGURE 5.   Electron photomicrograph of cells in an actively growing culture of *Escherichia coli*. The dark areas in the cells may be nuclear material. Enlarged 8500X. (Courtesy J. Hillier, S. Mudd, and A. G. Smith, and Radio Corporation of America.)

very difficult to demonstrate the presence of a definite, particulate **nucleus** in the protoplasm of the cell. The most recent work on this problem indicates that the bacteria possess some sort of nucleus, but either it is too small to be seen with an ordinary microscope, or the nucleoplasm is not contained in a structural unit similar to the nucleus of most other living cells. Microchemical tests and electron microscope studies have shown that some bacteria possess a well-defined nucleus or several nuclei. Figure 5 is an electron photomicrograph which shows intracellular, dense bodies that may be nuclei.

Probably the most important physical characteristics of bacterial protoplasm are that it has a high moisture content (70 to 85 per cent), that it is
colloidal, and that the cells of many species contain well defined **granules.**
These granules may be of the metachromatic type, meaning that, when
treated with a dye such as methylene blue, they stain more deeply, or perhaps a different color, than the rest of the cell's protoplasm. These granules
apparently consist of volutin, which is ribonucleic acid, a salt of nucleic

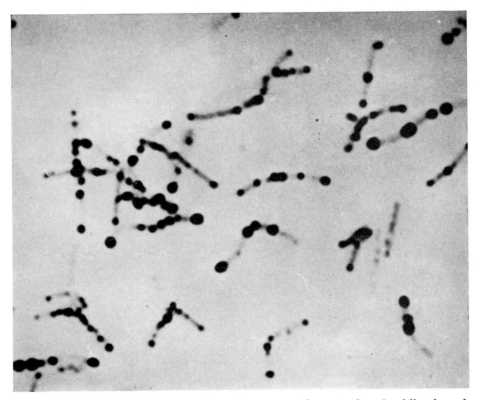

FIGURE 6.   Metachromatic granules. These unevenly stained and oddly shaped
cells of *Corynebacterium diphtheriae* contain deeply-stained metachromatic granules. Enlarged 2000X. (From J. Nowak.)

acid. Another type of granule found in some species consists of glycogen or
iogen, which are starch-like substances. Fat globules are also found in the
cells of some bacteria, whereas still others are known to contain granules of
sulfur. Certain species, for example, *Corynebacterium diphtheriae* and
Lactobacillus bulgaricus, are noted for the presence of metachromatic
granules in their cells, and this property serves as an aid in their recognition. The peculiar vacuolated appearance of the cells of certain root-nodule
bacteria and of *Azotobacter* is due to the presence of fat globules. The exact

function of these granules and fat globules is not known, but they are usually thought of as reserve substances. Figure 6 is a photomicrograph of cells containing metachromatic granules.

Endospores

The ability to form an **endospore** (spore within a cell) is possessed by some, but not all, of the bacillus forms and is extremely rare in the cocci and spirilla. Practically all of the bacteria which form endospores produce one spore per cell. With almost all spore-forming bacteria, conditions most

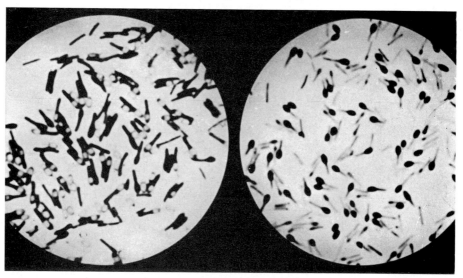

FIGURE 7. Photomicrographs showing endospores in a bacillus. Two different methods of staining were used to demonstrate spores in the same organism. One method stained the cells and left the spores clear, the other stained the spores and left the cells comparatively clear. Note that the spores of this organism are wider than the cells and are formed in a terminal position. Enlarged 1330X. (From J. Nowak.)

favorable to growth are also conducive to endospore formation, and spores are formed as the cells in a culture mature. Spore-forming bacteria go through a period of active growth and reproduction before they produce spores.

It is possible to cause some species of spore-forming bacteria to lose their ability to form endospores. This may be accomplished by continued cultivation of the bacteria under conditions unfavorable to spore formation. The loss in spore-forming power thus induced may be transient or permanent. It is possible that some species, now believed to be unable to form spores, may produce them under conditions as yet undetermined.

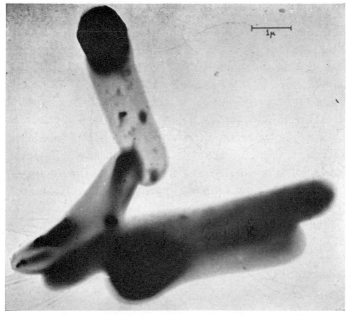

A

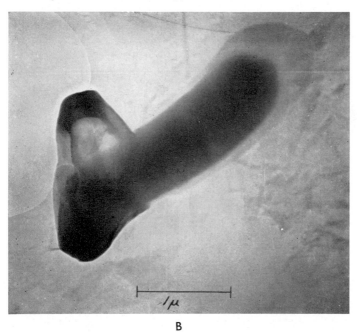

B

FIGURE 8. Electron photomicrographs of endospores and germinating spores. **A.** Cells of *Clostridium tetani* showing terminal or "drumstick" endospores. Magnified 10,000X. (Mudd and Anderson, S.A.B. No. 63.) **B.** Germinating cell of *Bacillus mycoides* growing out of ruptured spore. Magnified 23,330X. (Knaysi, Baker, and Hillier, S.A.B. No. 205.)

There has been considerable controversy over the mechanism of spore formation, but the most recent work on this problem has demonstrated the occurrence of certain definite steps in the process. At first, the protoplasm of the cells, which has been quite homogeneous during the period of active growth, begins to show definite granulation as the cells mature. Gradually one end of each cell becomes free from granules by a displacement of the granules with a homogeneous, denser mass of protoplasm. This mass, or primordium as it is termed, becomes surrounded by a thin membrane and continues to increase in density. Within the primordium a smaller, denser mass—the prespore—is now formed rapidly. The prespore surrounds itself with a membrane and migrates slowly to the position it will finally occupy in the cell. The endospore thus formed possesses a thickened wall which resists the penetration of dyes; it also has a thinner, more flexible outer wall. The significance of spore formation is incompletely understood, but it is known that the endospore contains the hereditary units needed to perpetuate the species.

The position of the endospore within the bacterial cell is fairly constant in each spore-forming species; in some, the spore is found in the center of the cell, whereas in others, it may be located in a subterminal or terminal position. Some species characteristically form spheroidal spores, whereas in others the endospores are ellipsoidal. In many species the endospore is no larger in diameter than the cell, but in others it is large enough to bulge the wall and cause the cell to assume a characteristic boat, spindle, or drumstick shape. Figure 7 shows endospores of bacteria.

When the endospore matures, the remaining portions of the cell disintegrate, and the spore is set free. It may remain viable for long periods of time as it is much more resistant to drying and other adverse conditions than the vegetative cells of the species. When the spore is placed under conditions favorable for germination, it swells and becomes less dense in appearance. In some species, the spore wall is absorbed or digested as the spore germinates, whereas in others, the spore wall ruptures and the vegetative cell which emerges sheds the ruptured wall. Electron photomicrographs of endospores and of a germinating spore are shown in Figure 8.

Inasmuch as each bacillus forms but one endospore, which may germinate to form only one vegetative cell, spore formation is simply a means of perpetuating the species; it is reproduction without multiplication.

Flagella

Bacteria possessing flagella are capable of moving under their own power. Very few of the cocci are flagellated, but a large proportion of the bacilli

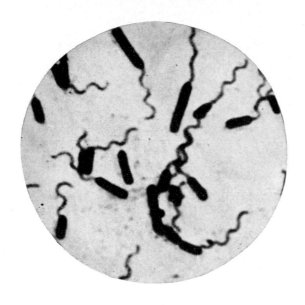

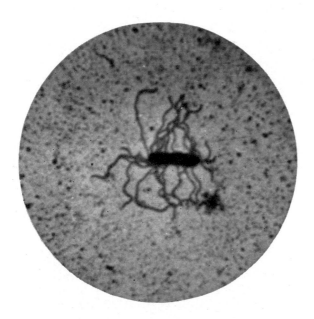

FIGURE 9. Photomicrographs showing two types of flagellation: the bacteria on the top are monotrichous; those on the bottom are peritrichous. In both instances the flagella have been made visible by coating them with a dye. Enlarged about 2000X. (Upper from J. Nowak; lower by M. C. Shepard.)

and most of the spirilla have flagella. Bacteria which lack flagella are moved about by molecular bombardment—Brownian movement—or by currents in the liquid in which they are suspended. Nonflagellated bacteria are said to be nonmotile because they do not move under their own power.

Flagella are long, thread-like, helicoidal structures, usually greater ...i length than the cell to which they are attached. Apparently, they originate within the cell and extend through the cell membrane. Flagella are very thin—about 0.03 μ in diameter—and in order to see them clearly with the ordinary microscope, special staining methods, involving the precipitation on the flagella of some opaque substance, must be used. The arrangement of flagella on the cell is quite constant for each flagellated species. If the cell possesses one flagellum at one end, it is said to be monotrichous; if there is a tuft of flagella at one end, it is lophotrichous; a cell with a tuft of flagella at each end is amphitrichous; when the flagella are scattered over the entire surface of the cell, it is peritrichous. Photomicrographs of bacteria stained to show their flagella are shown in Figure 9.

Flagella undergo a series of rhythmic contractions and extensions to cause movement of the bacterial cells to which they are attached. The flagella act not only as propellers, but also as rudders. Under ideal conditions, they may move bacterial cells at rates as high as 60 microns per second. This means that a bacillus two microns in length may move as much as 30 times its length in a second. If a six-foot man could move as rapidly, he would be able to run 180 feet in a second. However, motile bacteria seldom move in a straight line for any considerable period of time; even if they did, it would take a cell moving at its maximum rate of 60 μ/second about seven minutes to move one inch.

Flagella may be removed from flagellated bacteria by mechanical agitation, filtration, centrifugation, or by the action of detergents. Flagellated bacteria may be caused to lose their ability to form flagella by cultivation under certain conditions; for example, by the addition of detergents to the culture medium. This loss may be of a transient nature, but in some cases becomes permanent.

Flagella are made up to a large extent of complex proteins which are demonstrably different from the major protein constituents found within the cell. Furthermore, the proteins in the flagella of one bacterial species usually differ from those found in other species; in many cases there are marked differences among the protein constituents of the flagella of the various strains or varieties of a species. These characteristic differences may be employed in the identification of certain species or strains of bacteria.

Reproduction of Bacteria

All true bacteria reproduce by an asexual process known as **binary fission.** In this process, lateral projections form at opposite points on the inner surfaces of the cytoplasmic membrane and grow toward the center of the cell along its transverse axis, if it is a bacillus or spirillum. After these sections of the membrane grow together, the cell wall of each cell grows toward the center along the plate thus formed and splits the two cells apart.

Considerable controversy exists over the possibilities of there being other methods by which bacteria may reproduce. Budding and conidia formation have been observed in mature cultures of some of the "higher" bacteria which are more closely related to the more complex fungi and algae than are the true bacteria. Some investigators claim that even the true bacteria—the most primitive forms—may reproduce by sexual means and by forming conidia or buds. However, at present it is best to assume that fission, if not the only method of reproduction, is at least common to all bacteria and is the only method by which young, actively growing cells of true bacteria reproduce.

During the phase of most rapid growth, some bacteria—those which prefer to grow at high temperatures—may undergo fission every eight or ten minutes. On the other hand, some of the slow-growing types, cultivated at temperatures slightly above freezing may, even in their phase of most rapid growth, take as long as five or six hours to divide. Some of the bacteria that grow well in milk stored at room temperature divide every 30 minutes. This phase of rapid reproduction lasts only until the waste products of the bacteria begin to accumulate, or until some essential food becomes exhausted. If these agencies did not operate to control bacterial reproduction, the progeny of one single bacterial cell after 36 hours of steady multiplication involving a doubling of the number of cells every 30 minutes would, according to Löhnis and Fred, fill 200 trucks of 5 tons capacity each. For a period, however, during the development of a culture of bacteria, this geometric progression of numbers does occur, and for this reason the rapidity of growth of bacteria and the changes they cause in a relatively short period of time often seem miraculous.

Formation of Cell Aggregates

When a bacterial cell divides, the two cells formed may either break apart or cling together. Those cells which possess a well-developed slime layer or capsule tend to cling together, but others having less capsular coating exist typically as single cells. The aggregates of cells formed are, in some cases, quite typical and constant in occurrence and may be used as a characteristic of value in recognizing a particular species. The coccus forms may divide in different planes to form a variety of groupings, but the bacilli and spirilla, because they divide only along the transverse axis (perpendicular to the long axis), become arranged in chains or irregular masses, or exist as single cells.

If a coccus divides to form two cells which cling together and the majority of the progeny of these cells exist in pairs, the aggregate is called a **diplococcus.** The cells of diplococci remain spheroidal, but usually become flattened on their proximal surfaces while their distal surfaces may remain spheroidal or become cone-shaped. When a coccus divides in one plane and all of its progeny continue to divide in parallel planes, a chain of cocci is formed which is called a **streptococcus.** When a coccus divides in one plane to form two cells, which then divide in a plane at right angles to the first, a group of four cells is formed; this arrangement is called a **tetracoccus.** If a coccus forms a tetrad and then divides in a third plane, a cubical packet of eight or more cells is produced which is termed a **sarcina.** If a coccus divides and its progeny divide in different planes, an aggregate similar to a bunch of grapes is formed; this arrangement is known as a **staphylococcus.**

Colony Formation

When bacteria grow in or on semisolid media they tend to form colonies, which are masses of bacterial cells large enough to be seen without the aid of a microscope. A colony may originate from a single vegetative cell, a single spore, or a clump of cells or spores. As the cells reproduce they are held together by the medium and form either a surface or subsurface colony. Subsurface, or "deep" colonies of bacteria are more dense and compact than surface colonies. Colonies are composed of many cells, but there is little or no differentiation in function among the cells in a colony. The colony is not an individual organism; it is a mass of individual cells, each of which continues to function as an independent unit. In spite of this, the colonies of a bacterial species often exhibit a distinctive and characteristic form and structure. This form and structure may be altered by a change in the environment in which the colony develops, but under similar environmental conditions the colonies of a species of bacteria are fairly uniform. Colonies of spore-forming bacteria may show considerable variation in structure because the older cells of the colony are in the spore state while the young, growing cells at the edge are in the vegetative state. If allowance is made for the relatively small variations in form and structure of colonies,

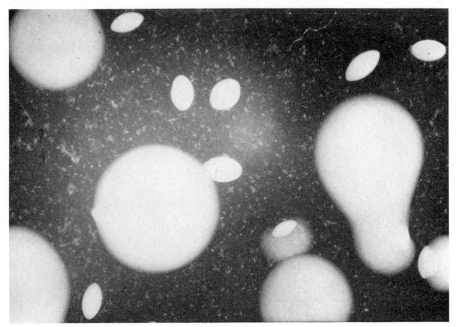

FIGURE 10. Subsurface and surface colonies. Subsurface colonies are small and lens-shaped, whereas surface colonies are relatively large, flat, and spreading. Enlarged 10X.

observation and description of them is of aid in identification and classification of bacteria. The variations which may occur in the form and structure of bacterial colonies are frequently of considerable importance, not only because such variations make the identification of a species or variety more difficult, but also because they indicate that the cells which make up the colony have undergone some significant change. Variations which may occur in the form and structure of bacterial colonies are discussed in Chapter 14. Figure 10 shows surface and subsurface colonies of bacteria growing in an agar culture medium.

REFERENCES

Breed, R. S., Murray, E. G. D., and Hitchens, A. P., *Bergey's manual of determinative bacteriology* (6th ed.). Baltimore, Md., Williams & Wilkins, 1948.
Dubos, R. J., *The bacterial cell*. Cambridge, Mass., Harvard University Press, 1945.
Knaysi, G., *Elements of bacterial cytology*. Ithaca, N. Y., Comstock, 1944.
Knaysi, G., "The endospore of bacteria." *Bact. Rev.* (1948), *12*:19–77.
Knaysi, G., "Cytology of Bacteria II." *Bot. Rev.* (1949), *15*:106–151.

2. RICKETTSIAE, FILTERABLE VIRUSES, AND BACTERIOPHAGES

Rickettsiae (Rickettsia Bodies)

These are strictly parasitic, bacteria-like bodies found under natural conditions only in the cells of infected tissues, or occasionally in the blood or feces of an insect, animal, or human being. As a rule they produce disease, but apparently some of them, while parasitic, do not harm their host markedly. Attempts to cultivate these organisms apart from living tissues have so far been unsuccessful. They can, however, be grown in artificial cultures of living tissue, and infect the cells in these tissues.

Rickettsia bodies are either spheroidal or cylindrical; the most common forms look like small, round-ended bacilli. They are, as a rule, very small, and vary from about 0.2 μ to 0.5 μ in their greatest diameter. Although reports are conflicting, the balance of evidence indicates that rickettsiae are not filterable; that is, filters which will hold back the smallest bacteria will also retain rickettsia bodies. Figure 11 is a photomicrograph showing rickettsiae in living tissue.

Typhus fever and Rocky Mountain spotted fever are important diseases of human beings caused by rickettsiae. These diseases also affect animals. For example, rats are susceptible to typhus fever; and goats, sheep, bears, coyotes, and rabbits become infected under natural conditions with the causative agent of Rocky Mountain spotted fever. Typhus fever is transmitted by the body louse; Rocky Mountain spotted fever is transmitted by a wood tick. The lice and ticks become infected by feeding on the blood of an infected individual, and in this way transmit the rickettsiae to susceptible human beings.

24

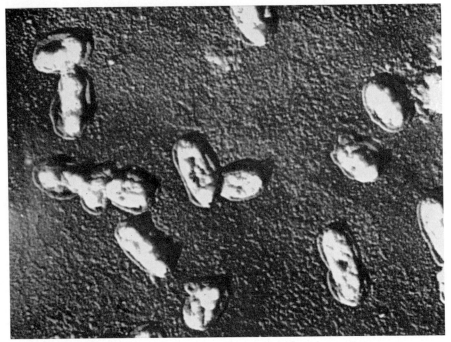

FIGURE 11. Electron microscope picture of the *Rickettsia* that causes typhus fever. These parasitic, bacteria-like organisms are carried from man to man by the body louse. Enlarged about 18,000X. (From *Textbook of Virology* by Rhodes and van Rooyen, Thomas Nelson & Sons, New York, 1949.)

FILTERABLE VIRUSES (ULTRAMICROSCOPIC VIRUSES)

Disease-producing agents which are so small that they cannot be seen, even with the aid of the best compound microscopes, and which will pass through a filter that will hold back bacteria, are known as filterable viruses. At present there is considerable controversy over their nature, but before outlining the theories that have been advanced to explain what they are, it might be well to consider a few of the general properties of viruses.

All viruses are strict parasites. They multiply, or increase in concentration, only in certain living tissues. Furthermore, they are extremely specific and develop only in one, or rarely a few, kinds of tissue. They have not, as yet, been cultivated, or caused to increase in concentration, in an artificial medium.

Viruses vary greatly in size, but all of the different kinds recognized at present are ultramicroscopic. Some of the smallest, such as those which cause foot-and-mouth disease, are about 0.008 μ to 0.012 μ (8–12 milli-microns, or mμ; 1 mμ = .001 μ) in size; others are as large as 0.1 μ (100 mμ), which is just beyond the range of visibility of the compound microscope. Probably the majority of the viruses are about 0.02 to 0.03 μ (20 to 30 mμ.) in size. The size of virus cells or particles may be determined by measurement with an electron microscope, by their rate of sedimentation in an ultracentrifuge, or by use of special collodion filters of known pore size. Photomicrographs of viruses taken through the electron microscope at magnifications as high as 30,000 to 100,000 times have been published. These show some viruses to be small cocci or bacilli; some of the coccoid

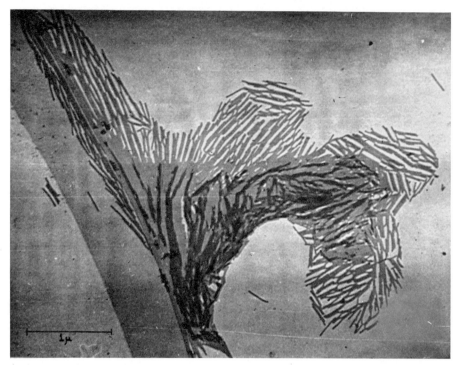

FIGURE 12.   Electron microscope picture of an aggregation of tobacco mosaic virus particles. This virus, like some of the other plant viruses, can be crystallized. (Stanley and Anderson, S.A.B. No. 49.)

forms have peculiar "tails." Some of the viruses appear to have a crystalline structure. Figure 12 is an electron photomicrograph of the "crystals" of tobacco mosaic virus. Figure 13 is an electron photomicrograph of chromium-shadowed influenza virus.

In general, the agencies that will kill or inhibit the activities and growth of bacteria will have the same effect on viruses, but some viruses are more resistant to adverse conditions than nonspore-forming bacteria, whereas other kinds of viruses are more easily inhibited or killed.

After reading these rather general, somewhat vague statements concerning the nature of viruses it is only natural to ask for some proof of their existence. That there are such ultramicroscopic, filterable agents which cause disease can be clearly demonstrated. For example, if a hog is afflicted with cholera, the presence of the causative virus in its blood stream can be demonstrated by taking a small quantity of the animal's blood aseptically, allowing the blood to clot, passing the serum which separates, under aseptic conditions, through a sterile filter that will retain bacteria, and finally inject-

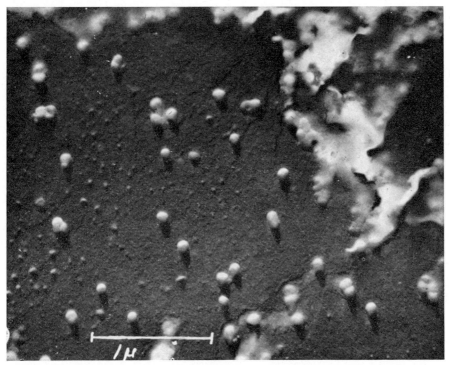

FIGURE 13. Electron microscope picture of the influenza virus shadowed with chromium. This virus, like other animal viruses, has not been crystallized and is more "cell-like" in morphology than the tobacco mosaic virus. Magnified about 32,000X. (Williams and Wyckoff, S.A.B. No. 136.)

ing a very small amount of the filtrate into a healthy, susceptible hog. If the virus of hog cholera is present in the filtrate, this injection will cause the inoculated animal to contract hog cholera. Examination of the filtrate under the microscope, or by cultural methods, will show it to be free from bacteria and from particles of any kind large enough to be seen with an ordinary microscope. Yet this filtrate causes hog cholera in the inoculated animal be- cause it contains the virus. This procedure can be repeated over and over again and the virus thus kept in an active state. In this way, it can be demonstrated that viruses exist and multiply, or increase in concentration, although it must be admitted that the proof involves a demonstration of the activity of the virus rather than showing its actual presence.

Proof that certain viruses exist can be carried one step farther, and the results of this work serve as the basis for one theory concerning the nature of viruses. It has been shown that an apparently pure protein of high molecular weight can be obtained in crystalline form from the filtered juice obtained from leaves of a tobacco plant afflicted with mosaic disease. This protein can be obtained by either a "salting-out" process or by sedimentation in the ultracentrifuge. It can be crystallized and dried; it has a molecular weight of approximately 17,000,000 to 500,000,000. When this purified protein is "dissolved" in sterile water, the solution filtered, and the filtrate rubbed on the leaves of a healthy, susceptible tobacco plant, the inoculated leaves in time become affected with the mosaic disease. Filtration of an extract of these diseased leaves yields, in turn, an infective filtrate from which the same protein can be crystallized in the pure state.

Work of this type is going on in many laboratories all over the world. However, few of the viruses which have been studied thus far with this objective in mind have been isolated in a crystalline state, possibly because they are too labile and lose their activity when subjected to the rather rigorous purification procedures employed. But it has been demonstrated conclusively that at least one virus, that which causes mosaic disease of tobacco, is a nucleoprotein of high molecular weight. These results provide the basis for one theory concerning the nature of viruses. This is that viruses are nucleoproteins which, when placed in contact with susceptible, healthy cells of the appropriate plant or animal, cause these cells to become diseased and also to produce more nucleoprotein similar to that of the original virus. Hence, the inoculation of a small quantity of the causative nucleoprotein would cause a progressive disease and would lead to the production of a relatively large quantity of the infective agent. That is, the "virus" would apparently "grow" or "multiply" in spite of its being an inanimate substance having no cell structure. However, before this theory can be accepted without reservations, it must be demonstrated that the nucleoprotein preparations secured from infective material are both chemically pure and sterile, i.e., free from all living cells. At present, these criteria have been satisfied for the tobacco mosaic virus, but much remains to be done in order to prove that all viruses are nucleoproteins capable of autocatalytic action in susceptible living tissues.

The second principal theory concerning the nature of viruses is the older of the two that are worthy of serious consideration. This theory states that viruses are living cells which are strictly parasitic and are much smaller than bacteria. It is based in part on the fact that viruses respond much like living cells to many adverse physical and chemical agencies. They can, for example, be killed or inactivated by heat, ultraviolet light, and certain disinfectants. Another fact that is used in support of this theory is that viruses are particulate, and that the particle size varies considerably with different viruses. A third basis for this belief lies in the fact that viruses multiply. For example, if a susceptible, 200-pound hog is inoculated with 1 ml. of a filtrate containing hog cholera virus, every drop of the approximately 11 liters of blood in the animal's body will contain the virus at the height of the disease. This is evidence that the virus has multiplied, or increased in concentration, and it is further supported by the fact that the virus can be passed from animal to animal and caused to multiply in each susceptible individual. The fourth basis for this theory is that electron microscope photographs show that many viruses look like small bacteria. (See Figure 13.)

There exist several modifications of the theory that viruses are small, living cells. One is that viruses are a filterable stage in the life cycle of protozoa; another states that viruses are "naked nuclei" that can multiply only when they become imbedded in the cytoplasm of susceptible cells.

Perhaps, for the time being at least, it may be assumed that some viruses are small, living, strictly parasitic cells, and that others are inanimate, high molecular weight proteins capable of causing susceptible living cells to become abnormal and to produce more of the high molecular weight protein. At present, the causative agent of tobacco mosaic has been shown to be a high molecular weight protein. There are at least 50 other kinds of viruses of unknown nature which, for all practical purposes, may be considered as small, living cells.

BACTERIOPHAGES (BACTERIAL VIRUSES)

Bacteriophages (bacterial viruses) cause disease of bacteria; they bring about the dissolution, or lysis, of young, actively growing bacterial cells. They have the same general properties as filterable viruses, but instead of causing disease in animals or plants, they are specific for bacteria. The same theories advanced to explain the nature of filterable viruses may be used in an attempt to describe the nature of bacteriophages.

Bacteriophages may be found in old cultures of bacteria, in sewage, in feces, and in many other places where bacteria are growing or have grown. Their presence in sewage may be demonstrated by mixing some untreated domestic sewage with a very young, actively growing broth culture of bacteria such as *Escherichia coli*, a common inhabitant of the large intestine, incubating the mixture for about 12 hours, and then passing it through a sterile filter which is capable of retaining bacteria. If some of the filtrate thus obtained is added to a fresh, actively growing broth culture of *Escherichia coli,* and the mixture incubated, the following changes will be noted. The broth culture will start to get cloudy due to the growth of bacteria, and then, if the added filtrate contains phage, the culture will, in a short time, become almost as clear as sterile broth. This is the phenomenon of bacteriophagy. A filtrate obtained from the cleared culture will contain a

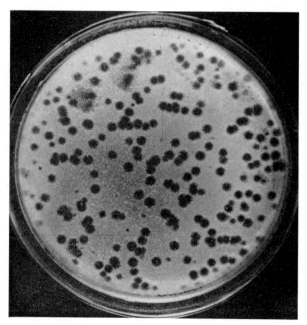

FIGURE 14.   Plaques caused by bacteriophage in a poured plate culture of *Rhizobium.* A mixture of bacteria and phage were incubated together for 48 hours. Dense masses of colonies formed in and on the agar except in those areas where the bacteriophage was present. In the clear areas, or plaques, the phage has killed the bacteria and has prevented colony formation. (Kleczkowska, S.A.B. No. 145.)

greater concentration of phage than the original filtrate, which shows that the phage has multiplied, or increased in concentration while causing lysis of the bacteria.

Another way in which to demonstrate bacteriophage action involves the use of a semisolid culture medium. The phage-containing filtrate, free from bacterial cells, is mixed with a young culture of bacteria. The phage-bacteria mixture is then added to melted, cooled, sterile nutrient agar. After transferring this inoculated culture medium to a petri dish, the agar is allowed to solidify, and the dish is incubated. Colonies of the bacteria form in and on the agar of the petri dish culture, but if bacteriophage is present, it attacks the bacteria and prevents colony formation. As a result, such a petri dish culture appears to have "holes," or clear areas, in the agar, called plaques, in which phage action has occurred. Such a petri dish culture is shown in Figure 14.

Many different bacteriophages have been isolated. Like the viruses, they are known by the effect which they produce and the organisms which they attack, rather than by any specific name. Thus we have an *Escherichia coli* phage, a *Micrococcus pyogenes* phage, and phages that are capable of attacking other specific bacteria. Electron microscope photographs of phages show most of them to be spheroidal, or small cocci with "tails." Figure 15 shows a series of electron photomicrographs of bacteriophage entering and lysing bacterial cells. These pictures show the phage particles clearly.

The particles of bacteriophages are of about the same range of size as are those of filterable viruses. They may be, as one of their discoverers, Dr. d'Herelle stated, ultramicroscopic living cells which are parasitic on bacteria; or they may be nucleoproteins of high molecular weight that are self-propagating in their action. Whatever their exact nature may be they serve to illustrate again the truth of Augustus de Morgan's famous verse:[1]

> Great fleas have little fleas
> Upon their backs to bite 'em,
> And little fleas have lesser fleas,
> And so, ad infinitum.

Following their discovery by Twort and by d'Herelle, bacteriophages were studied intensively because of their ability to lyse bacterial cells, and because it was hoped that they might be useful as therapeutic agents in the treatment of infectious diseases. However, it was found that they were of limited value for practical use in this field.

Bacteriophages may cause trouble in fermentation industries and in the dairy industry, in processes that rely upon pure cultures of bacteria to produce chemical changes. If these bacterial cultures become infected with bacteriophage, they become "sick" and fail to produce the desired chemical changes. Protection of bacterial cultures against phage contamination, and the development of phage-resistant strains of bacteria have become necessary procedures in certain industries and have opened up new fields of research.

Many investigators have become interested in the bacteriophages because it is believed that studies on their nature and mode of action may lead to a

---

[1] Augustus de Morgan. *Budget of paradoxes*, 1872. P. 377.

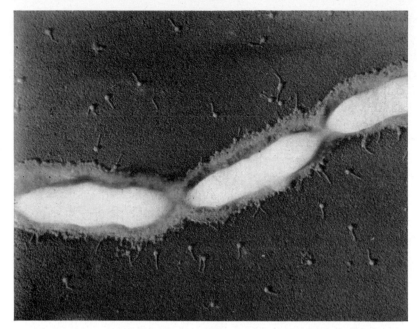

A

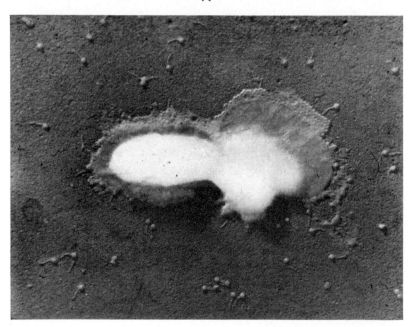

B

FIGURE 15.   Electron microscope pictures of bacteriophage infecting and lysing cells of *Streptococcus lactis*. **A.** Rapidly dividing cells of *Streptococcus lactis* about to be infected with virus. Note the slime layer on the bacteria and the "tails" on the virus particles. **B.** Infection has been completed and the cell is swelling and bursting.

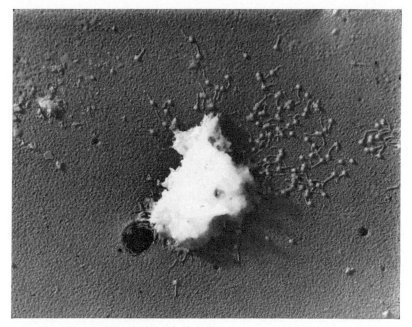

C

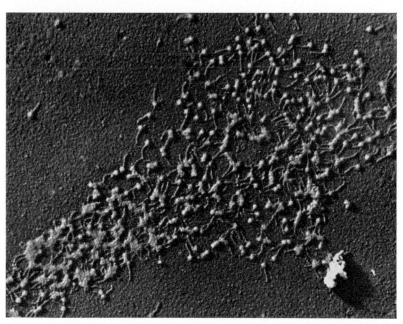

D

C. A completely disrupted cell spilling out protoplasm and newly formed virus particles. **D.** Newly formed viruses. Magnified approximately 20,000X. (From C. E. Parmelee, P. H. Carr, and F. E. Nelson, 1949, *Journal of Bacteriology*, 57:391–397. Reproduced by permission of the authors and The Williams & Wilkins Company, publishers.)

better understanding of all viruses. The bacteriophages are similar to viruses which cause diseases of animals or plants in that they:

1. Have a similar range in size: 10 mμ to 80 mμ; also similar morphologically to many viruses
2. Reproduce only inside a living host cell
3. May have a wide host range or may be specific for one species
4. May destroy the host cell or may continue to exist within it in a latent state
5. May extend or change their host specificity by adaptation or mutation
6. May show interference phenomena; that is, the presence of one phage in a susceptible host cell may interfere with the infection of that cell by another phage
7. Are antigenic (when injected into an animal, they will stimulate the animal to form specific antibodies against them)

These similarities are the basis for recommending phage and susceptible bacterial cells as a model system for fundamental studies on all viruses. In this perspective, bacteriophages may well come to occupy a key position in fundamental biological science. In addition, bacteriophages are proving to be useful in work on the identification and classification of bacteria.

REFERENCES

Craigie, J., "The significance and applications of bacteriophage in bacteriological and virus research." *Bact. Rev.* (1946), *10:*73–88.

Delbrück, M., "Bacterial viruses or bacteriophages." *Biol. Rev.* (1946), *21:*30–40.

Pinkerton, H., "The pathogenic Rickettsiae with particular reference to their nature, biologic properties, and classification." *Bact. Rev.* (1942), *6:*37–78.

Rivers, T. M. (ed.), *Viral and rickettsial infections of man.* Philadelphia, Pa., Lippincott, 1948.

Stanley, W. M., "The architecture of viruses." *Physiol. Rev.* (1939), *19:*524–556.

3. ALGAE

Oceans, lakes, ponds, rivers, and other bodies of water exposed to sunlight are the natural habitat of algae, but they are also found in the soil and on rocks and trees. The "blooming" of a lake, which may occur during the late spring or summer months, is the result of the growth of great numbers of free-floating algae. Other kinds of algae grow attached to rocks and other solid objects in a body of water. Approximately 17,000 different kinds of algae have been described; and their appearance and habits of growth differ markedly.

Some kinds of algae are unicellular and are the simplest plants that contain chlorophyll; others are multicellular and are almost as complex in structure as some of the ferns and mosses. The algae which are green in color are grouped in one class; the brown algae make up a second class; the red algae are grouped in a third class; the blue-green algae are placed in a fourth class. Algae of any color contain chlorophyll, but the presence of other pigments masks the color of the chlorophyll in all but the green algae. Because they contain chlorophyll all algae can utilize the energy of sunlight to synthesize organic matter and their own protoplasm from CO_2, water and inorganic substances.

The algae are of considerable practical importance in bodies of water. It has been said that "algae are to a fish what grass is to a cow." They also serve as food for other aquatic animals, which in turn may be eaten by fish. Unfortunately, however, the growth of algae in water is at times a great nuisance. When excessive numbers of algae grow in a body of water many of them die, and when these dead cells are decomposed by bacteria, bad odors may result. For this reason it is often necessary to prevent excessive growth of algae in a reservoir or other body of water used for human consumption or for recreational purposes.

Algae are found on or just beneath the surface of nearly all soils, where they are able to grow if they can get sunlight, air, and plenty of moisture and inorganic foods. Their growth results in the accumulation of organic matter in the soil, and their dead cells serve as food for the fungi and bacteria which are present. The decomposition of dead algal cells by fungi and bacteria, subsequent to the growth of algae on rocks, aids in the gradual disintegration of the rocks and the formation of soil.

The red algae and most of the brown algae are not studied in bacteriology because they are large marine plants. However, a product called agar, or agar-agar, which is obtained by water extraction of any one of several species of *Gelideum*, a red alga that grows in the ocean off the coasts of California, China, and Japan, is of importance in bacteriological work. This substance, which is a galactan (a complex carbohydrate that yields the sugar, galactose, when hydrolyzed), is used as a solidifying agent in culture media employed in bacteriological laboratories.

The Diatoms are brown algae which are of interest because they are unicellular microorganisms that grow in the ocean and in fresh water and surround their cells with a siliceous shell. When they die, their shells fall to the bottom of the lake or ocean and, over a period of many years, great deposits of these shells are built up because the silica in them is resistant to decomposition. These deposits are known as beds of "diatomaceous earth." Diatomaceous earth is used as a filtering agent, a polishing powder, an insulating material, and a carrier for nitroglycerine in dynamite.

Diatoms may float free in the water or grow attached to some solid object such as a rock. They attach themselves by means of a gelatinous stalk, which is produced by the cell. Several cells growing together in a colony may exhibit a rather complex structure, but each organism in the colony still functions as an individual.

Green algae are abundant in water, in the soil, and on the bark of trees and wet surfaces of rocks; many of them can be cultivated in the laboratory. The green algae constitute a very large group of organisms varying from unicellular, microscopic types up to multicellular forms that are almost as complex in structure as some of the higher plants. Vegetative reproduction occurs by fission, but most green algae are also capable of sexual reproduction. One or more chloroplasts (bodies containing chlorophyll) are always found in their cells, and within these are pyrenoids, which are centers of starch synthesis. The cell walls of green algae are made of cellulose; some

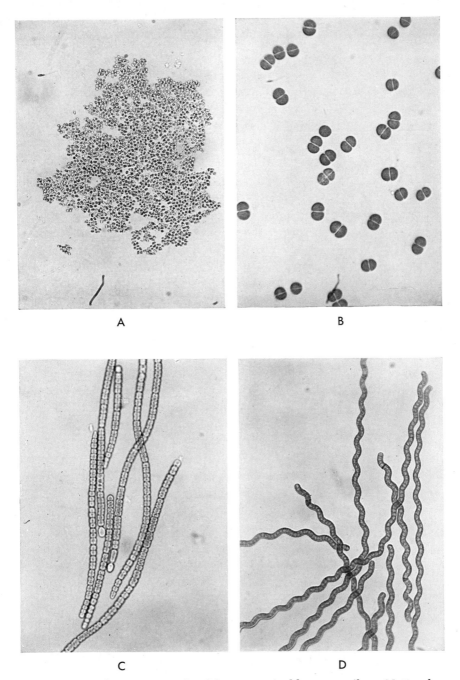

FIGURE 16.   Photomicrographs of four common blue-green algae. Notice the morphological relationship between these algae and the true bacteria. **A.** *Microcystis aeruginosa,* enlarged 305X. **B.** *Chroococcus turgidus,* enlarged 125X. **C.** *Cylindrospermum licheniforme,* enlarged 305X. **D.** *Arthrospira Jenneri,* enlarged 125X. (Courtesy of Gerloff and Fitzgerald, University of Wisconsin.)

are covered with spiny protuberances, whereas others are surrounded by a gelatinous or slimy coating. Most of the flagellated, free-swimming forms do not have any structures covering the cell wall.

The blue-green algae are the simplest plants that contain chlorophyll. Of all plants that contain chlorophyll, the blue-green algae are most similar in morphology to the bacteria. They are unicellular, but are usually found in colonies or long filaments. In colonies, the cells are held together by a gelatinous capsule; long filaments are enclosed in a sheath. Individual cells reproduce by fission, and although there are modifications of this process in some species, sexual reproduction does not occur. The cells of blue-green algae do not have a distinct nucleus, but are known to contain nucleoplasm. The chlorophyll of their cells is diffused throughout the protoplasm and is not bound in a chloroplast. In addition to chlorophyll, they contain phycocyanin, a blue pigment, but although blue-green is the predominant color, some species are yellow, olive-green, or brownish-green due to the presence of other pigments. They store carbohydrate in the form of glycogen, or "animal starch," which is characteristic of fungi and animals, not as starch as do typical green plants. They are found in bodies of water everywhere, even in hot springs where the temperature is as high as 75° C. Blue-green algae are universally distributed in soils, but are not present in as large numbers as the bacteria. Figure 16 shows photomicrographs of common blue-green algae.

REFERENCES

Smith, G. M., *Cryptogamic botany,* Vol. I (*Algae and fungi*). N. Y., McGraw-Hill, 1938, pp. 1–350.

Smith, G. M., *et al., A textbook of general botany* (4th ed.). N. Y., Macmillan, 1942, pp. 241–301.

Tiffany, L. H., *Algae, the grass of many waters.* Springfield, Ill., C. C. Thomas, 1938.

4. MOLDS

Molds, which are multicellular, filamentous fungi, are very widely distributed in nature. Usually, they are found growing on solid substances, such as wood, paper, cloth, leather, meat, fruits, vegetables, and many other materials. Each mold produces enormous numbers of spores which are light in weight and are easily carried from one place to another by air currents. Molds are the most important causative agents of plant diseases and are responsible for some infections of animals. In the laboratory, and in many industries where bacteria and yeasts are employed, molds are about as welcome as weeds are to a gardener—and as difficult to combat. But in spite of their undesirable activities in food spoilage and in the production of certain plant and animal diseases, they may be very useful. In the soil they are responsible for decomposition of much of the organic matter that is resistant to bacterial action. They are used in several industrial processes and are responsible for the appearance and flavor of such cheeses as Roquefort and Camembert. The most widely used antibiotic—penicillin—is the product of a mold.

DESCRIPTION OF MOLDS

Molds are multicellular fungi which form a filamentous branching growth known as a **mycelium.** The individual filaments of the mycelium are known as **hyphae.** In some molds the hyphae are continuous, multinucleate cylinders which have no cross walls; these are known as **nonseptate** hyphae. In other molds, the hyphae have cross walls which divide them into a chain of individual cells, each with one nucleus, or occasionally with two nuclei. Hyphae with cross walls are known as **septate** hyphae.

Those hyphae through which the mold obtains its foods, and which anchor the mold to its substrate, but which are not directly concerned with reproduction, are called **vegetative** hyphae to distinguish them from the **fertile** hyphae, which are responsible for spore production. Fertile hyphae are usually aerial, whereas vegetative hyphae are as a rule submerged in or lie upon the medium on which the mycelium is developing.

The mycelium is usually colorless and distinctly filamentous looking. The fruiting bodies, or asexual spores, of a mold are often colored; black and green are common colors, but pink or brown spores are sometimes observed. The mycelium may be microscopic in size, but under suitable conditions, for example on the surface of silage, it may be several feet in diameter. The mycelium increases in size by repeated division of the cells at the tips of the vegetative hyphae, occasionally by division of cells within the interwoven hyphae of the mycelium.

FIGURE 17. Photomicrograph of *Rhizopus nigricans*. This mold is classified as a phycomycete because the hyphae are nonseptate and asexual spores, sporangiospores, are borne inside of a sac-like sporangium. Note the root-like rhizoids that gather nutrients and anchor the mycelium to the substrate. Enlarged about 200X.

Each cell of a septate hypha contains the structures characteristic of cells in general. It is surrounded by a fairly rigid cell wall composed of chitin. The cytoplasm, which is surrounded by a cytoplasmic membrane, is usually rather homogeneous in young cells, but as they mature it becomes vacuolated and granular. Carbohydrate is stored in the cytoplasm as glycogen; fat globules are often present; granules of volutin are frequently found. Vacuoles, when present, seem to be filled with cell sap which is less dense than the cytoplasm. As a rule, each cell contains only one nucleus, which is small and rather hard to distinguish. Mycelia made up of nonseptate hyphae are multinucleate, hence are considered to be multicellular.

Reproduction of Molds

Molds reproduce by the formation of spores; those capable of both asexual and sexual spore formation are usually classified as either *Phycomycetes* or *Ascomycetes;* molds which produce spores by asexual means only are classed as *Fungi Imperfecti.*

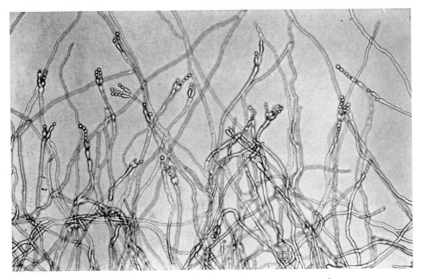

Figure 18. Photomicrograph of *Penicillium notatum* showing septate hyphae and conidia. This mold is classified as an ascomycete and was one of the first penicillia to be used for penicillin production. Enlarged about 300X. (Courtesy of The Abbott Laboratories, North Chicago, Ill.)

Asexual Spores

There are four main types of spores which may be formed asexually by different molds.

1. **Chlamydospores** may be produced by any of the molds by filling one or more of the cells within the mycelium with reserve food, and surrounding it with a rather heavy wall. Apparently, any spore thus formed can remain dormant for considerable periods of time, is fairly resistant to drying, and will germinate to form a new mycelium when placed under favorable conditions for growth.

2. **Sporangiospores** are asexual spores formed by molds classed as *Phycomycetes*. These are alga-like fungi which form a nonseptate mycelium, and are found in water and on fruits and starchy foods. Such molds have

FIGURE 19.   Photomicrograph of the mold *Aspergillus niger,* a common ascomycete. The vegetative hyphae are septate and large clusters of conidia have formed on aerial nonseptate conidiophores. Enlarged about 200X.

sporangiophores, which, when the mycelium is growing on a fairly dry substrate, are aerial, fertile hyphae which bear specialized cells at their tips which reproduce to form large numbers of **sporangiospores** that remain inside sac-like structures called sporangia. Eventually, each sporangium ruptures and sets free its spores. The spores are microscopic, usually pigmented cells covered with a tough, dry spore wall; they are resistant to drying and can remain dormant for long periods of time. In *Phycomycetes* found on foods and in the soil, the sporangiospores are dry and depend mainly upon air currents for their dissemination. Figure 17 shows sporangiophores and sporangia of *Rhizopus nigricans.*

3. **Conidia** are asexual, exposed spores formed by molds classed as *Ascomycetes;* a few of the *Phycomycetes* and *Basidiomycetes* and many *Fungi Imperfecti* are also known to form conidia. Conidia are formed either at the tip or by growth from fertile hyphae known as **conidiophores,** which are usually aerial structures. The usual process of conidia formation involves first the pinching off of a cell at the tip of the conidiophore. Immediately, another cell is constricted off, pushing the first one ahead of it; this process is repeated with the result that a chain of conidia is formed, with the youngest conidium at the base. Occasionally, however, the tip cell of a coniodiophore buds, and then the daughter cell buds; repetition of this process leads to the formation of a chain of conidia, with the youngest cell at the tip. Conidia formed by either process remain attached to the conidiophore until they mature; maturation involves thickening of the spore wall and, in some cases, development of pigment. Each conidium is microscopic and resistant to drying, can remain dormant for a long time, and is capable, upon germination, of forming a new mycelium. Figures 18 and 19 show the microscopic structure and conidia of two common *Ascomycetes.*

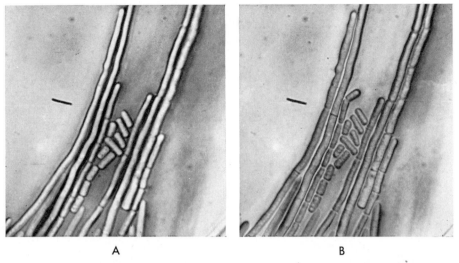

A   B

Figure 20. Photomicrographs of arthrospore formation in *Geotrichum candidum*, a common *Fungi Imperfecti*. Note the fragmentation of the mycelium that occurred during the 10 minutes that elapsed between photographing **A** and **B**. Enlarged about 420X.

4. In addition to sporangiospores and conidia, which are true asexual spores, and chlamydospores, which are spore-like bodies, many molds may form—by asexual means—other reproductive units, known as **arthrospores** or **oidia**. Arthrospores are cells formed by the fragmentation of any part of the mycelium—even from vegetative hyphae. As a rule, arthrospores are produced by molds that are made up of septate hyphae; they are shorter, thicker-walled cells than the active, vegetative cells of the hyphae. Arthrospore formation by *Geotrichum candidum* is shown in Figure 20.

Sexual Spores

The manner of sexual spore formation is used as the main basis for classification of the fungi. If a fungus does not form sexual spores, it is classed with the *Fungi Imperfecti*. If sexual spores are formed, the way in which they are produced, together with their structure, serves as a means for identifying and classifying the plant as a basidiomycete, phycomycete or ascomycete. Very few of the filamentous fungi known as molds are *Basidiomycetes;* hence the sexual method of spore formation of this class will not be described.

Among the *Phycomycetes,* the aquatic types form **oöspores** by union of a small male gamete and a large female gamete. These are sexual spores that are protected by resistant walls and can remain dormant for some time; they are very resistant to drying. Those *Phycomycetes* commonly found in the soil and on foods form **zygospores** by the union of two cells that are apparently alike, and which may come from either the same or from different mycelia. Like oöspores, zygospores are covered by a tough wall, can resist drying, and remain dormant for long periods of time. Zygospore formation by *Rhizopus nigricans* is shown in Figure 21.

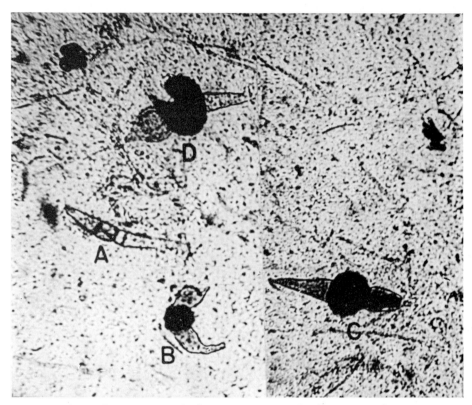

FIGURE 21.   Photomicrograph showing stages in the formation of a zygospore in one of the *Phycomycetes, Rhizopus nigricans*. **A.** Two hyphae have fused and the zygospore has just started to form. **B.** The zygospore is larger and has become pigmented. **C.** The mature zygospore. **D.** An opened zygospore after germination. Note that the two hyphae that fused remain attached to the zygospore. Enlarged 250X.

In the *Ascomycetes*, the sexual spores are known as **ascospores.** They are formed following the union of two cells from the same mycelium or from two separate mycelia. When these cells unite, their nuclei fuse and either immediately or sometime later after going through an intermediate step, the fusion nucleus divides and redivides to form two to sixteen nuclei. Each of these nuclei becomes surrounded by dense cytoplasm and is covered with a spore wall. The spores are retained within an ascus, or sac. When several asci are formed in one part of a mycelium, the cells of the nearby hyphae branch and rebranch to form a covering for the asci. Such a covering is known as a **perithecium.** Eventually the spores are set free when the perithecium and asci disintegrate. Each ascospore is resistant to drying, can remain dormant for a long period of time, and will produce a new mycelium upon germination.

Physiology of Molds

The great majority of molds are saprophytic (use nonliving matter for food), but there are a few species which may cause infectious diseases in man or animals and many which cause infectious diseases of plants. Saprophytic molds are noted for their ability to produce a wide variety of enzymes that will enable them to digest and make use of many different complex organic foods. In fact, there are few organic compounds known that are not subject to attack by some mold. In their respiration processes, molds produce many important by-products, but in general, given time and an ample supply of oxygen, they will oxidize organic substances completely.

Many different molds and mold-like organisms are known which will produce substances antagonistic to other living organisms, particularly the bacteria. Penicillin is the most widely used and important antibiotic thus produced; it is formed under certain conditions by *Penicillium notatum* or *Penicillium chrysogenum.*

REFERENCES

Foster, J. W., *Chemical activities of fungi.* N. Y., Academic Press, 1949.

Skinner, C. E., Emmons, C. W., and Tsuchiya, H. M., *Henrici's molds, yeasts, and actinomycetes* (2nd ed.). N. Y., Wiley, 1947.

Smith, G., *An introduction to industrial mycology* (3rd ed.). London, E. Arnold and Co., Ltd., 1946.

Smith, G. M., *Cryptogamic botany,* Vol. I (*Algae and fungi*). N. Y., McGraw-Hill, 1938, pp. 351–512.

Wolf, F. A., and Wolf, F. T., *The fungi,* Vols. I and II. N. Y., Wiley, 1947.

5. YEASTS

OCCURRENCE OF YEASTS

In nature, yeasts may be found in many different places, but are not as widespread in occurrence as the bacteria. The surfaces of fruits, exuded sap of trees and of plants such as corn, the nectar of flowers, and the leaves of plants are all places where yeasts may be found. They also exist in the soil of vineyards and of orchards, and in various animals; insects in particular carry yeasts in their digestive tracts. Yeasts prefer to grow in acid foods containing sugar. They are also rather common in dairy products, particularly in cream, butter, and certain types of fermented milks.

DESCRIPTION OF YEASTS

The term, yeast, is a common one and has no significance in a botanical classification. Most yeasts are microscopic, unicellular fungi, which do not form a permanent, multicellular, branching structure known as a mycelium, but exist as single cells; most yeasts reproduce vegetatively by budding, but a few reproduce by fission. One species of yeast has been described which reproduces by both fission and budding. Some kinds of yeasts form a multicellular mycelium, but most of the common yeasts are unicellular.

In addition to these methods of vegetative reproduction, one large group of yeasts may reproduce by the formation of sexual spores. The great majority of the spore-forming yeasts are classified in the *Ascomycetes*, but a few are classed as *Basidiomycetes*.

There is a large, heterogeneous group of yeasts which do not form sexual

46

spores, and hence are classed as *Fungi Imperfecti.* Yeasts in this class reproduce only by budding, fission, or by the formation of asexual spores.

An outline of the classification of yeasts may be found in Appendix C.

MORPHOLOGY AND STRUCTURE OF YEASTS

Morphology

The yeasts are such a large, heterogeneous group of microorganisms that
it is not possible to describe the morphology of a "typical" yeast cell. As a
rule, yeast cells are from four to twenty times longer than the cells of true
bacteria. Some yeast cells are spheroidal, others may be ellipsoidal, sausage-
shaped, lemon-shaped, or cylindrical. The morphology of the cells of individual species of yeasts is fairly constant and can be used as one of the
characteristics employed in their identification and classification.

Structure of the Yeast Cell

All yeast cells have a cell wall, probably composed of chitin, which surrounds the cell proper. When the cell is young, the wall is rather thin and
flexible, but becomes thicker and more rigid as the cell matures. Surrounding the protoplasm within the cell wall is a cytoplasmic membrane which is
differentially permeable. Yeasts do not have flagella and, as a rule, do not
possess capsules or slime layers.

Within the yeast cell is a large **vacuole.** At one end of this vacuole is
a small, dense body which some workers believe to be the nucleus. Other
workers are convinced that the entire vacuole is a nuclear vacuole, and
that the dense body at one end is merely one part of the nucleus; these investigators claim that the vacuole contains the chromosomes which carry
the hereditary units, or genes. It is not possible at present to state which of
these opinions is correct, but the weight of evidence appears to support the
latter view. At any rate, it is certain that the yeast cell contains a nucleus.

The cytoplasm which surrounds the vacuole of a yeast cell is granular in
appearance, particularly in mature cells. The granules may consist of the
storage products: volutin, fat, or glycogen. Small structures of unknown significance, called mitochondria, also exist in the cytoplasm and give it a granular appearance.

REPRODUCTION OF YEASTS

Vegetative Reproduction and Asexual Spores

The most common method of vegetative reproduction of yeasts is by budding, but a few species can reproduce by fission; one species can reproduce

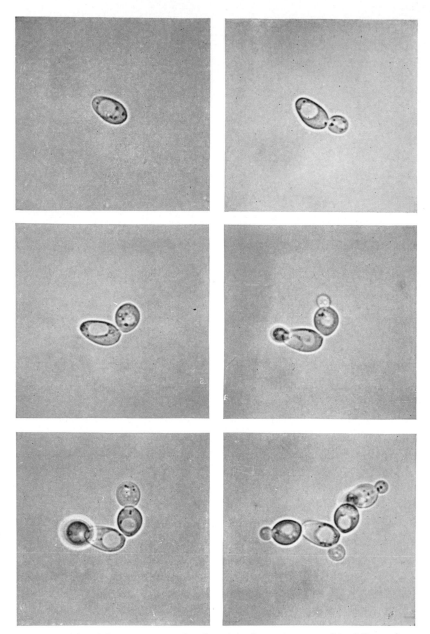

FIGURE 22. Photomicrographs showing the sequence of budding of a rapidly growing cell of the common yeast, *Saccharomyces cerevisiae*. In 4 hours one cell has increased to 4 adult cells each with a bud. Enlarged 1500X. (Courtesy of the Fleischmann Laboratories.)

by both budding and fission. In budding, some of the protoplasm of the cell bulges out the cell wall, and the bud thus formed grows until it is similar to the original cell in form and size. When the bud reaches maturity, it usually becomes separated from its mother cell. Actively growing yeasts may bud at several points on the cell, and the daughter cells may in turn start to bud before they reach the size of the mother cell. Thus, for a time, the yeast may exhibit a primitive mycelial structure, which may be only temporary if the cells formed by budding ultimately break off and exist as single cells. During the formation of a bud, the nucleus of the cell divides, and one of the nuclei, along with some of the cytoplasm, migrates into the bud. The series of photomicrographs in Figure 22 shows the budding of yeast cells.

In the few species of yeast that reproduce vegetatively by fission, the process is similar in many respects to that which occurs in bacteria. The yeast cell becomes somewhat elongated, nuclear division occurs, and a cross wall is laid down along the transverse axis of the cell, dividing it into two daughter cells, each equipped with a nucleus and cytoplasm, and surrounded by a cell wall.

In some of the yeasts, cells in old cultures develop thickened walls, become filled with granular, reserve material, and apparently go into a resting stage. These are called **chlamydospores** and are more resistant to drying than are ordinary vegetative yeast cells. When placed under suitable environmental conditions, a chlamydospore germinates and forms a new vegetative cell. This process, like endospore formation in bacteria, results in reproduction without multiplication.

The yeasts which can produce a mycelium may produce chlamydospores either at the tip of a hypha or within the chain of cells which goes to make up a hypha. In addition, some of the mycelium-forming yeasts produce **blastospores,** which are spheroidal or ellipsoidal reproductive units formed from the hypha by budding. A third type of asexual spores which may be produced by mycelium-forming yeasts are **arthrospores;** these are produced by the breaking up of a septate hypha into its component cells. The arthrospores, or oidia, are usually cylindrical, and have rather square-cut ends; this characteristic makes possible their differentiation from blastospores, which are spheroidal or ellipsoidal in shape.

Sexual Reproduction

It is now believed that all ascospore-forming yeasts reproduce by sexual means. There are two main types of ascospore-forming yeasts: (1) The usual vegetative cell is haploid (half the number of chromosomes that are found in sexual spores), and sexual spores are formed following the union (conjugation) of two cells; the diploid spores are retained in an ascus and upon germination, divide to form haploid vegetative cells. This type of sexual reproduction is typical of yeasts in the genera *Zygosaccharomyces* and *Schizosaccharomyces*. (2) The usual vegetative cell is diploid, and when nuclear division occurs within the cell, nuclei containing half the normal number of chromosomes are formed. These nuclei become surrounded by walls and are retained within the mother cell wall, which is then called an ascus. The haploid spores may conjugate to form diploid cells, which upon emer-

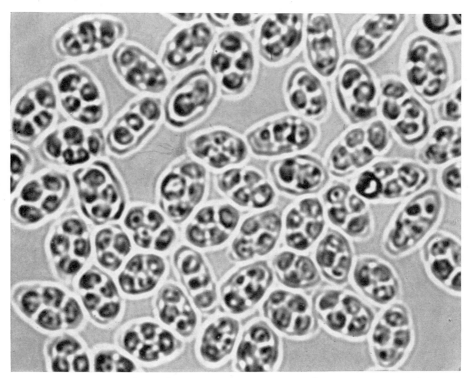

FIGURE 23.   Asci of *Saccharomyces cerevisiae*. Each ascus contains 4 ascospores. (Courtesy of The Fleischmann Laboratories.)

gence from the ascus become vegetative cells; in some cases, the ascus breaks open to liberate the haploid spores which then unite to form diploid vegetative cells. This type of sexual reproduction is most common among the yeasts of industrial importance. Figure 23 shows asci formed by *Saccharomyces cerevisiae*; each ascus contains four ascospores.

Sexual spore-formation in yeasts results in multiplication, but the increase in numbers is not as rapid as that which occurs during vegetative reproduction by budding or fission. The spores of yeasts are formed only under special conditions, and it is often difficult to induce spore-forming yeasts to produce spores. In the laboratory, cultivation of the yeast on a medium containing carrot infusion or carrot extract in the presence of a little calcium sulfate may bring about spore formation in time if the temperature, oxygen supply, and moisture content of the environment are suitable.

At present, many different kinds of yeasts are classified as imperfect fungi because they have been found to reproduce only by vegetative means, or by the formation of asexual spores.

Cultural and Physiological Characteristics of Yeasts

Different kinds of yeasts exhibit not only morphological and structural differences, but vary tremendously in cultural characteristics and physiology.

On solid culture media, **mycelium-forming** yeasts form a mold-like growth which often is difficult to distinguish from a mold. The typically unicellular yeasts form colonies much like those produced by bacteria.

On liquid media, **film-forming** yeasts grow on the surface and usually remain in this location until the film is broken or becomes so heavy that it sinks. Other yeasts, called "top" yeasts, have cells which gather in clumps and are carried to the top of the fermenting liquid by gas caught in the clumps. Yeasts of a third type are known as "bottom" yeasts, the cells of which stay fairly well separated, and settle toward the bottom of a fermenting liquid.

In general, the film-forming yeasts bring about oxidation of organic foods such as sugars, alcohols, and organic acids. Bottom and top yeasts usually are fermentative in their use of carbohydrate foods, and produce carbon dioxide and varying quantities of ethyl alcohol as their main by-products.

The fermentative yeasts are of great importance in baking, the manufacture of alcoholic beverages, and the industrial production of ethyl alcohol.

REFERENCES

Lindegren, C. C., *The yeast cell, its genetics and cytology*. St. Louis, Mo., Educational Publishers, 1949.

Skinner, C. E., Emmons, C. W., and Tsuchiya, H. M. *Henrici's molds, yeasts, and actinomycetes* (2nd ed.). N. Y., Wiley, 1947.

Smith, G. M., *Cryptogamic botany*, Vol. I (*Algae and fungi*). N. Y., McGraw-Hill 1938, pp. 427–431.

Wolf, F. A., and Wolf, F. T., *The fungi*, Vols. I and II. N. Y., Wiley, 1947.

6. PROTOZOA

Occurrence of Protozoa

Protozoa, like other microorganisms, are widely distributed in nature. They are particularly abundant in oceans, but are also found in large numbers in lakes, rivers, and ponds. The upper six inches of the soil contains numerous protozoa; as a rule there are larger numbers in soils high in organic matter than in sandy soils. The intestines of nearly all animals contain protozoa, most of which, like those that exist in the mouths of many animals, are apparently harmless; but some of the parasitic protozoa produce disease. Malaria is the most important of the protozoan diseases of man, but there are, unfortunately, many others.

Description and Classification of Protozoa

Protozoa are the simplest of all animals; they are one-celled, and usually are microscopic in size. About 15,000 species of protozoa are known to exist, and they vary tremendously in size, shape, methods of reproduction and physiology. They are usually grouped in four classes, which are differentiated largely on the basis of morphology, as follows:

Phylum *Protozoa*
    Class   I.   *Sarcodina*. Those which move by means of pseudopodia (foot-like structures)
    Class   II.   *Mastigophora*. Flagellated forms
    Class III.   *Sporozoa*. Have no special structures to cause motility; produce spores at one stage in their life cycle
    Class IV.   *Ciliata*. Ciliated forms

SHAPES OF PROTOZOA

The most famous of the *Sarcodina, Amoeba,* has no fixed shape because its protoplasm is constantly flowing into pseudopodia that are projected in different directions. Some of the *Sarcodina* are covered with a shell, and therefore are quite constant in shape. Some of the *Mastigophora* are spheroidal, others ellipsoidal, and a few are cigar-shaped. The *Sporozoa* may

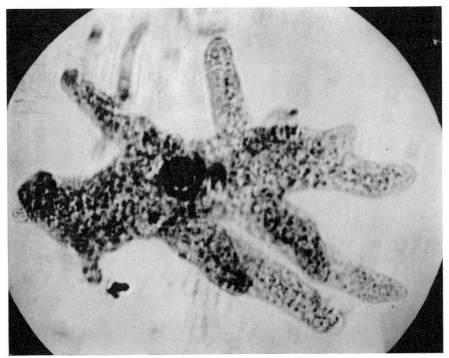

FIGURE 24. An amoeba showing pseudopodia. Enlarged 630X. (From J. Nowak.)

vary from small, spheroidal cells to fairly long, rod-forms. Some of the *Ciliata* are bell-shaped; others trumpet-shaped; a few are slipper-shaped; many are ellipsoidal. The smallest protozoa are not much larger than bacteria, but some of the larger ones may be nearly a quarter of an inch long. The cells of any one species are quite constant in morphology, but considered as a group, protozoa show tremendous differences in size and shape.

CELL STRUCTURE OF PROTOZOA

All protozoa are surrounded by a cytoplasmic membrane which, in some forms, such as *Amoeba,* is extremely thin and flexible. Many other forms, such as *Paramecium,* have a thickened cell membrane which, although rather flexible, holds the cell in shape. Still others are covered with a shell composed of calcium carbonate, silica, or sand grains, and hence their shape is fixed.

The *Sarcodina,* such as *Amoeba,* move by means of foot-like structures, or pseudopodia. When not resting, which means nearly all of the time, an amoeba is constantly, although slowly, moving about by sending out a pseudopod and then literally flowing into it. The cell membrane is so thin and

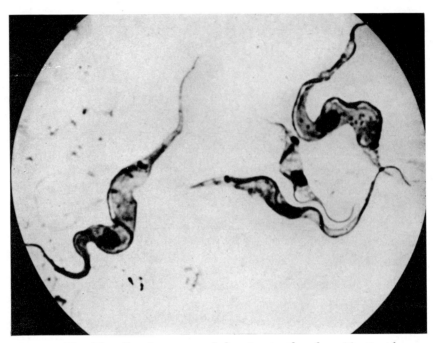

FIGURE 25. Flagellated protozoa belonging to the class *Mastigophora.* Enlarged 1600X. (From J. Nowak.)

flexible that an amoeba is almost like a small bit of rather weak jelly; hence its projection of pseudopodia and the subsequent flowing movement is apparently not difficult. Some of the *Sarcodina* have long, slender, ray-like pseudopodia which are used more for food-getting than for motility. Figure 24 is a photomicrograph of an amoeba.

The *Mastigophora,* or whip-bearers, have one or more flagella, which are comparatively long, protoplasmic structures that originate within the cell, stick out through the cell membrane, and are covered with a thin, highly flexible membrane of their own. The flagellates are capable of comparatively rapid movement caused by the lashing of their flagella. A few of the flagellated forms are also capable of amoeboid motion. Figure 25 is a photomicrograph of flagellated protozoa.

The cilia of *Ciliata* are shorter, finer, and more hair-like than flagella; also, a ciliated cell usually has thousands of cilia, whereas there are comparatively few flagella on the cells of flagellates. *Paramecium*, the best-known of the ciliates, is well covered with cilia that carry it through the water in which it lives in a spiral course, the axis of which is a straight line. The cilia may also serve to create currents in the liquid surrounding a rather stationary form, such as *Vorticella*, and thus, draw food particles into its mouth. In some of the ciliates, such as *Stylonichia*, several cilia have fused together to form spine-like structures that enable the cell to creep along on solid objects. Figure 26 is a photomicrograph of *Stylonichia*.

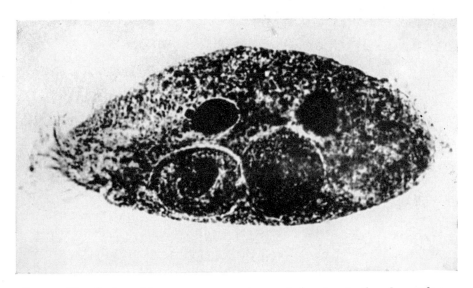

FIGURE 26. *Stylonychia*, a common protozoan belonging to the class *Ciliata*. The cilia are not visible without special treatment. Enlarged 480X. (From J. Nowak.)

Although protozoa are the simplest of animals, their internal structure is, compared to that of bacteria, rather complex. The cytoplasm of protozoa is usually heavily granulated and may contain several vacuoles. The granules consist of food undergoing digestion and stored materials such as glycogen and oils. Some protozoa contain a contractile vacuole which is able to discharge its liquid contents by contraction, and then expand once more as it refills with the liquid wastes of the cell.

All protozoa contain a nucleus or several nuclei. A protozoan cell cannot exist without its nucleus as this structure apparently exerts control over cellular metabolism as well as functioning in reproduction.

Some of the plant-like flagellates contain chlorophyll in chloroplasts imbedded in the cytoplasm. However, most protozoa do not contain chlorophyll, and their cells are colorless. Those forms which contain chlorophyll carry on a metabolism similar to algae; they absorb carbon dioxide, inorganic nitrogen compounds, and minerals in solution, and with the aid of the energy they get from sunlight, manufacture their own organic foods and reserves. Most of the protozoa, however, exist on a diet much like that of higher animals. All protozoa absorb food by osmosis, but some kinds also are able to engulf or ingest solid particles of food. Bacteria, algae, other protozoa, and small particles of dead organic matter make up the main food of these types. The parasitic protozoa that live in the intestines of termites eat the small particles of wood that are chewed and swallowed by the insect, but most of the other parasitic types either use food that has been partially digested by the host, or consume the cells of the host.

Reproduction of Protozoa

Protozoa can reproduce asexually in several different ways. The formation of cysts is common to nearly all species and occurs when the cells are placed under adverse conditions—particularly when they are dried or when their waste products accumulate. In the process of encystment, the cell's protoplasm becomes more dense and is then surrounded by a heavy wall. In this encysted form the cell is resistant to drying and can remain dormant for rather long periods of time. When the cyst reaches a favorable environment, it may burst open to liberate one cell; in some cases, nuclear division, with the formation of several cells, may precede opening of the cyst's wall. Thus, encystment may be merely a means for perpetuating an individual cell, or it may result in an increase in numbers of cells.

The most common asexual method of reproduction of protozoa is fission. In this process, a cell matures, its nucleus divides, and two cells are formed, each with a nucleus. Many flagellates divide along the longitudinal axis; other protozoa undergo transverse fission. In a multinucleate cell there is an equal division of nuclei between the two cells when fission occurs. In the *Sporozoa,* a process known as **schizogony** takes place in which several daughter cells are formed from a single mother cell.

Sexual reproduction does not occur in all protozoa, but there are some species in each class that are capable of reproducing by sexual means. Sexual reproduction involves first the union of two cells which may be different but usually look alike. This union is followed by a fusion of the nuclear material of the two cells and the subsequent division of the fusion nucleus results in the formation of spores or of new cells which then divide by fission.

REFERENCES

Hegner, R., *Big fleas have little fleas, or who's who among the protozoa.* Baltimore, Md., Williams & Wilkins, 1938.
Kudo, R. R., *Protozoology* (3rd ed.). Springfield, Ill., C. C. Thomas, 1946.

7. HIGHER BACTERIA AND APPARENT RELATIONSHIPS BETWEEN BACTERIA AND HIGHER FORMS OF LIFE

Orders of the Class Schizomycetes

All bacteria are *Schizomycetes*. This means that they are microscopic, unicellular, chlorophyll-free plants that reproduce asexually by fission, and exist either as spheroidal, cylindrical, spirillar or filamentous forms. The "higher" bacteria, although they are *Schizomycetes,* possess certain structures similar to, or develop in a manner much like that of certain other forms of life. Two of these groups of higher bacteria, the *Spirochaetales* and *Actinomycetales,* are of great importance owing to their ability to produce disease in man and animals; the *Actinomycetales* are also important agents in the decomposition of organic matter in nature, and some of them are used in industry to produce antibiotics such as streptomycin. The chief characteristics of each order of the higher bacteria will be described, and a discussion of the important activities of the two groups mentioned will be found in those chapters dealing with the decomposition of organic matter in nature and the production of disease.

Spirochaetales (Spirochetes, or Protozoan-Like Bacteria)

These are spiral forms of bacteria which usually are more or less cork-screw-shaped. They differ from the spirillum forms of true bacteria because their cell membranes are flexible, their motion is snake-like, and their cells are not flagellated; whereas the spirilla are equipped with rigid cell walls, move through liquid like a corkscrew, and have flagella. Almost all of the spirochetes are parasites, only a few being nondisease-producing aquatic forms, whereas the great majority of spirilla are nonparasitic.

58

The spirochetes resemble to a slight extent some of the *Mastigophora* known as trypanosomes, but this relationship is not very close. The spirochetes apparently lack a well-defined nucleus, and divide by transverse fission; the trypanosomes have a nucleus and undergo longitudinal fission.

Probably the chief claim for the relationship of this group of bacteria to the protozoa lies in their physiological characteristics. They produce diseases which resemble in many respects certain infections caused by protozoa, and chemicals used to combat protozoan parasites are often effective in preventing or treating diseases caused by spirochetes.

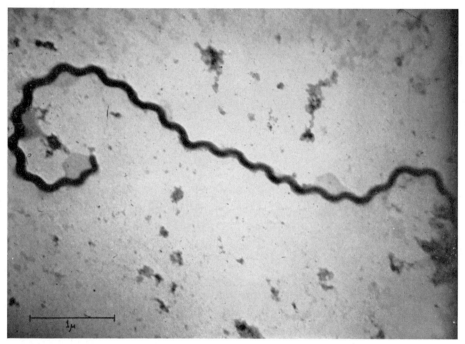

FIGURE 27. An electron photomicrograph of *Leptospira icterohaemorrhagiae*, a higher bacterium of the order *Spirochaetales*. This organism is protozoan-like because of its flexible cell wall and motility without the aid of flagella. (Morton and Anderson, S.A.B. No. 83.)

The cells of the *Spirochaetales* are usually rather small in diameter and vary a great deal in length. In some species the cells appear as tightly coiled spirals, but in others they look more like a long, wavy line. As a rule, it is difficult to stain spirochetes with the dyes which are commonly used in staining cells of the true bacteria. Figure 27 is an electron photomicrograph of one of the *Spirochaetales*.

The most important of all spirochetes is *Treponema pallidum*, the cause of syphilis.

Myxobacteriales (Slime-Mold-Like Bacteria)

Comparatively little is known about the *Myxobacteriales*. In nature they grow on manure and on dead mold mycelia. They may be isolated from soil, but whether or not they grow there and what changes they might cause, are not known.

When these bacteria grow, their cells are surrounded by a large amount of slime, and hence the colonies which they form have a very moist appearance. The cells move about in the colony by a sort of gliding or slithering motion, the cause of which is not known. As the colony matures, some of the cells pile up on the surface and form stalk-like structures on the ends of which fruiting bodies are developed. These fruiting bodies become surrounded by a wall and form a cyst, which in some cases may be a rather complex structure. As long as it is dry, the cyst, and probably the cells within it, remain dormant. When placed under conditions suitable for growth, the cyst breaks open, and the bacteria within move out into the surrounding medium to form new, slime-covered colonies.

Actinomycetales (Actinomycetes, or Mold-Like Bacteria)

Some of the microorganisms belonging to this order are definitely mold-like; others are very similar to the true bacteria, and a third group appears to be intermediate between the two extremes.

Members of the family *Mycobacteriaceae* are similar in many ways to the true bacteria, but have some characteristics which indicate their relationships to the mold-like bacteria. The *Mycobacteriaceae* are straight or slightly curved rods which frequently grow in long, hypha-like filaments and often show peculiar swellings. It is unusual for these cells to branch, and they do not form a mycelium. The cells reproduce by fission and do not form conidia. All members of this family are classified in the genus *Mycobacterium*. These bacteria are **acid-fast.** This means that they are difficult to stain; usually a strong dye such as carbol fuchsin must be used, and heat must be employed to make the stain penetrate the cells. Once stained, the bacteria are acid-fast; that is, they are not easily decolorized by ethyl alcohol containing 3 per cent HCl. Nonacid-fast bacteria are easily and quickly decolorized by such treatment. It is believed that the property of acid-fastness of the mycobacteria is caused by the presence of relatively large amounts of lipoids in their cells. Mature cells contain greater quantities of these lipoids and lipoproteins, and hence are more acid-fast than young cells.

All species of the genus *Mycobacterium* are aerobic, Gram-positive, acid-fast, nonmotile, and nonspore-forming. *Mycobacterium tuberculosis,* the cause of tuberculosis in man and animals, is the most important species of this genus. Some other species of this genus are also disease producers, but many are nonpathogenic, and are found in the soil, on hay or grass, and on the skin and exposed mucous membranes of man and animals.

The second family of the order *Actinomycetales* is made up of bacteria which are more mold-like than the *Mycobacteriaceae,* and are classified as *Actinomycetaceae.* As a rule, members of the *Actinomycetaceae* form a my-

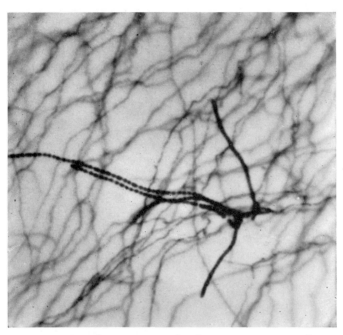

FIGURE 28. Photomicrograph of *Streptomyces antibioti-cus,* a mold-like higher bacterium in the order *Actinomy-cetales.* In the background is the network of branching, slender hyphae. In the foreground are the more dense chains of conidia. Enlarged about 1500X. (Courtesy of S. A. Waksman.)

celium composed of nonseptate, slender hyphae (never more than 1.5 μ in diameter) which later may become septate and break up into rod-shaped or coccus-shaped cells; however, some members of this family produce a mycelium which does not fragment, remains nonseptate, and produces ae-rial hyphae on which conidia are borne. Some species of *Actinomycetaceae* are partially acid-fast, but this is not true of the majority.

The obligate aerobic members of the *Actinomycetaceae* are classified in the genus *Nocardia.* Members of this genus are aerobic, Gram-positive, and nonmotile. They are widely distributed in nature and are active in the decomposition of organic matter. There are few pathogenic species in this genus.

The anaerobic, parasitic, nonacid-fast members of the *Actinomycetaceae* are classified in the genus *Actinomyces*. These organisms produce disease in man and animals; lumpy-jaw of cattle, caused by *Actinomyces bovis* is the most important of these diseases.

The third family of the order *Actinomycetales* contains the most mold-like organisms; they are classified in the family, *Streptomycetaceae*. These organisms form a mycelium composed of nonseptate, branching hyphae not over 1.5 μ in diameter, which do not fragment. Conidia are formed which are borne upon aerial hyphae by members of the genus *Streptomyces*, and on nonaerial hyphae by members of the genus *Micromonospora*. The *Streptomyces* produce chains of conidia, but the *Micromonospora* form a single conidium at the tip of each conidiophore. Figure 28 is a photomicrograph of *Streptomyces antibioticus*.

Members of the family *Streptomycetaceae* are widely distributed in nature; most of them are not pathogenic. They are important in the decomposition of organic matter. Some are thermophilic (grow best at temperatures above 45° C.) but most of them grow best at mesophilic temperatures (15° to 45° C.). They are numerous in soils, rotting manure, and lake muds. *Streptomyces griseus* is used industrially to produce the antibiotic, streptomycin. Several other *Streptomyces* species are known to produce antibiotic substances of potential value.

CHLAMYDOBACTERIALES (SHEATHED, ALGA-LIKE BACTERIA)

These bacteria grow in water in long chains of rod-shaped cells surrounded by a sheath. In some species this sheath is anchored at one end to some solid object, but in others it floats free and unattached. The sheath may be composed of colloidal ferric hydroxide, of organic matter containing granules of ferric hydroxide, or of organic matter in which no iron salts are precipitated. Figure 29 is a photomicrograph of *Sphaerotilus natans*, a species which has a sheath made up of organic matter.

Because many of these bacteria either have a sheath composed of ferric hydroxide or one in which this substance is precipitated, they are often called the "iron bacteria." They are found growing in reservoirs, and may even grow in wells or pipes if the water is rich in ferrous compounds. Apparently, the bacteria do not cause the oxidation of the ferrous carbonate in the water to ferric hydroxide, but this reaction occurs on the surfaces of their cells and on their sheaths. One group of filamentous, sheathed bacteria

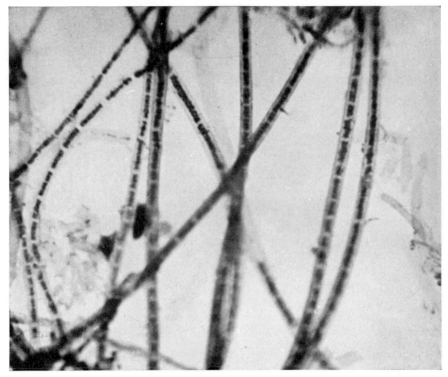

FIGURE 29. Photomicrograph of *Sphaerotilus natans*, a sheathed higher bacterium in the order *Chlamydobacteriales*. The sheath around these organisms does not become impregnated with ferric hydroxide. Enlarged about 1115X. (Photomicrograph by M. C. Shepard.)

in this order may contain granules of sulfur in their cells when growing in water containing sulfides.

Bacteria classified as *Chlamydobacteriales* reproduce by fission, by the formation of conidia, or by production of motile reproductive units called swarm cells. These motile swarm cells are produced by repeated division of the "normal" bacterial cells at the tip of an ensheathed filament. Each of these swarm cells is able to start the formation of a new, ensheathed filament when it is placed under suitable conditions.

SUB-ORDERS OF EUBACTERIALES RELATED TO HIGHER BACTERIA

The true bacteria are classified in the order *Eubacteriales* in which the suborder *Eubacteriineae* is made up of the "typical" true bacteria; these have been described in Chapter 1. However, there are other groups of true bacteria which possess structures or physiological characteristics that indicate their relationships to the higher bacteria.

The suborder *Caulobacteriineae* is made up of true bacteria which are found in lakes, streams and oceans growing attached to some solid surface. Some of these bacteria have a stalk that attaches them to the solid surface, but others are sessile and have no stalk. The stalk, if present, is composed of ferric hydroxide or of gummy organic matter on which ferric hydroxide is deposited. The cells occur singly, in pairs, or in short chains. They do not form filaments and do not have sheaths. Reproduction is by fission, and the cells do not form spores.

The suborder *Rhodobacteriineae* is made up of true bacteria that possess red, purple, brown, or green pigments which enable them to carry on a photosynthetic process. The photosynthesis caused by these bacteria does not liberate oxygen and can be carried on anaerobically if suitable oxidizable foods are available. These bacteria are found in lakes, streams, and oceans. Many of them are called sulfur bacteria because they contain globules of sulfur when they are grown in the presence of sulfides. Their cells are spherical, rod-, vibrio-, or spiral-shaped. Some are small—less than 1 μ in size—while others may be as large as 20 μ. All are Gram-negative, nonspore-formers; some are motile. There is strong evidence that one of these bacteria, *Rhodospirillum rubrum*, can fix atmospheric nitrogen in its cells.

REFERENCES

Breed, R. S., Murray, E. G. D., and Hitchens, A. P., *Bergey's manual of determinative bacteriology* (6th ed.). Baltimore, Md., Williams & Wilkins, 1948.

Skinner, C. E., Emmons, C. W., and Tsuchiya, H. M., *Henrici's molds, yeasts, and actinomycetes* (2nd ed.). N. Y., Wiley, 1947.

Waksman, S. A., "The actinomycetes." *Annales Cryptogamici et Phytopathologici* (1950), 9:1–230 + xviii. Waltham, Mass., Chronica Botanica Co., 1950.

PART II

The Physiology
of Microorganisms

Microorganisms, like other living things, consume food, grow and reproduce, and finally die. They are sensitive to various environmental influences, and are capable of causing both physical and chemical changes in their surroundings. A study of the physiology of microorganisms involves consideration of their extremely varied life processes. Most attention will be given to bacteria, but the physiology of yeasts and molds will also be discussed briefly.

8. NUTRITION AND METABOLISM . OF MICROORGANISMS

The algae and some of the photosynthetic bacteria are, like the higher plants, able to obtain energy from sunlight and make use of it in the photosynthesis of organic compounds. Foods consumed by these forms of life are used mainly for growth. With the exception of those few protozoa that contain chlorophyll, all animals and all microorganisms other than those mentioned are unable to use the energy of sunlight. From the foods which these forms of life use must be derived energy as well as the elements essential for growth. Some microorganisms, like animals, also must be supplied with small amounts of accessory substances (vitamins) in order to grow normally.

Food for Energy

Most of the food consumed by microorganisms that are incapable of photosynthesis is used in respiration processes which supply energy to the cell. The uses to which microbial cells put the energy thus obtained are not completely understood, but it is known that energy is needed for the following purposes: all of the cell's synthetic activities require the expenditure of energy; all of the reduction reactions which occur within the cell require the expenditure of energy; some energy is no doubt expended in performing mechanical work, such as movement; and finally, some of the remaining energy is used to maintain the living state. Saying that some of the energy available is used to maintain the living state, or as "energy of maintenance," of course does not explain how it is used, but merely points out the fact that energy is needed for this purpose. In addition, much of the energy liberated by microorganisms in their respiration processes is wasted.

Food for Growth and Syntheses

A relatively small proportion of the food consumed by microorganisms is used for manufacturing protoplasm and for other synthetic processes. Of course the kinds of food used by different microorganisms vary tremendously, but certain elements in these foods are apparently essential, and growth cannot occur unless they are present. The elements needed by each of the thousands of different kinds of microorganisms are not known, and years of painstaking work will have to be done in order to obtain this information. Bacteria, for example, are so small and are able to grow, i.e., increase in numbers, upon such minute quantities of certain foods that it is extremely difficult to determine exactly which elements in these foods are absolutely necessary for growth. But in spite of these difficulties, it has been fairly well established that most microorganisms require about the same elements as other living things. Carbon, hydrogen, oxygen, nitrogen, phosphorus, and sulfur are absolutely essential; iron, calcium, magnesium, potassium, sodium, and chlorine are probably essential; manganese, zinc, copper, boron, molybdenum, iodine, and silicon are elements that may be essential for some microorganisms, but not for all.

Accessory Substances (Vitamins)

In addition to the foods used to supply the cell with energy, and those used in synthetic processes, microorganisms also require minute amounts of certain accessory substances or vitamins. Probably all kinds of microorganisms need these accessory substances because they function as enzymes and coenzymes in the chemical changes necessary to continued life and activity of the cells. Some microorganisms are able to synthesize the accessory substances which they need, but others are unable to bring about the necessary syntheses, and hence the required accessory substances must be provided in the nutrients supplied. In general, microorganisms which require simple foods are able to synthesize the accessory substances which they need; but microorganisms which require complex foods usually must be provided with one or more accessory substances if they are to live and grow normally.

It is not possible in the space available in this chapter to describe in detail the many different kinds of accessory substances which microorganisms need, or the uses to which these substances are put in the life processes of microbial cells. Reference is made to the review by W. H. and M. S. Peterson, listed at the end of this chapter, for detailed information on these subjects. However, it may be pointed out that nearly all of the accessory substances that have been shown to be required by microorganisms are water-soluble; vitamin K, which is fat-soluble, is known to be required by one species of acid-fast bacteria, but not by others. Most of the water-soluble accessory substances known to be required by microorganisms are members of the vitamin-B complex; however, some of those substances that are needed by microorganisms do not have any known role in animal nutrition. The needs of all kinds of microorganisms for these accessory substances have not been determined with accuracy, nor have the abilities of certain microorganisms to synthesize the known accessory substances which they require been established. The following list includes those accessory substances which have been shown to be necessary for microorganisms:

Biotin	Para-aminobenzoic acid
Nicotinic acid (or nicotinamide)	Riboflavin
Pantothenic acid	Thiamin
Pyridoxine (or pyridoxal)	

In addition, inositol, hemin, choline, pimelic acid, glutamine, and several other substances have been shown to have value as accessory substances for some microorganisms.

It is believed necessary to repeat that only those microorganisms which cannot synthesize needed accessory substances must be provided with these vitamins in the nutrients supplied.

If a particular kind of microorganism is known to require a certain vitamin, i.e., if it cannot synthesize the substance, that microorganism can be used in vitamin assay work. The microbiological assay of foods to determine their content of certain B-vitamins is an accurate and useful method. The quantities of accessory substances required by microorganisms are very small. For example, *Lactobacillus casei* is known to require only 0.05 microgram (one microgram = one millionth of a gram) of riboflavin per milliliter of culture medium in which it is grown. This organism can be used to determine with accuracy riboflavin concentrations ranging from 0 to 0.05 microgram per milliliter. If the need of a microorganism for one or more vitamins can be established on a quantitative basis, that microorganism can then be employed in determinations of the amounts of the required vitamin (or vitamins) in foods.

Grouping of Microorganisms According to Foods Used

Autotrophs

Those microorganisms which use simple compounds or elements as their main food, and obtain the carbon which they need from CO_2, are called autotrophs. One group of autotrophs is made up of the algae, those protozoa which contain chlorophyll, and the bacteria which contain either bacterioviridin or bacteriopurpurin. These organisms are autotrophic because they obtain carbon from CO_2 and the other elements which they need from inorganic compounds; their energy is secured from sunlight. A second group of autotrophic microorganisms is made up of a rather small number of true bacteria that are unable to cause photosynthesis and must, therefore, obtain energy from foods which they consume. They are remarkable because they are able to derive energy from the oxidation of elements or of very simple compounds. For example, one kind of nonphotosynthetic autotrophic bacteria obtains energy from the oxidation of sulfur, another oxidizes ammonium salts to nitrites, and a third oxidizes nitrites to nitrates. These bacteria get the carbon they need from CO_2 or from carbonates; the other elements which they require are obtained from inorganic compounds.

Heterotrophs

Most microorganisms are heterotrophic; they are unable to use CO_2 as a sole source of carbon, and must obtain this element from organic foods; they derive energy from relatively complex organic food substances. **Saprophytic,** heterotrophic microorganisms use dead organic matter as their main food. **Parasitic,** heterotrophic microorganisms obtain their food from living tissue. Some microorganisms such as *Salmonella typhosa,* the cause of typhoid fever, are facultative or adaptable parasites because they can grow either in living tissue or in inanimate substances such as nutrient broth or milk. Some heterotrophic bacteria, such as *Azotobacter chroococcum,* which grows in soil and fixes atmospheric nitrogen, are strict saprophytes. Others, such as *Treponema pallidum,* the cause of syphilis, are strict parasites and have not been cultivated on inanimate material. Heterotrophic microorganisms need all of the essential elements and of course must obtain some of them from inorganic compounds, but the majority of their food is organic in composition. Their food requirements are somewhat similar to those of animals. Some of the heterotrophic microorganisms require certain accessory substances; others, like most of the autotrophs, can grow without being supplied with accessory materials, and apparently synthesize those which they need.

Whether or not a microbial cell can utilize a substance as food depends upon the enzymes which it possesses or can produce. **Enzymes** are organic compounds which have catalytic action and are produced only by living cells. Their properties are described later in this chapter. Enzymes which are liberated into the surrounding medium to catalyze the hydrolysis reactions necessary to decompose complex, insoluble foods into simple, soluble substances, are called **extracellular** enzymes. Whether or not a cell can use a complex, organic substance as food usually is determined by its ability to produce the extracellular enzyme needed to catalyze hydrolysis of that substance. Enzymes which remain inside the cells of microorganisms catalyze the syntheses, the oxidations, and the reductions which are necessary to the life of the cell; these are called **intracellular** enzymes. The oxidation and reduction reactions which occur in the respiration processes within the cells are of particular importance because their net result is the liberation of energy. These reactions are very complex, and many enzymes and coenzymes are required for their catalysis. The kinds of respiration reactions which a cell can cause, the kinds of foods which it can use in respirations, and the by-products formed, are dependent upon the kinds of respiratory enzymes which a cell possesses or can produce.

How Microorganisms Obtain Food

Some of the protozoa consume such solid foods as the cells of bacteria, algae, or other protozoa, and dead material such as wood or bits of plants. Other protozoa and all other microorganisms are unable to ingest solid food. Their food must be in solution, and must pass through the cell membranes into the cell by diffusion.

The relatively simple foods of autotrophic microorganisms are in solution or can easily be dissolved in sufficient quantities; this is also true of the inorganic compounds used by heterotrophic organisms, and of many of the organic foods which these forms require. However, many heterotrophic microorganisms are able to utilize complex, insoluble organic foods in a manner rather similar to that employed by higher animals. Some bacteria, for example, can use starch as food; but they must first digest it by means of hydrolytic changes catalyzed by enzymes which are secreted into the surrounding medium before the constituent food elements of the starch can be taken into their cells. Such a digestion is similar to that which occurs in the stomach and small intestine of a human being. Starch in the food which has been ingested by man is acted upon by the enzymes **amylase** and **maltase,** and is digested, i.e., hydrolyzed, to maltose and finally to glucose. The glucose is then absorbed into the blood stream and transported to the tissues where it is used as food. The way in which the insoluble substance must first be digested or hydrolyzed into simple, soluble components before it can be utilized as food is similar in both cases. The substance cannot be used by the organism until it is in the cell; it must be in solution in order to get there; the action of the proper extracellular, hydrolytic enzyme is necessary to bring about the hydrolysis reaction needed to change the substance to more simple, soluble compounds.

Enzymes Which Catalyze Hydrolysis of Complex Foods

An enzyme is an organic catalyst produced by a living cell. It is able to alter the rate of a reaction already started, or may even be capable of initiating a reaction between two substances with which it is in contact. While temporarily tied up in a labile compound with one or both substances, the enzyme becomes liberated in its original state as the reaction proceeds. A very small quantity of enzyme is able to catalyze chemical changes in relatively enormous amounts of reacting substances, and is not used up in the process. Enzymes alter the rate of a chemical reaction; they may either accelerate or decelerate a reaction between two substances, but they are usually of importance because of their ability to speed it up. Theoretically, most reactions catalyzed by enzymes are reversible, but an enzyme is usually important because of its ability, under certain conditions, to catalyze a reaction to the extent that equilibrium is quickly established.

Of the many theories advanced to explain the nature of enzymes, only two are widely accepted at this time. One theory states that the enzyme consists of two parts: a colloidal carrier and a specific, reactive substance held on this carrier. The opposing point of view is that enzymes are pure proteins, and that their specificity is determined by the arrangement of the atoms of the molecule. Within recent years several enzymes have been isolated in a pure, crystalline state. This lends considerable support to the view that enzymes are proteins, but until all enzymes have been obtained in a pure, crystalline condition, it is necessary to accept the possibility that both theories are correct. There is considerable evidence to support the view that the enzymes which catalyze hydrolysis reactions are pure proteins, but those responsible for the catalysis of respiration processes which take place within cells are composed of colloidal carriers with an adsorbed, active group.

Probably enzymes function in the following manner when they catalyze the hydrolytic decomposition of a substrate such as starch:

1. Enzyme + substrate $\rightleftharpoons$ Enzyme − substrate compound
2. Enzyme − substrate compound $\rightleftharpoons$ Enzyme + decomposition products

Whether or not an enzyme can catalyze a certain reaction, and its activity as a catalyst, are determined by several factors:

1. Enzymes are specific in that they will catalyze only certain kinds of reactions; in addition they will act on but one kind of substance.

2. The activity of enzymes is influenced by temperature. That temperature which is best for enzyme activity is known as the optimum. At low

temperatures, enzyme activity is decreased. At temperatures above the optimum, the activity of enzymes decreases rapidly, and at the maximum temperature their activity is much below that exhibited at the optimum. Heating at temperatures above the optimum will, in time, inactivate the enzyme completely; heating to a temperature above the maximum will inactivate it rapidly.

3. The activity of enzymes is influenced by the reaction of the solution in which they are working. Some enzymes are most active in an acid solution, others in a neutral solution, and some in an alkaline medium. Every enzyme

TABLE 2.   Some of the Extracellular Hydrolytic Enzymes Produced by Microorganisms

Enzyme	Substrate ($+H_2O$)	End Products of Hydrolysis
I. Esterases		
1. Lipases	glycerides (fats)	glycerol + fatty acids
2. Phosphatases		
a. Lecithinase	lecithin	choline + H_3PO_4 + fat
II. Carbohydrases		
1. Fructosidases		
(sucrase)	sucrose	fructose + glucose
2. Alpha glucosidases		
(maltase)	maltose	glucose
3. Beta glucosidases		
(cellobiase)	cellobiose	glucose
4. Beta galactosidases		
(lactase)	lactose	galactose + glucose
5. Amylase	starch	maltose
6. Cellulase	cellulose	cellobiose
7. Cytase	hemicelluloses	simple sugars
8. Pectinase	pectins	simple sugars and uronic acids
III. Enzymes hydrolyzing nitrogen compounds		
1. Proteinases	proteins	polypeptides
2. Polypeptidases	polypeptides	amino acids
3. Desamidases		
a. Urease	urea	CO_2 + NH_3
b. Asparaginase	asparagin	aspartic acid + NH_3
4. Deaminases	amino acids	NH_3 + organic acids

has a range of reaction in which it can operate. As the acidity of the solution is increased beyond the optimum, the activity of the enzyme is decreased until it disappears; this also occurs when the alkalinity is increased beyond the optimum.

4. The activity of enzymes may be influenced by the presence of neutral salts such as NaCl and KNO_3. Optimal concentrations of these substances accelerate the action of enzymes. Salts of heavy metals, such as $HgCl_2$ and $CuSO_4$ will, in time, inactivate enzymes.

5. In relation to the activity of enzymes and the optimum conditions for their action, time is an important factor. The effect of temperature on en-

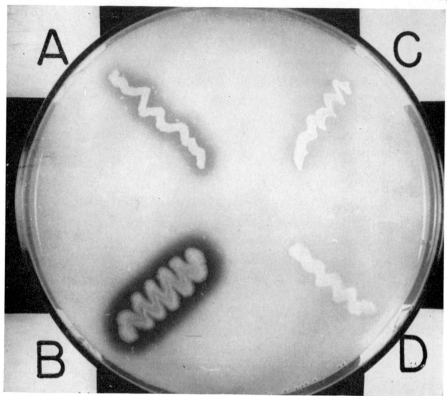

FIGURE 30.   An example of an enzyme that catalyzes the hydrolysis of an insoluble, complex protein. The milk-containing agar medium in the petri dish was streaked with four different kinds of bacteria and incubated. *Bacillus cereus* in streak **A** produced an extracellular hydrolytic caseinase that catalyzed the hydrolysis of the complex insoluble casein in the milk to simple soluble compounds so that a clear zone was formed in the milk agar around the streak of growth. Likewise, *Pseudomonas fluorescens* (streak **B**) produced much caseinase and a large clear zone was formed. However, *Micrococcus pyogenes* var. *aureus* and *Escherichia coli* (streaks **C** and **D** respectively) produced no caseinase so no clear zone was formed in the agar surrounding the streaks of growth.

zyme activity serves to illustrate the importance of time. A comparatively high temperature may appear to be optimum if the reaction is allowed to go on for only a short time; however, if the reaction is allowed to proceed for a much longer time, a lower temperature may be found to be optimum for the same enzyme in that acting at a slower rate, it may continue to be active for a longer time and hence catalyze a greater total amount of chemical change.

Microorganisms which produce enzymes capable of catalyzing hydrolysis of complex, insoluble foods probably secrete these enzymes into the surrounding medium. At any rate, the enzymes are found in the solution surrounding the cell, are spoken of as extracellular enzymes to distinguish them from those which are intracellular, and are liberated only when the cell is disintegrated. Table 2 on page 73 lists some of the more important types of extracellular, hydrolytic enzymes that may be produced by microorganisms. The hydrolysis reaction involves addition of water to a complex compound and the splitting of the compound into more simple and more soluble products.

Of course, every heterotrophic microorganism does not produce all of the extracellular, hydrolytic enzymes that have been listed. Some bacteria, for example, are noted for their ability to produce amylase; others can produce proteinases, etc. The ability of pure cultures to produce certain extracellular enzymes is determined in the identification and classification of bacteria. Figure 30 shows variation in the ability of four different kinds of bacteria to produce caseinase, a proteinase which catalyzes hydrolysis of casein.

In summary, it may be stated that a pure culture of a heterotrophic microorganism can make use of a complex, organic food only if it can produce an extracellular enzyme which will catalyze the hydrolysis of that food into more simple soluble substances which can enter the cell by diffusion. However, when several different kinds of microorganisms are growing in association, and one or more of the types present in the mixture produces an extracellular enzyme which catalyzes the hydrolysis of a complex food, the other organisms present in the immediate neighborhood may absorb the products of hydrolysis just as rapidly as do the cells which produced the enzyme.

USE OF FOODS THAT ENTER THE CELL BY DIFFUSION THROUGH CELL MEMBRANES

Foods taken into the cell by diffusion are acted upon by the intracellular enzymes which are present. The reactions catalyzed by these enzymes are of two main types: synthesis and respiration.

Synthesis

One type of change catalyzed by intracellular enzymes involves synthetic reactions in which the simple, soluble foods taken into the cell are built up into protoplasm, enzymes, reserve materials, pigments, or some other complex product. It is believed that the same enzymes which cause hydrolysis when acting outside the cell are present within it to catalyze these syntheses. It is known that the extracellular, hydrolytic reactions are reversible. This fact serves as a basis for the above hypothesis. Synthetic reactions use energy and are extremely complex. Consider, for example, the syntheses which must be carried on by a bacterium such as *Nitrosomonas*, which will grow in a medium containing only $(NH_4)_2SO_4$, K_2HPO_4, $MgCO_3$, $MgSO_4$, NaCl and $FeSO_4$. It obtains carbon from CO_2 in the air; oxygen is supplied by air; its nitrogen comes from $(NH_4)_2SO_4$; and the other essential elements are secured from the compounds listed. This organism builds protoplasm and the enzymes it needs from these very simple foods—a most remarkable feat.

Even heterotrophic microorganisms, which obtain their carbon from sugars, proteins or fats, their nitrogen from proteins, and their other essential elements from inorganic compounds, must still perform truly miraculous syntheses in order to build up protoplasm out of the comparatively simple fragments of food taken into the cells. The chemistry of these syntheses is almost entirely unknown at present.

Respiration

As a rule, the greatest part of the food consumed by microorganisms incapable of photosynthesis is used in respiration: any change occurring within the cell in which energy is liberated. If free oxygen is used, the process is known as **aerobic** respiration; if no free oxygen is employed, it is called **anaerobic** respiration. Microorganisms which need free oxygen for respiration, and cannot grow unless it is provided, are known as **aerobes:** those that grow in the absence of free oxygen, and are unable to use it in their respiration, are **anaerobes.** Those microorganisms which can either utilize free oxygen or grow without it are termed **facultative.** Microorganisms which require a definite, but small amount of free oxygen are termed **microaerophilic.**

Respiration reactions are catalyzed by intracellular enzymes which are very difficult to obtain and study apart from the cell. The nature of these enzymes and the mechanisms of the respiration processes which they catalyze are being studied intensively at this time. It is not the function of this book to attempt a detailed description of the mechanisms which have been proposed for each of the respiratory processes carried on by microorganisms. In a study of general and applied microbiology, knowledge of respiration is important because it is the process which provides energy for the maintenance and growth of microorganisms; because in respiration processes microorganisms decompose certain foods; and because, as by-products of respiration, microorganisms produce acids, alcohols, gases and other products of practical significance. Examples of each of the different types of respiration will be given, and it must be remembered that these are no more than type reactions. It is known, for instance, that one species of bacteria,

Pseudomonas putida, can utilize at least 77 different organic compounds in its respiration processes. When the large number of species of bacteria and the truly tremendous variety of substances these organisms can use as sources of energy are considered, it becomes apparent why only type reactions will be given.

All respirations involve oxidations and reductions. In general, an oxidation is any chemical reaction between two substances in which one loses one or more electrons, thereby becoming oxidized, and the other accepts these electrons and is reduced. For example:

$$2 \text{ FeCl}_2 + \text{Cl}_2 \rightleftharpoons 2 \text{ FeCl}_3$$

If the reaction proceeds from left to right, the iron increases in valence, i.e., loses an electron, and is oxidized. When the reaction proceeds from right to left, the iron decreases in valence, i.e., gains an electron, and is reduced.

In respiration processes that go on in the cells of microorganisms, oxidations and reductions involving the addition or removal of oxygen or hydrogen are of primary importance. The main changes involved in these processes may be summarized as follows:

Oxidation	Reduction
1. Addition of oxygen to a substance	1. Removal of oxygen from a substance
or	or
2. Removal of hydrogen from a substance	2. Addition of hydrogen to a substance

Most microorganisms oxidize organic compounds, such as simple carbohydrates, by the removal of hydrogen from the organic molecule. Enzymes known as dehydrogenases remove the hydrogen from the organic compound, an atom at a time, and pass it on from one enzyme system to another until it is used to reduce the final hydrogen acceptor. The substance which acts as the final hydrogen acceptor is determined by the aerobic or anaerobic character of the cells.

Whenever an oxidation occurs in a respiration process, a reduction must occur simultaneously. In the oxidation energy is liberated, while in the reduction energy is consumed. However, the net result of the oxidation-reduction processes in respiration is that more energy is liberated than is used up, and the excess is available for use by the cell.

Aerobic Respiration

1. Complete oxidation. During recent years the mechanisms by which living cells oxidize foods have been studied intensively, and it has been found that this process is not as simple as it was once thought to be. For ex-

ample, an aerobic or facultative, heterotrophic microorganism grown in a medium containing glucose and supplied with an abundance of oxygen, is known to bring about the following change:

$$C_6H_{12}O_6 + 6 O_2 \longrightarrow 6 CO_2 + 6 H_2O + 689,800 \text{ calories}$$
glucose

This process is similar to the oxidative changes occurring in animal respiration and was at one time thought of as a simple combustion. However, it has been shown that the complete oxidation of the glucose involves a long series of chemical changes in which many different enzymes are involved. The hydrogen that is removed from the glucose molecule is transferred through a series of enzyme systems until it is used finally to reduce atmospheric oxygen, with the result that H_2O is formed.

In some aerobic respirations, the oxygen used is reduced to H_2O_2 instead of H_2O. Inasmuch as H_2O_2 is poisonous, the cell must either have some enzyme to catalyze its destruction or one to aid its use in another process, or it will in time be killed. Some microorganisms contain an intracellular enzyme called catalase which catalyzes the decomposition of H_2O_2 to H_2O and O_2. Others contain enzymes known as peroxidases, which catalyze the oxidation of organic substances by H_2O_2 or other peroxides.

Molds, yeasts, and both aerobic and facultative types of bacteria have the systems of intracellular enzymes needed to carry on aerobic respiration and to cause complete oxidation of the foods which they utilize. There are, apparently, differences in the enzyme systems possessed by different microorganisms; no one organism is able to oxidize all of the oxidizable organic foods with which it might be provided.

Many aerobic, autotrophic bacteria may cause complete oxidation of substances which they use as food for energy. A good example is *Thiobacillus thiooxidans*, which gets its energy from the oxidation of elemental sulfur in this manner:

$$2 S + 2 H_2O + 3 O_2 \longrightarrow 2 H_2SO_4 + 237,000 \text{ calories}$$

Little is known concerning the mechanisms of this respiration, or the nature of the enzymes which catalyze the oxidations and reductions involved. Further information on the mechanism of aerobic respiration may be obtained from Porter's or Stephenson's books, to which reference is made at the end of the chapter.

2. Incomplete oxidation. Some microorganisms regularly cause only partial oxidation of the food used in their aerobic respirations. Others, given plenty of time and an abundant supply of oxygen, will bring about complete oxidation, but in a short time or under a restricted supply of oxygen, cause only incomplete oxidation. Probably the same intracellular enzymes

that catalyze the oxidations and reductions involved in complete oxidations also function in incomplete oxidations. An example of an incomplete oxidation caused by a **heterotrophic** microorganism is:

$$C_6H_{12}O_6 + 1\frac{1}{2} O_2 \longrightarrow C_6H_8O_7 + 2 H_2O + 199{,}000 \text{ calories}$$

glucose   citric acid

This oxidation is caused by certain molds. The oxidation is incomplete because the same mold, given more oxygen and a longer time to work, will oxidize the citric acid to CO_2 and H_2O. It will also be noted that this partial oxidation of glucose to citric acid sets free only 199,000 calories, while complete oxidation liberates 689,800 calories from the sugar molecule.

An example of an incomplete oxidation caused by *Nitrosomonas*, an aerobic, **autotrophic** organism, follows:

$$2 NH_3 + 3 O_2 \longrightarrow 2 HNO_2 + 2 H_2O + 66{,}500 \text{ calories}$$

Apparently, this organism is not equipped with enzymes which will catalyze a complete oxidation of ammonia to nitric acid. A related type, *Nitrobacter*, causes the final oxidation in this manner:

$$2 HNO_2 + O_2 \longrightarrow 2 HNO_3 + 35{,}000 \text{ calories}$$

Anaerobic Respiration

1. Intermolecular oxidation-reduction. Under anaerobic conditions, there is no free oxygen available to add directly to a substance or to serve as a hydrogen acceptor. Certain microorganisms are equipped with intracellular oxidizing and reducing enzymes which make it possible for them to bring about oxidation-reduction reactions within their cells without the use of free oxygen. The foods used in the respiration reactions of these microorganisms must be of two types: an oxidizable substance and a reducible material. An example of this type of respiration carried on by a **heterotrophic** organism is as follows:

$$C_6H_{12}O_6 \quad + \quad 12 KNO_3 \longrightarrow 12 KNO_2 + 6 H_2O + 6 CO_2 + \text{energy}$$

[glucose (oxidizable)] (reducible)   (reduced)   (oxidized)   (oxidized)

Not as much energy is available for the use of the cell in which this oxidation-reduction has occurred as was liberated in complete oxidation with free oxygen because some of the energy set free is used in the reduction of the nitrate.

Some **autotrophic,** anaerobic or facultative organisms cultivated under anaerobic conditions are capable of causing rather similar intermolecular oxidation-reduction reactions in their respiration processes. For example:

$$6 HNO_3 \quad + \quad 5 S \quad + \quad 2 H_2O \longrightarrow 5 H_2SO_4 \quad + \quad 3 N_2 \quad + \quad \text{energy}$$

(reducible)   (oxidizable)   (oxidized)   (reduced)

Microorganisms which obtain energy from intermolecular oxidation-reduction reactions may utilize a wide variety of oxidizable and reducible substances; the enzyme systems with which they are equipped determine which compounds can be used. The products formed are either the incompletely or completely oxidized form of the main food of the organism along with the partially or wholly reduced reducible substance employed.

2. Intramolecular oxidation-reduction. Of all forms of respiration, this is probably the simplest and most primitive. This is the process known as **fermentation.** It can be carried on only by anaerobic or facultative heterotrophic microorganisms. In this method of respiration, the cell absorbs the food, which is usually a simple sugar, such as glucose or some other soluble organic compound of sufficient complexity to allow both oxidation and reduction to take place within its molecular structure. This compound is then acted upon by the oxidizing and reducing enzymes within the cell with the result that the molecule is broken down in successive stages; part of it is oxidized by removal of hydrogen, while the other part is reduced by the addition of the hydrogen taken from the oxidized fragment. The most famous of the intramolecular oxidation-reduction reactions is the alcoholic fermentation of glucose by yeast, represented by the following equation:

$$C_6H_{12}O_6 \xrightarrow{\text{yeast}} 2\ C_2H_5OH + 2\ CO_2 + 31,200 \text{ calories}$$

The oxidation-reduction nature of the reaction becomes more evident when structural formulas of the compounds are considered.

$$
\begin{array}{l}
\text{CH}_2\text{OH} \\
|\\
\text{CHOH} \\
|\\
\text{CHOH} \\
|\\
\text{CHOH} \\
|\\
\text{CHOH} \\
|\\
\text{CHO} \\
\text{(Glucose)}
\end{array}
\xrightarrow{\text{yeast}}
\begin{array}{l}
\text{CH}_3 \\
|\\
\text{CH}_2\text{OH} \quad \text{(ethyl alcohol)} \\
+ \\
\text{CH}_3 \quad \text{(ethyl alcohol)} \\
|\\
\text{CH}_2\text{OH} \\
+ \\
2\ \text{CO}_2
\end{array}
$$

From this equation it may be seen that the first carbon atom of each of the molecules of alcohol is more reduced, i.e., has more hydrogen atoms, than any carbon atom in the glucose. The carbon of CO_2 is more oxidized than any of the carbon atoms in glucose.

The mechanism of this fermentation, and the enzymes, coenzymes and carriers which operate in each step of the process are now known. Students who wish to study the chemistry of this fermentation may find a complete description of it in Porter's or in Stephenson's book.

In this respiration, as in the others for which type reactions have been given, the microorganisms within which the oxidations and reductions occur benefit by securing energy. The products formed are useless to the cell and upon accumulation in sufficient quantity are even poisonous to it. The by-products of intramolecular oxidation-reduction respirations vary with different microorganisms because they contain different systems of oxidizing and reducing enzymes. For example, *Streptococcus lactis*, the common cause of the souring of milk, ferments glucose with the formation of lactic acid; other bacteria produce such by-products as acetic, propionic and butyric acids, butyl and isopropyl alcohols, and gases such as H_2 and CH_4 when acting on glucose.

In conclusion, it must be repeated that no attempt has been made to describe all of the chemical changes which microorganisms may cause. The purpose of the information presented in this chapter is to provide the student with a concept of how microorganisms obtain food and the different ways in which they may use it. The chemical and physical changes which microorganisms cause will be described in the chapters on soil microbiology, the microbiology of sewage treatment and disposal, industrial fermentations, the microbiology of milk and dairy products, and the microbiology of foods.

REFERENCES

Foster, J. W., *Chemical activities of fungi.* N. Y., Academic Press, 1949.

Lardy, H. A. (ed.), *Respiratory enzymes* (rev. ed.). Minneapolis, Minn., Burgess Publishing Co., 1949.

Peterson, W. H., and Peterson, M. S., "Relation of bacteria to vitamins and other growth factors." *Bact. Rev.* (1945), 9:49–109.

Porter, J. R., *Bacterial chemistry and physiology.* N. Y., Wiley, 1946.

Stephenson, M., *Bacterial metabolism* (3rd ed.). N. Y., Longmans, Green, 1949.

Williams, R. J., "Growth-promoting nutrilites for yeasts." *Biol. Rev.* (1941), 16: 49–80.

9. GROWTH OF MICROORGANISMS

A study of the growth of microorganisms is of considerable practical importance as well as of scientific interest. From studies of the growth histories of microorganisms and of the factors which influence the rate and extent of their growth, information may be obtained which is of value to those interested in favoring microbial development; similar knowledge is often useful in attempts to retard growth of microorganisms. For example, a cheese maker wishes a starter (which is a culture of desirable bacteria that is added to the milk to be made into cheese) to be as active as possible. The bacteria in this starter must be able to grow rapidly in the milk to which they are added in order to produce the desired changes. Knowledge of the growth habits and history of the bacteria employed in the starter aids the cheese maker in cultivating and using them to best advantage. The farmer whose cows produce milk to be used in cheese making applies his knowledge of the factors influencing the growth of microorganisms to the problem of preventing their development in milk. He knows that growth of microorganisms will result in changes in the milk and in the presence of large numbers of microorganisms that may be undesirable to the cheese maker; he must use this knowledge to inhibit or retard their growth.

The term "growth," when applied to unicellular microorganisms, usually means an increase in number of cells, i.e., multiplication. However, it is also used to designate an increase in size, weight, or volume of a single cell or of a colony. It is always necessary to use care in deciding whether a description of growth refers to an increase in numbers or an increase in size, but in this discussion, the term, growth, means an increase in numbers of cells of unicellular organisms.

Before describing the growth history of bacteria, some of the main factors that influence the rate and extent of their growth will be described.

Factors Influencing Growth of Microorganisms

The following are the more important factors that influence the growth of microorganisms.

1. *Food.* The foods required by microorganisms have been considered in Chapter 8. Two main types of foods must be supplied: those which are used in the cell's synthetic processes, and those used in respiration processes to supply energy. In addition, some organisms require certain accessory substances, or growth factors. The lack of any food substance will inhibit growth. Growth will be favored by the presence in sufficient quantity of the proper kinds of foods.

2. *Moisture.* Microorganisms need moisture to carry foods in solution into the cell, to carry wastes in solution out of the cell, and to maintain the moisture content of the protoplasm of their cells. This moisture must be free, not bound by the colloids of the medium. For example, milk, which contains approximately 87.5 per cent moisture, is an excellent culture medium for bacteria, as is meat broth, which contains about 98 per cent moisture. If enough agar is "dissolved" to make a 4 per cent solution in the broth, the moisture content of the medium will be approximately 94 per cent. However, very few bacteria will be able to grow on the broth containing 4 per cent agar because the agar, which is a hydrophilic colloid, has "bound" the water and made it relatively unavailable to the bacteria. This medium still contains more moisture than milk, 94 per cent as compared with 87.5 per cent, but milk is the better medium because the moisture in it is not bound; it is free and therefore available to the cell. In general, yeasts will grow in media containing less available moisture than is required for bacteria; molds need even less moisture than yeasts.

Another condition that will influence the availability of moisture to microorganisms is the osmotic pressure of the medium. This is controlled largely, other factors being constant, by the number of particles of solute dissolved in a liquid. If the osmotic pressure of a medium surrounding a cell is similar to that of the liquid within a cell, the solution is said to be **isotonic**. A **hypertonic** solution has a greater osmotic pressure than the liquid within the cell, while a **hypotonic** solution has a lower osmotic pressure than that of the liquid in the cell.

In a hypotonic solution, moisture will rush into the cell in an attempt to balance the concentration of substances in solution on each side of the cell membrane. Of course some of the solutes in the cell will pass out into the surrounding solution at the same time, but the water moves in so rapidly that if the cell does not have either a very rigid or an extremely flexible membrane it may burst. Hypotonic solutions are not conducive to growth and may even cause death of microorganisms.

In a hypertonic solution, moisture will be drawn out of a cell, and solute particles will tend to pass into it through the cell membrane in an attempt to balance the osmotic pressure on each side of the cell membrane. If the moisture is drawn out of the cell rapidly, the protoplasm within the cell shrinks, and the cell is said to be **plasmolyzed.** Plasmolysis of a cell causes inhibition of its growth and activity, and in time, may cause death. Some bacteria, for example, those that grow in the Great Salt Lake where the concentration of NaCl is about 28 per cent, and those that grow on salted hides, are rather indifferent to high osmotic pressure. Some yeasts can grow in honey; molds are known which grow on jellies and jams that have a high sugar content. There are, however, many kinds of microorganisms that are sensitive to increased osmotic pressure and will be unable to grow in any but an isotonic solution.

3. *Temperature.* The temperature which is best for the growth of a microorganism is known as its **optimum** temperature. In determining the optimum temperature, time, as well as temperature, must be considered. For example, a culture may grow very rapidly for a short time at a high temperature, and then die. At a slightly lower temperature, it may grow more slowly, but form more cells and live longer. The temperature which provides for most rapid growth combined with a maximum yield of cells is the optimum for that organism.

A few degrees above the optimum is the **maximum** temperature at which growth will occur. At the maximum temperature the rate of growth is usually rapid for a short time, but the amount of growth, i.e., the total number of cells produced, is not as great as it is at the optimum temperature.

The **minimum** temperature for growth is usually many degrees below the optimum. The rate of growth decreases as the temperature is lowered, and is much slower at the minimum than at the optimum temperature.

Some microorganisms are very particular in their temperature requirements for growth. The variety of *Mycobacterium tuberculosis* which causes most human cases of the disease grows best at 37° C., and has a minimum growth temperature of 30° C. and a maximum growth temperature of approximately 40° C. Many other bacteria are not at all particular; for example, *Escherichia coli* grows best at 37° C., but will also grow at 10° C. and at 45° C.

All microorganisms have been classified into groups on the basis of their **optimum** temperature for growth. Those species which have **optimum** growth temperatures above 45° C. are called **thermophiles;** those who **optimum** lies between 15° and 45° C. are termed **mesophiles;** the few forms which have **optimum** growth temperatures below 15° C. are called **psychrophiles.**

It is safe to say that in any natural substance, such as raw milk, which contains a mixed flora of microorganisms, there will be various species present capable of growing at temperatures ranging from 0° to 65° C. Of course the growth at 0° C. will be very slow, but will nevertheless take place in time. Conversely, in raw milk incubated at 65° C. growth of the thermophiles that are present will be rapid.

When an attempt is made to favor the growth of microorganisms, a temperature must be provided that will be optimal for their development; in retarding growth, low temperatures are usually employed. No growth occurs in completely frozen materials because the moisture present is changed to solid ice crystals and is not available to microorganisms. The low temperature of the frozen material is also a factor in preventing growth.

4. Oxidation-Reduction Condition of the Medium, and Supply of Free Oxygen. Aerobic microorganisms use free oxygen in the oxidation-reduction reactions involved in their respiration. Anaerobes do not use free oxygen and grow best in its absence. Facultative types are rather indifferent to the supply of free oxygen; they can use it in their respiration or can get along without it; they will grow either in its presence or its almost complete absence. Microaerophilic microorganisms require a definite, small amount of free oxygen.

The supply of free oxygen is important to the growth of microorganisms, but in addition, the oxidation-reduction character of the medium has been found to have considerable effect on growth. It is known that oxidizing substances, such as KNO_3, have a tendency to poise a medium at an oxidized level. Conversely, reducing substances, such as KNO_2, tend to maintain a medium in a more reduced state. That is, if a medium contains a relatively large amount of KNO_3 along with plenty of available oxidizable substances, it may be so oxidizing that even aerobic microorganisms will develop in it under nearly anaerobic conditions. It is also possible to put enough reducing substances into a medium to allow some anaerobic bacteria to be grown in it under aerobic conditions.

When most bacteria grow in a medium, such as milk, they usually change its oxidation-reduction character; they oxidize its oxidizable substances, reduce its reducible materials, and use up any dissolved oxygen that may be present. Some species bring about this change toward the reduced state at a more rapid rate than others. The rate and extent of reduction can be measured electrometrically, and the results expressed as the **oxidation-reduction potential,** or it can be measured with certain chemical indicators. Methylene blue and litmus are good examples of such indicators. In the oxidized state methylene blue is blue, but when reduced it changes to a colorless compound. If, for example, 1 ml. of a sterile, aqueous solution of methylene blue, containing about 1 part of the dye in 30,000 parts of water, is added to 10 ml. of milk, it will color the milk a robin's-egg blue. If the tube containing the milk-dye mixture is placed at 37° C., the dye will sooner or later, depending upon the number and reducing activities of the bacteria and other cells present, change to a colorless compound, i.e., become reduced. The chemical change which takes place is as follows:

$$(CH_3)_2N \text{—} \cdots \text{—} N(CH_3)_2 \quad \xrightarrow[(-2H)]{+2H} \quad (CH_3)_2N \text{—} \cdots \text{—} N(CH_3)_2$$

Methylene blue (chloride)   Leuco (reduced) Methylene blue

This reaction is described because it illustrates what is meant by the statement that microorganisms reduce substances in a medium. It explains the visible change which occurs in the methylene blue test used to determine the bacteriological quality of milk. It is also given in order to re-emphasize the fact that oxidation and reduction do not necessarily involve transfer of oxygen. Lastly, it shows another way in which a medium may be poised at an oxidized level, i.e., by adding to it a considerable quantity of a substance such as methylene blue. The chemical composition of litmus is complex and cannot be shown by means of a simple formula. However, in the oxidized state it will be colored, but when reduced it is changed to a colorless substance.

5. *Hydrogen-Ion Concentration.*   The reaction of a medium, expressed in terms of its hydrogen-ion concentration (usually in terms of pH), exerts considerable influence on the rate and extent of growth of microorganisms. All microorganisms have an optimum pH at which they grow best; a minimum pH, which is the most acid reaction in which they will grow; and a maximum pH, which is the most alkaline reaction which will permit their growth. Although some bacteria are known which will grow at pH 3.0 or perhaps in even more acid media, most species have an optimum some-

where between pH 6.0 and pH 8.5. A few bacteria are known which prefer definitely alkaline media of pH 8.5 or above. Most yeasts grow well in acid media of pH 3.5 to 4.5, but may grow in media as acid as pH 3.0 and as alkaline as pH 7.5. Molds may grow in media as acid as pH 2.0 and as alkaline as pH 8.5.

Some bacteria, for example *Streptococcus lactis*, prefer to grow in a medium of approximately pH 6.0 to 7.0. However, during their growth they produce lactic acid as a by-product of the use of a sugar, such as glucose, in their respiration. The lactic acid which they produce dissociates and hence increases the hydrogen-ion concentration of the medium, with the result that the pH drops to a point below the optimum for growth unless there are **buffers** present to maintain the hydrogen-ion concentration at its original level. The following is an example of a substance which acts as a buffer:

$$K_2HPO_4 + H^+ \rightleftarrows KH_2PO_4 + K^+$$

When an excess of H^+ ions is present, the reaction proceeds from left to right. In the presence of an excess of OH^- ions, the reaction proceeds from right to left, and the H^+ ions liberated react with the free OH^- ions to form H_2O. Amino acids also have amphoteric properties (act either as acids or bases) and hence serve as buffers.

Any medium has a certain buffer capacity. This means that the buffers present will resist a change in hydrogen-ion concentration until they become saturated with H^+ ions or until they have set free all of their H^+ ions in the presence of free OH^- ions. As soon as the buffer capacity of a medium is reached, any further addition of H^+ ions or OH^- ions results in a change in the pH of the medium. For example, when *Streptococcus lactis* grows in milk, it produces lactic acid as a by-product of its use of lactose. If normal, sterilized milk of pH 6.6 to 6.7 is inoculated with *Streptococcus lactis* and incubated at 21° C., several hours elapse, and the number of bacteria increases from a few thousand to several million per ml. before the buffer capacity of the milk is reached; then the reaction changes rapidly as these organisms, and the new ones formed, produce lactic acid. The reaction of the milk soon reaches pH 4.3 to 4.5, and then growth ceases. If no buffers had been present in the milk, the reaction would have been changed to pH 4.5 with comparative rapidity, and little growth would have occurred. It is possible to adjust the reaction of a medium to a desired pH, buffer it at that point, and in this way control the growth of microorganisms.

6. *Accumulation of inhibitory substances.* The by-products of microbial respiration are wastes and usually tend to poison the cells that are responsible for their formation. Acid-forming bacteria in time inhibit their own growth because of the accumulation of the acids which they produce. Yeasts pro-

duce alcohol and carbon dioxide in the fermentation of sugars, and these substances accumulate to the point where they stop growth. Some products of protein decomposition also become poisonous to the cells responsible for their formation and eventually stop growth. As a rule, neutralization or removal of waste products will enable growth to continue for a much longer time than when such wastes are allowed to accumulate.

7. *Surface tension.* This is the force that tends to hold together the molecules at the surface of a liquid. The surface tension of water, and of most aqueous solutions used as culture media, is rather high. However, if soaps, bile salts, or sulfonated alcohols are added to a solution, the surface tension is lowered. Some bacteria, especially those capable of growing in the intestinal tracts of animals, are able to multiply in media having a relatively low surface tension. Most microorganisms prefer to grow in media of relatively high surface tension.

8. *Presence of CO_2.* It is believed that all kinds of bacteria require the presence of at least a little CO_2 in order to grow normally. This substance is necessary for the growth of autotrophic forms because they use it as a source of carbon, but in addition, it has been shown that heterotrophic bacteria also need some CO_2. Too much CO_2 will retard growth; the complete absence of CO_2 may prevent growth entirely.

There are other, minor factors which influence the growth of microorganisms, but those which have been listed are of greatest importance. It is rather obvious, but nevertheless important to remember, that for best growth, all conditions must be optimal; growth may be inhibited by making unfavorable any one of the several conditions that have been considered.

GROWTH HISTORY (GROWTH CURVE) OF BACTERIA

When bacteria are placed in a new environment under conditions suitable for growth, and kept in this environment for a time, they pass through several consecutive states of development that together constitute what is known as the **growth history** of a culture. Changes occur in the morphology of cells during their growth history, but the feature of main interest is the change in number of cells. First, some of the methods available for measuring the number of bacteria will be considered because these procedures must be employed in order to obtain the information needed to study the growth history of a culture.

Methods for Measuring Numbers of Bacteria

1. *Direct Microscopic Methods:* (a) Counting chamber. This is a rather thick glass slide in which there is a small, hollowed-out area 0.02 mm. deep.

On the bottom of this depression are fine, criss-cross lines which form squares 0.0025 sq. mm. in size. The liquid containing the bacteria to be counted is placed in the counting chamber and a cover glass fitted over it so as to seal in the liquid. The bacteria over each ruled square are then counted with the aid of a microscope. In this way, the average number of cells per square may be determined.

Since liquid over each square represents $\dfrac{1}{20,000,000}$ ml. ($0.02 \times 0.0025 \times 0.001 = \dfrac{1}{20,000,000}$), the average number of cells per square, multiplied by 20,000,000 gives the total number per milliliter.

This method gives the total number present, but, because living and dead bacteria look alike, does not tell how many viable cells are in the liquid. It is not satisfactory for counting bacteria in solids (such as soil) or liquids containing solids which interfere with microscopic examination, but for use with clear liquids or suspensions prepared from solid media, it is a satisfactory procedure.

(b) Breed method. One hundredth of one milliliter of the liquid containing the bacteria to be counted is spread evenly over a rectangular or circular area of 1 sq. cm. on a clean glass slide. After drying and fixing, the film is stained with some dye such as methylene blue. The number of bacteria present in each of at least 50 different microscopic fields is then determined, and the average number per field calculated. The microscope used for counting the bacteria must be standardized by determining the diameter of its field, and calculating from this figure the area, and finally the fraction of one square centimeter represented by the area of the field. With the oil immersion objective and a 10 × ocular, the area of the microscopic field is usually about 1/5000 sq. cm. Therefore, if 0.01 ml. of liquid is spread over 1 sq. cm. and the average number of bacteria per field is, for example, found to be 12, the number of bacteria per ml. of liquid would be: $12 \times 5000 \times 100 = 6,000,000$ per ml.

This method, or modifications of it, may be used on a wide variety of substances. It gives the total number of bacteria present, but does not distinguish between living and dead cells.

There are other methods for direct counting of bacteria under the microscope, but the two which have been described are used more than any of the others.

2. *Cultural methods:* (a) Dilution. This is a rather inexact procedure for estimating the number of living bacteria or other microorganisms present in a substance. The liquid or solid on which the determination is to be made is diluted quantitatively, and a unit quantity of each dilution is inoculated

into a suitable culture medium. Following incubation of the inoculated medium, the number of microorganisms present in the original substance is estimated on the basis of the highest dilutions which show growth.

This procedure, though admittedly inexact, is used in estimating the number of certain pathogenic bacteria and viruses which will not grow in laboratory media. In such cases, susceptible animals or plants are inoculated with the diluted material, and the results calculated on the basis of the highest dilution causing infection. It is also used for estimating numbers of bacteria which cannot be cultivated easily on agar media.

(b) Plating method. One gram of solid or 1 ml. of liquid containing the bacteria to be counted is diluted quantitatively in a series of sterile "water blanks" (bottles containing 99 ml. sterile water) as shown in Figure 31. One ml. or 0.1 ml. quantities are then pipetted under aseptic conditions from the water blanks into sterile petri dishes. For example, 1 ml. from the 1-100 dilution will add 1/100 of the original material to a petri dish; 0.1 ml.

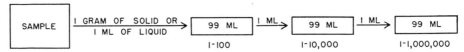

FIGURE 31. Diagram of a procedure for making quantitative dilutions of a solid or a liquid containing bacteria.

from the 1-100 dilution will add 1/1000 of the original substance; 1 ml. from the 1-10,000 dilution will add 1/10,000 of the original substance; 0.1 ml. from the 1-10,000 dilution will add 1/100,000 of the original substance, etc.

Melted, sterile agar medium, cooled to 45° C. is then added under aseptic conditions to each petri dish, which is immediately tilted back and forth in order to mix the medium with the diluted material. The agar is allowed to gel, and the petri dishes are incubated at a temperature suitable for growth of the bacteria that are present. Colonies will form in or on the agar in these plates from each viable cell or clump of cells present in the diluted material, providing conditions are suitable for their growth. These colonies are counted and multiplied by the dilution factor to obtain the number of bacteria per ml. (or gram) of original substance. For example, if 200 colonies grow on the plates inoculated with 1 ml. each of the 1-10,000 dilution, it is calculated that there were 200 × 10,000, or 2,000,000 bacteria per ml. (or gram) in the original material.

At best, this procedure gives only a fairly accurate estimate of the numbers of living bacteria present in a substance. Colonies may develop from clumps of cells as well as from single cells; it is almost impossible to avoid slight errors in pipetting; small colonies may be missed when the plates are counted; and the medium and conditions of cultivation may not be favorable to all of the bacteria in the original substance. These are but a few of the more important factors which make the results of the plate count procedure of relative rather than of absolute value. However, it is the most widely used method for determining the numbers of living bacteria in a substance.

3. *Increase in cell mass.* By measurement of the dry weight of bacterial cells in or on a substance, it is possible to obtain a fair estimate of their numbers. More important, though, is the fact that the results of such determinations are dependent upon the total quantity of cell substance, and are influenced by increases in size as well as increases in numbers of cells. Modifications of this procedure involve determination of turbidity or measurements of the volume occupied by the cell mass removed from a liquid by centrifuging.

Determinations of cell mass or volume, or of turbidity, must be standardized against some counting procedure. The facts that capsular materials and gums also increase the apparent cell mass and that different microorganisms vary in size and weight must also be taken into consideration. If this is done, these procedures provide a relatively accurate estimate of the amount of microbial cell substance and numbers of cells present in a medium. They do not, of course, distinguish between living and dead cells.

There are other methods available for measuring the number of bacteria present in or on a substance, but those which have been described are the ones most commonly used. By employing one or more of these procedures the bacterial population of a substance can be determined at intervals.

Growth Curve of a Culture of Bacteria

If bacteria are added to a substance in or on which they will grow, and suitable conditions are provided for their development, it will be found, by measuring the bacterial population at frequent intervals, that the culture passes through a certain series of phases known as its growth history. A typical growth curve is shown in Figure 32.

After inoculation at point A (see Figure 32), there ensues a period of lag during which multiplication is relatively slow. This **lag phase** lasts till point B; its duration is influenced by several factors. If the inoculum consists of a small number of cells, if these cells are old, if they are in the spore state, or if the environment is unfavorable in any respect, the lag phase will be comparatively long. Conversely, if the inoculum is large, if it consists of young, actively growing cells, and if the environment is favorable, the lag phase will be shortened, or may not occur. Numerous theories have been advanced to explain the lag phase, but these may be condensed into three general explanations. The first is that cells placed in a new environment take time to become accustomed to their new surroundings before they start to multiply. The second hypothesis is that cells placed in a new environment must alter it to suit their needs, and that this alteration, however slight, takes time. The third concept of the lag phase involves the belief that cells must go through a resting stage prior to rapid multiplication. Certainly the first two explanations can be accepted without hesitation, but the third does not necessarily hold in all cases. That multiplication does not occur or takes place very slowly during the lag phase, is an established fact,

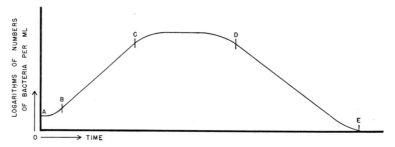

FIGURE 32.   A typical growth curve of a culture of bacteria. The phases of the growth curve are: **A** to **B**, lag phase; **B** to **C**, logarithmic phase; **C** to **D**, maximum stationary phase; **D** to **E**, phase of decline.

but it has also been shown that cells increase in size and respire actively during this stage of their development; therefore, they are not resting. If conditions are favorable, the cells soon start to divide, and continue to redivide at frequent intervals.

From points B to C (Figure 32), the culture is in its **logarithmic phase** of growth, so called because during this period the logarithms of the numbers of bacteria per ml., plotted against time, yield a straight line. Under optimum conditions, multiplication during this phase will go on at the most rapid rate possible for the organism concerned. Some thermophilic bacteria divide every ten minutes, and many common mesophilic bacteria reproduce every twenty to thirty minutes; but some of the mesophiles are not capable of dividing more often than every hour or two, and psychrophilic bacteria reproduce very slowly. The number of generations of bacteria formed during the logarithmic phase may be determined as follows:

$$n = \frac{\log c - \log b}{\log 2}$$

where n is the number of generations, $\log c$ is the logarithm of the number of bacteria per ml. at point C; $\log b$ is the logarithm of the number of bacteria per ml. at point B; and log 2 is the logarithm of 2. This formula may also be written as follows, since the logarithm of 2 is 0.301:

$$n = 3.3 \log \frac{c}{b}$$

In this formula, c = number of bacteria per ml. at point C; b = number of bacteria per ml. at point B.

The generation time may be calculated as follows:

$$G = \frac{T}{3.3 \log \frac{c}{b}}$$

where G is the generation time and T is the total time in minutes from point B to point C.

The duration of the logarithmic phase of growth is controlled by the various factors which influence growth. Eventually the rate of multiplication decreases until the numbers of bacteria remain practically constant. This **maximum stationary phase** is shown in Figure 32 between points C and D. During this phase the cells continue an active metabolism, but do not divide rapidly. If multiplication does occur, it takes place slowly and is balanced by the death of other cells.

Just why the logarithmic phase of growth does not continue, and the reasons for the maximum stationary phase are not entirely understood. The depletion of one or more essential foods or accessory growth substances will cause cessation of rapid multiplication as will the accumulation of waste products of the cells' metabolism. Probably these are the best explanations available, but they are not the final answer to the question.

The length of time that bacteria or other microorganisms can be maintained in the maximum stationary phase of development is dependent upon the kind of organism as well as on the environment. Some kinds of microorganisms start to die rapidly soon after reaching the peak of their growth. An example of such an organism is *Neisseria meningitidis*, the cause of epidemic meningitis. Other bacteria, such as *Escherichia coli*, have a prolonged maximum stationary phase under suitable conditions. In general, bacteria which have reached the maximum stationary phase of development can be kept from going into a phase of decline by removal or neutralization of poisonous metabolic products, by provision of an abundance of essential foods, by drying the culture, or by storage at a rather low temperature. Decrease of the temperature reduces the rate of metabolism, and will help maintain most microorganisms in their stationary state. Practical use is made of this knowledge by manufacturers and distributors of such products as compressed yeast, cultures of root-nodule bacteria for use in inoculating legume seed, and cultures of bacteria used as starters in cheese making. The microorganisms in these products must be maintained in the maximum stationary phase of growth for as long a time as possible, or at least until they are used.

Following the maximum stationary phase, the numbers of bacteria start to decline, slowly at first, and then more rapidly. The **phase of decline** is shown in Figure 32 between points D and E. During this phase there is little or no multiplication, and the cells die at a rate that varies considerably with different organisms and environmental conditions. Cultures of *Diplococcus pneumoniae* die very rapidly and may contain no living cells within a few days after entering the phase of decline. Other bacteria, such as *Mycobacterium tuberculosis,* die slowly over a period which may last months. Removal or neutralization of metabolic products, drying the culture, or storage of the bacteria at a low temperature decreases the rate of decline. Eventually, however, all of the cells of a culture die and become autolyzed. **Autolysis,** or self dissolving, is the result of the continued activities of the cell's enzymes following its death. Enzymes which catalyze hydrolytic and synthetic reactions within the cell are probably responsible for its hydrolytic decomposition upon death of the cell.

Changes in Morphology During the Growth History of Bacteria

While in the lag phase of growth, most bacteria increase in size and their protoplasm becomes more homogeneous in appearance as granules of volutin and other reserve substances disappear. The cells as a rule are of maximum size at the point where rapid multiplication begins.

During the logarithmic phase of growth the cells usually begin to decrease in size, but their protoplasm remains homogeneous. As growth slows up toward the end of the logarithmic phase, the cells become smaller, and in some species, granules begin to appear in the protoplasm.

When the stationary phase is reached, the cells are in general fairly uniform in size and smaller than they were in the early stages of the logarithmic phase of growth. Fat globules and granules of glycogen or volutin appear in the cells of some species. Spores form in the cells of spore-forming species upon reaching this stage of development. Most routine microscopic observations of morphology and staining properties are made while bacteria are in the early stages of the stationary phase.

As the culture ages and the cells go into the phase of decline, their morphology may change markedly. It is not unusual to find swollen, irregular cells in old cultures, and many cells become heavily granulated as they age.

The endospores of spore-forming species are liberated, and the cells which formed them disintegrate. The morphology of old cells is quite different from that of young bacteria—one of the most striking differences is the lack of uniformity in size and shape.

When these old, often peculiarly shaped cells are placed in a suitable environment, they repeat the history of development that has been described. If the cells of a pure culture are cultivated under carefully controlled, uniform conditions and are always examined late in their logarithmic phase or early in their stationary phase of growth, their morphology is remarkably constant.

REFERENCES

Henrici, A. T., *Morphologic variation and the rate of growth of bacteria.* Springfield, Ill., C. C. Thomas, 1928.

Porter, J. R., *Bacterial chemistry and physiology.* N. Y., Wiley, 1946.

10. INHIBITING AND KILLING MICROORGANISMS

In nature, many agencies may operate to kill microorganisms or to inhibit their activities and growth. These natural regulators of microbial populations keep the earth from becoming overgrown with saprophytic microorganisms and help prevent those capable of producing disease from killing all other living things. Some of these agencies have been adopted by man in his efforts to control the activities of microorganisms, and during the comparatively short time that scientific work has been done in an attempt to exert such control, remarkable advances have been made. However, much bacteriological and chemical work remains to be performed in order to explain the action of the various agencies which can be used, to refine and improve the techniques available, and to develop new means of control. This is a broad problem, but an important one, for everyone at some time is confronted with the task of inhibiting or killing microorganisms. The actual procedures used cannot, for want of space, be described in detail, but it is the purpose of this chapter to describe the different agencies involved and to discuss briefly the principles of the action of each.

FACTORS INVOLVED IN ANTISEPSIS, DISINFECTION, AND STERILIZATION

Any agency which inhibits the activity or growth of a microorganism is said to be **antiseptic.** Low temperatures are antiseptic as are certain chemicals which inhibit, but do not kill microorganisms. An agency which kills microorganisms is known as a **disinfectant** or **germicide.** High temperatures, applied for a sufficient period of time, kill microorganisms as will certain chemicals such as mercuric chloride.

Sterilization is a procedure which involves freeing a substance of all living things. This may be accomplished by means of physical agencies, such as heat, by the use of chemical disinfectants, or by removing the microorganisms from the substance.

Certain factors influence the various agencies which may be put to practical use in antisepsis, disinfection, and sterilization. Each of these factors must be considered when describing and attempting to explain the action of these agencies, and in reaching a decision concerning which physical or chemical procedure is to be used for some practical purpose. The very fact that these different factors may influence any attempt to inhibit or kill microorganisms makes it necessary to describe them briefly before proceeding to a consideration of the various agencies which may be employed.

1. *Intensity or Concentration, and Time of Action.* At high intensity or concentration, sterilization or disinfection may be accomplished in a short time, but at low intensity or low concentration, a longer time will be needed to accomplish the same result. The intensity or concentration of the agency may be low enough so that its effect is only antiseptic; it may even be low enough to have no effect. In some cases, very small quantities of antiseptic or disinfectant substances exert a stimulating effect on growth.

2. *Numbers of Microorganisms.* As a rule it is more difficult to inhibit or kill large numbers of microorganisms than small numbers. This is due to one or both of two things: (a) a greater quantity of the agency is required to inhibit or kill a large number of cells; (b) in mixed populations there is a greater chance for resistant types being present in a large number of cells than in a small number.

3. *Kinds of Microorganisms.* Some microorganisms are inhibited or killed very easily; others are comparatively resistant. In general, the spores of spore-forming bacteria are more resistant than vegetative cells, and capsulated varieties of a species are as a rule harder to kill or inhibit than noncapsulated varieties. Acid-fast bacteria, though nonspore-forming, are harder to kill than the vegetative cells of nonacid-fast bacteria. Other, so far unexplained, differences in resistance exist between various microorganisms.

4. *Age of Microorganisms.* In general, young, actively multiplying cells in the late lag phase and early stages of logarithmic growth are more easily killed than are cells which have reached the maximum stationary phase of growth. Old, senile cells are also less resistant than mature, active cells of

the same species. Spore-forming microorganisms are most resistant when in the spore stage; spores remain viable and resistant for relatively long periods of time.

5. *Previous History of Microorganisms.* As a general rule, cultivation of microorganisms under optimum conditions causes them to possess their maximum resistance to inhibitory or lethal agencies. However, it also appears that the resistance of bacteria to certain antiseptic or disinfectant agencies can be increased or decreased to a limited extent by varying the conditions under which they are grown or exposed. This might be interpreted as a "training" process, i.e., a change in the resistance of the individual cells in the culture. Another explanation is that by varying the conditions of cultivation, more resistant or more susceptible types are favored and allowed to develop at a greater rate than all other cells present in the culture. The diagram shown in Figure 33 illustrates the basis for this concept. A small number of cells in the culture have low resistance (points A-B); most of the cells have a medium resistance

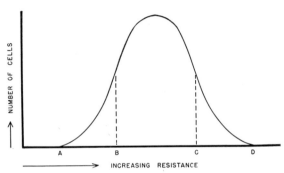

FIGURE 33. A frequency distribution curve showing the resistance of cells in a culture to a lethal agency.

(points B-C); a third group has a comparatively high resistance (points C-D). Cultivating the cells under conditions that will select or favor the less resistant forms will result in the majority of the population being made up of these forms and a lowered resistance of the resulting culture. Cultivation under conditions that will select and favor the more resistant forms will result in an increased resistance of the culture. Such variation is, however, limited to the range of points A to D. Variation in resistance beyond point D or below point A would indicate a change in the cells of the culture beyond the normal limits. Such a change would involve alteration of the cells by a training process or by a change in the heritable characteristics of the cells.

6. *The Medium Surrounding the Microorganisms.* (a) Moisture: Most of the agencies which kill or inhibit microorganisms operate to best advantage in the presence of moisture. For example, it is easier to kill microorganisms with heat in the presence of moisture than with heat in the absence of moisture; dry chemical disinfectants have little or no effect upon dry cells, but in solution they act upon moist cells with comparative rapidity. (b)

Presence of colloidal matter or solids: Such substances provide the microorganisms with some degree of protection; they are resistant to the penetration of both physical and chemical agencies. (c) Presence of substances in solution: Some materials in solution tend to protect microorganisms, others increase their susceptibility to antiseptic or disinfectant agencies. (d) Hydrogen-ion concentration of medium: In general, microorganisms will be more resistant to adverse agencies when suspended in a medium the pH of which is satisfactory for their growth. If the medium is made more acid or more alkaline in reaction, the resistance of the microorganisms will be lowered. However, the hydrogen-ion concentration of the medium may have an effect upon the antiseptic or disinfectant agency. For example, chlorine disinfectants decompose more slowly, and therefore do not kill microorganisms as rapidly in alkaline solutions as they do in solutions of a neutral or slightly acid reaction. Hence it is necessary to consider the effect of hydrogen-ion concentration on the agency as well as its effect on the microorganisms.

In addition to these few factors involved in the influence of the medium, there is the whole problem of trying to inhibit or kill microorganisms present in or on living tissue. This is particularly difficult because the protoplasm of the microbial cells is so similar to that of the tissue cells that an agency which harms the microorganisms is bound to have some effect upon the tissue.

Other factors influencing each agency will be mentioned in describing and discussing its action, but those which have been given are of greatest general importance.

AGENCIES WHICH KILL MICROORGANISMS OR INHIBIT THEIR ACTIVITIES

For purposes of description and discussion the agencies which act by primarily physical means will be separated from those whose action is mainly chemical.

PHYSICAL AGENCIES

1. *Desiccation.* In nature, desiccation is one of the chief agencies which inhibit the activities and growth of microorganisms. Dried substances often contain large numbers of microorganisms, but do not decompose because the microbial cells present cannot carry on metabolism or grow without moisture. Wood, textiles, grains, hay, straw, powdered milk, and dried fruits are a few examples of the many substances in or on which microorganisms are kept from acting by lack of moisture. Of the three kinds of microor-

ganisms—bacteria, yeasts, and molds—which must be kept from growing if substances which microorganisms can use as a source of food are to be preserved, molds need the least amount of moisture in the medium and are usually the most difficult to inhibit by desiccation.

Some microorganisms die very quickly upon desiccation, but others may live for long periods of time. While the spores of yeasts and molds are more resistant to desiccation than are the vegetative cells of these organisms, the spores of bacteria are more resistant to drying than any other form of life.

Drying may even be used to keep microorganisms alive for long periods of time. If the cells of a culture are suspended in a fresh, suitable medium and then frozen and dried under vacuum, they can be kept alive for long periods of time (providing the vacuum is maintained, and the container stored in a cool place).

2. **Osmotic Pressure.** In general, hypertonic solutions are antiseptic because they cause plasmolysis of the cells of microorganisms. High osmotic pressure is employed in the preservation of hides, meats, and fish by salting, and of fruits by sugaring. Microorganisms vary a great deal in their resistance to osmotic pressure. Bacteria are known which can grow on salted hides; some yeasts can grow in honey; mold-spoilage of jams, jellies, and sugared fruits is fairly common. But the growth of most bacteria, yeasts, and molds can be inhibited by high osmotic pressure. When moist substances which can be used as food by microorganisms are dried, the loss of moisture increases the concentration of substances in solution. Preservation by desiccation, therefore, also involves the influence of increased osmotic pressure.

3. **Pressure.** Microorganisms are capable of withstanding tremendous pressure. Pressures of from 6000 to 15,000 pounds per square inch are needed to exert any appreciable inhibition upon the activities of bacteria and yeasts. Pressures of 90,000 pounds per square inch, applied for 14 hours, kill most vegetative cells of bacteria and yeasts, but bacterial spores withstand 180,-000 pounds per square inch for the same period of time. However, if a gas such as CO_2 is added under high pressure to a liquid medium, and the pressure is suddenly released, it is possible to kill many of the microorganisms in the medium.

4. **Surface Tension.** When a liquid is placed in contact with an immiscible gas, solid, or liquid, the attraction between the molecules at the surface of that liquid results in a state of tension. Substances such as soaps, which reduce surface tension, tend to collect at any surfaces that may exist in the liquid. Thus, when surface tension depressants are added to liquids containing microorganisms, they become concentrated on the surfaces of the microbial cells. Here they may interfere with osmosis or exert some chemi-

cal effect on the cells. By mixing surface tension depressants with disin fectants it is sometimes possible to increase the killing power of the latter.

5. *Low Temperatures.* Practically all microorganisms are resistant to low temperatures. In fact, most microorganisms live longer at low temperatures than at the higher temperatures optimal for their growth. This is probably due to reduction in the rate of metabolism, a consequent decrease in the rate of production of waste products, and the fact that the poisonous effects of these waste products on the cells is lowered by cold. Low temperatures, above the freezing point of a substance, inhibit the activities and growth of microorganisms, but are not markedly germicidal.

At temperatures below the freezing point, metabolism ceases because of the low temperature and because all moisture present is in the crystalline condition. Freezing, however, does not kill microorganisms rapidly even when they are suspended in water. Exposure to $-252°$ C. for as long as two hours has only antiseptic effect on common nonspore-forming bacteria. When present in frozen meats, vegetables, fruits, and ice cream, microorganisms remain alive for considerable periods of time. For example, it has been shown that *Mycobacterium tuberculosis* remains viable and capable of producing disease when stored in frozen milk for as long as two years and eight months. *Salmonella typhosa*, the causative agent of typhoid fever, may live for two years and four months in heavily contaminated ice cream stored at approximately $0°$ F. Many fruit juices—such as orange juice, which has a reaction of about pH 3.5—are, at normal temperatures, somewhat germicidal to *Salmonella typhosa*; but this organism can survive for at least one week in frozen orange juice. The spores of spore-forming bacteria, such as *Clostridium botulinum*, the organism which produces botulinus toxin (the cause of botulinus poisoning), can live almost indefinitely in frozen foods. It is important to keep in mind the fact that cold is antiseptic; even extremely low temperatures do not kill microorganisms rapidly.

6. *High Temperatures.* If microorganisms are exposed to temperatures above their maximum for growth they will in time be killed. Heat is the most important and most widely used agency available for killing microorganisms. In all probability it kills the cells by coagulating the proteins of their protoplasm and inactivating the enzymes which catalyze metabolic processes. The temperature and time needed to kill microorganisms is influenced by several factors which must be considered when heat is used for this purpose. A brief discussion of each of these factors which influence **thermal death time** follows:

a. Time and temperature: A high temperature will kill in a relatively short time, while a lower temperature will take longer to accomplish the same result. For example, similar numbers of spores of *Clostridium per-fringens,* suspended in 0.85 per cent sodium chloride solution can be killed in 10 minutes at 100° C.; 15 minutes at 95° C.; 35 minutes at 90° C., and 80 minutes at 85° C. *Mycobacterium tuberculosis* in milk is killed in 10 minutes at 61.1° C. (142° F.), and in 6 minutes at 62.8° C. (145° F.).

b. Presence of moisture: Heat in the absence of moisture is much less effective in killing microorganisms than when moisture is present. Spores of *Bacillus anthracis* exposed in a relatively dry condition to dry air are killed in 1½ hours at 160° C.; the same spores exposed to heat in the presence of moisture are killed in 10 minutes at 100° C. In the laboratory, sterilization of dry glassware is accomplished by heating in the oven at 160°–180° C. for from two to three hours; liquids can be sterilized in the autoclave by steam under 15 lbs. pressure (121° C.) in about 20 to 30 minutes.

Use of the flame (incineration) is another means of employing "dry" heat. A culture loop or needle heated red-hot in the flame of a Bunsen burner can be sterilized quickly and effectively. Burning contaminated bandages, clothing, and bedding is an effective method of killing microorganisms present in them, but, for the latter articles at least, is hardly an economical procedure.

c. Kind of microorganism: Under a given set of conditions, there exists a wide variation among different kinds of microorganisms in their resistance to heat. In general, the spores of spore-forming bacteria are more resistant than either the vegetative cells of the spore-forming species or the cells of nonspore-forming bacteria. Bacterial spores are more heat-resistant than either yeast or mold spores. Thermophilic microorganisms are usually more heat-resistant than those which are mesophilic or psychrophilic. Finally, there exist differences in heat resistance between many species of bacteria which possess no outstanding properties to which such a variation might be attributed. For these reasons, sterilization by heat has to be aimed at destruction of the most heat-resistant microorganisms which may be present in or on the substance.

d. Previous history of microorganisms: Although much work remains to be done on this subject it appears that certain bacteria, when cultivated at their optimum temperature, are more resistant than when grown at a lower temperature or at a temperature above their optimum. For example, spores of a species of *Bacillus* grown in milk at 21° C. were killed at 116° C. in 6 minutes; the same number of spores of the same organism, grown at the optimum temperature (37° C.), required 17 minutes for their destruction at 116° C.; a like number of spores of the same species, grown at 45° C., were killed in 6 minutes at 116° C. Cells of *Escherichia coli,* a nonspore-forming bacterium, have been found to be much more resistant to heat when grown at their optimum temperature of 38.5° C. than when cultivated at 28° C.

e. Numbers of cells or spores: A longer time or a higher temperature, i.e., a greater quantity of heat, is needed to kill a large number of cells or spores than is needed to kill a small number. For example, a suspension containing 900,000,000 spores of *Clostridium botulinum* per ml. required 48 minutes at 105° C. for their complete destruction; 9,000,000 spores per ml., 36 minutes at the same temperature; 90,000 spores per ml., 20 minutes; and 900 spores per ml., 14 minutes.

f. Age of organisms: Young cells in the late lag or early logarithmic phase of growth are killed with comparative ease; cells of the same species in the maximum stationary phase of growth are more resistant; old cells of the same species well along in the phase of decline are again comparatively easy to kill. Since spore-forming bacteria form spores when they reach the maximum stationary phase of growth, they become much more heat-resistant at this age. The heat resistance of spores decreases very slowly with age.

g. Medium: Microorganisms are killed more easily in a moist than in a dry medium. They are killed more easily in an acid medium than in a neutral or slightly alkaline medium. They are killed more easily in a medium which contains their waste products than in a fresh medium which is free from these substances. Any solids or substances in solution which resist the penetration of heat into the medium will make their destruction more difficult. These and other minor factors make it necessary to determine the thermal death times of the microorganisms to be killed in the specific medium involved. For example, the spores of *Clostridium botulinum* can be killed in 50 minutes at 100° C. when suspended in a peptone solution, but in canned corn, an exposure of 100 minutes at 100° C. is needed to kill the same number of spores.

The time and temperature used is also influenced by the effect on the medium itself and by economic considerations. For example, in the sterilization of cans of evaporated milk, it is necessary to employ a temperature and a time of exposure that will sterilize the product without giving it too much "cooked" taste or causing it to have a burnt or caramelized appearance. Excessive exposures are also avoided because of the added expense.

Consideration of these factors emphasizes the fact that any statement concerning the temperature and time needed to kill a certain microorganism must be qualified by describing the conditions under which the determination was made. Practical application of this knowledge is made in canning factories, dairy plants which practice pasteurization, industries which use heat for sterilization of equipment and materials, hospitals, bacteriological laboratories, and in the home.

7. *Light and Other Radiations.* In general, light is harmful to microorganisms which lack chlorophyll or some other pigment that enables them to use radiant energy in photosynthetic processes. Radiations of such short wave lengths that they are invisible are usually more germicidal than visible light. The diagram presented in Figure 34 shows the radiations known to exert antiseptic and disinfectant action and their relation to some other radiations. The unit of measurement employed in expressing the wave length

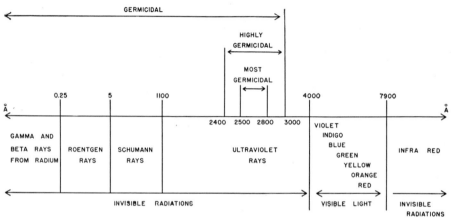

FIGURE 34. A portion of the spectrum showing germicidal and nongermicidal radiations.

of light and other radiations is the Ångström unit, Å, the value of which is 0.0001 μ (0.1 mμ).

Sunlight contains a relatively low concentration of germicidal radiations (usually under 0.1 per cent), and fog, clouds, smoke, and glass may filter out practically all of these ultraviolet rays. But if direct, unfiltered sunlight can reach microorganisms it will in time cause their death.

Artificial sources of ultraviolet rays, such as the quartz mercury vapor lamp or the carbon arc, provide a relatively great concentration of germicidal radiations and can be put to practical use. As shown in Figure 34, ultraviolet rays of from 2400 Å to 3000 Å are highly germicidal—those of from 2500 Å to 2800 Å are particularly effective in killing microorganisms.

The spores of spore-forming bacteria are somewhat more resistant to the germicidal action of ultraviolet light than are the vegetative cells of the same species or the cells of nonspore-forming bacteria. Some viruses, particularly the cause of tobacco mosaic, are even more resistant than bacterial spores.

Bacteria suspended in water that is free from other suspended matter can be killed with comparative case by ultraviolet light. Spores of molds present on the surfaces of solid substances such as meat and bread can also be destroyed rather easily. But if the microorganisms are suspended in milk, water containing solids which absorb or reflect the rays, or are present in soil or cloth, they are well protected against germicidal radiations. Attempts to kill microorganisms on or just beneath the surface of the skin must be made with great care to avoid painful and often serious burns.

Roentgen rays (commonly known as X rays) are somewhat germicidal, but are less effective than the longer Schumann rays, and much less effective than ultraviolet radiations. The beta and gamma rays from radium exert some germicidal effect; however, a greater amount of radiant energy is required to kill microorganisms with these radiations than with ultraviolet radiations. In general, the lethal radiation must be absorbed by some constituent of the cell if it is to cause injury or death. Some of the radiations of very short wave length tend to pass through the cell without being absorbed. Bacterial spores and some of the viruses are much more resistant to Roentgen rays and the beta and gamma emanations from radium than are the vegetative cells of bacteria.

8. *Electricity.* Passing an alternating current through a liquid in which microorganisms are suspended induces physical and chemical changes which may be antiseptic or even disinfectant. Whether or not the electricity has any direct effect on the microbial cells is a question that remains to be answered. When an electric current is passed through a substance, heat is produced; the greater the resistance and the higher the amperage, the more heat will be generated. Production of heat is the chief physical change caused by the current and is apparently mainly responsible for its lethal effects. Equipment is available for pasteurizing milk or fruit juices by passing a 60 cycle, 110 or 220 volt alternating current through such liquids as they flow between two carbon electrodes.

While heat appears to be the main factor in the killing of microorganisms by electricity, it is also possible that the current may cause the formation of ozone and chlorine in a liquid such as milk. Although produced in very small quantities, these substances, acting at the high temperatures developed, may aid in the germicidal activity.

9. *Agitation, Grinding, High-Frequency Sound Waves, etc.* The effect of each of these agencies is to disintegrate the cells of microorganisms. They are not particularly efficient means for killing microorganisms, but may be employed for this purpose under some conditions.

10. *Removal of Microorganisms from a Gas or Liquid.* Although such a procedure does not kill microorganisms, it removes them from a substance thereby bringing about its sterilization. One method by which removal can

be accomplished is **sedimentation;** a process of considerable importance in nature. Microorganisms are heavier than air or water and will ultimately settle out or sediment if undisturbed (currents in air or water tend to keep microorganisms suspended). In water sedimentation can be hastened by adding alum and lime, which causes the formation of a flocculent precipitate of aluminum hydroxide; as this precipitate settles in undisturbed water, it carries with it most of the microorganisms which were present. Rain and snow hasten the settling of microorganisms from the air—in modern ventilating systems air is often passed through a fine spray in an attempt to accomplish the same result.

In the laboratory sedimentation of microorganisms can be hastened tremendously with a **centrifuge.** In this apparatus the liquid is whirled around at such a high rate of speed that the cells are literally thrown out of suspension. In a continuous centrifuge the liquid containing the cells is fed upward through a cylinder rotating at a high rate of speed. Any cells present are thrown to the outside while the relatively cell-free liquid passes on up through the cylinder. Such a centrifuge is used in the manufacture of compressed yeast for separating yeast cells from the liquid in which they have grown. The more common type of centrifuge consists of a circular disc in which tubes or flasks of liquid can be mounted and whirled around at speeds up to 2500 revolutions per minute. This causes sedimentation of cells and solids to the bottom of the container. **Ultra centrifuges** have been developed which rotate at speeds high enough to develop a force as great as 700,000 times that of gravity. Such centrifuges can be used to sediment viruses and bacteriophages as well as bacterial cells.

Even more common, both in nature and in practical fields, is the use of **filtration** for removal of microorganisms from a gas or liquid. Under natural conditions water is filtered as it seeps through soil. Filtration is used in various ways in the laboratory and in hospitals and industries. In ventilating and air conditioning apparatus many different kinds of filters are employed. Cloth, cotton, steel wool, and glass wool impregnated with oil are the most commonly employed filtering agents in such units. Their action is dependent not so much on the small size of the pores through which the air passes as upon the crookedness of the air passages and the presence of water or oil on the exposed surfaces. Most of the microorganisms in air are carried on dust particles which will adhere to a wet or oily surface or will be trapped in a substance such as cotton.

Microorganisms may be removed from liquids by filtration through a wide variety of substances. Ground or sintered glass, thick layers of paper pulp, asbestos, plaster of Paris, unglazed porcelain, diatomaceous earth, and sand are examples of substances which can be used as filtering agents. More so than in the filtration of air, pore-size is important, but the crookedness of the path through the filtering agent also affects the efficiency of these filtering agents. In addition, the electric charge of the material is significant. Plaster of Paris carries a positive charge, but practically all other filters are negatively charged. Microorganisms also carry a negative charge in solutions of approximately neutral reaction, but the strength of this charge varies with different species and in different media. A negatively charged particle or cell will be attracted to and held by a positively charged filter. A cell carrying a weak negative charge will be repelled less by a negatively charged filter than will a cell carrying a strong negative charge; the cell with the strong negative charge will be less likely to be held by such a filter. Figure 35 shows a laboratory filtration procedure.

FIGURE 35. A filter for the removal of microorganisms from a liquid. The liquid is sterilized by drawing it through a fine sintered glass disc that holds back the bacteria. The flask in which the filter is mounted is connected with a suction pump in order to obtain the negative pressure needed to draw the liquid through the filter. (Courtesy of Corning Glass Works, Corning, New York.)

The medium in which the cells are suspended plays a considerable role in determining whether or not they can be removed by filtration. It is necessary to make tests to determine the effect of the medium on the filtration process, because accurate predictions are difficult to make.

As a rule, the smaller the organism, the more difficult it becomes to remove it by filtration. However, some rather large cells, because their cell membranes are extremely flexible, are able to pass through filters of very fine porosity. There is also a possibility that fragments of some cells may be able to regenerate new cells after passing through filters capable of retaining whole cells of the species.

Filtration has been studied extensively because of its use in the laboratory to separate bacteria from filterable viruses and bacteriophages, and because of its uses in water purification and in various industries. It is not a simple process, but when adequately controlled can be used to advantage in removing microorganisms from liquids or gases.

CHEMICAL AGENCIES

Just as it is at present impossible to tell exactly how and why microbial cells live and grow, it is almost as difficult to attempt an explanation of why certain chemical agencies cause their inhibition or death. Yet many substances are known which are either antiseptic, or disinfectant. The more important groups of such chemical agencies will be described and an attempt made to explain the manner in which they may affect microorganisms.

The factors influencing the antiseptic or disinfectant action of various agencies have been described at the beginning of this chapter. At this point, it might be well to list the main factors which must be considered when a chemical agency is to be used to inhibit or kill microorganisms; these are:

1. Kinds of microorganisms involved
2. Numbers of microorganisms involved
3. Age and previous history of the microorganisms
4. The tissue or substance in or on which the microorganisms exist
   a. The effects of the chemical on the tissue or substance
   b. The effects of the tissue or substance on the chemical
5. The poisonous properties of the chemical (if taken internally)
6. The time allowed for the chemical to act and the concentration which can be employed
7. The influence of temperature on the chemical and upon the tissue or substance involved

When these different factors are considered, it becomes apparent why there is no such thing as a "universal disinfectant" that can be used for all purposes. Consideration of these many factors also brings out the difficulties encountered in attempts to measure the value of disinfectants or antiseptics which are to be employed for various purposes.

METHODS FOR MEASURING AND COMPARING THE ACTION OF DISINFECTANTS

In the United States the method used by the Food and Drug Administration of the Federal Government is the official method for testing and comparing disinfectants. Briefly, the effect of the test chemical upon *Salmonella typhosa* is compared with that of phenol, under carefully controlled conditions. From the results of this comparison, the **phenol coefficient** of the chemical is computed by dividing the greatest dilution of the chemical capable of killing the bacteria in ten minutes, but not in five minutes, by the greatest dilution of phenol found to effect this same result. Chemicals which have a phenol coefficient greater than 1 are more effective under these conditions than phenol; those with a phenol coefficient less than 1 are less effective under these conditions than phenol.

From a consideration of the various factors which influence the action and use of chemicals as disinfectants it may be concluded that the phenol coefficient is a purely arbitrary evaluation which may or may not have practical significance. Not only the effect of the disinfectant on microorganisms but also the effect on living tissues should be considered; therefore some of the new methods for evaluating disinfectants take both of these factors into consideration.

Many chemotherapeutic agents, particularly certain antibiotic substances derived from fungi, e.g., penicillin and streptomycin, have very low phenol coefficients. However, when these substances are injected intravenously or intramuscularly, or are introduced into the body of an animal or human being by other means, they have remarkable abilities to combat certain invading microorganisms without causing great injury to the individual. Hence it is necessary to evaluate the potency of these antibiotic substances on the basis of "units" of antibiotic activity rather than in terms of their phenol coefficients. For example, the antibiotic activity of penicillin is assayed by inhibition of growth of a standard strain of *Micrococcus pyogenes* var. *aureus*. In this assay nutrient agar is inoculated with *Micrococcus pyogenes* var. *aureus* and poured into a sterile petri dish. When the agar has solidified, small cylinders of glass, porcelain, or stainless steel are placed on the surface of the inoculated agar, and filled with 1 ml. quantities of aqueous solutions containing varying dilutions of penicillin. Following incubation, there is a clear zone surrounding each cylinder containing inhibitory quantities of penicillin. If the zone of inhibition is 24 millimeters in diameter at the end of 24 hours' incubation, the solution is said to contain one Oxford unit of penicillin per ml. A typical penicillin assay plate is shown in Figure 36. A tentative International Unit has been adopted which is defined as the activity of 0.6 micrograms of the pure, crystalline sodium salt of penicillin G or II, a quantity of which has been set aside for use as a standard. The International Unit of penicillin is for all practical purposes identical with the Oxford Unit. In a similar manner, "units" have been worked out for streptomycin and other antibiotics. Unfortunately, these assay units are arbitrary and do not predict with absolute accuracy the efficacy of the antibiotic under the many different conditions which may be encountered during its use for therapeutic purposes.

Assay and evaluation of the sulfonamides, which are used extensively in chemotherapeutic work, is also very difficult. At present, methods are employed which indicate the concentration of a sulfonamide in the blood or urine of the patient after it has been given by mouth or parenterally. On the

FIGURE 36.   A typical penicillin assay plate. A solution was placed in the cylinders where it diffused out into the inoculated nutrient agar and inhibited growth of *Micrococcus pyogenes* var. *aureus*, a sensitive assay organism. The zone of inhibition is proportional to the concentration of penicillin in the solution. (Courtesy of Commercial Solvents Corporation, Terre Haute, Ind.)

basis of such determinations, the physician administering the drug can maintain levels of concentration which have been shown by experimentation to be inhibitory to certain pathogenic microorganisms.

In summary, it must be admitted that the problem of evaluation of disinfectants or antiseptics remains unsolved. The methods now available are inadequate because they do not give a complete answer to the question of what the disinfectant will do under varying conditions and acting upon different microorganisms.

CHEMICALS WHICH MAY ACT AS DISINFECTANTS

The chemicals which possess potential disinfectant properties may be grouped together, on the basis of their composition, into 14 main classes. An attempt is made in listing these main classes of chemical agencies to point out the principal mode of action which may be involved in the inhibitory or lethal action of each substance.

1. *Soaps and Other Detergents.* In practical use, soaps act mainly by causing mechanical removal of microorganisms from skin, various utensils, floors, clothing, etc. They also have some antiseptic action due to one or more of the following effects: (a) lowering the surface tension; (b) causing an alkaline reaction; (c) liberation of fatty acids that are antiseptic; (d) action of alcohol or other antiseptics mixed with the soap. The action of soaps is enhanced when they are used with hot water. It has been shown that the addition of sufficient hexachlorophene (G-11) to liquid soap to give a final concentration of 1 per cent of the chemical in the soap solution greatly increases the germicidal action of the soap on microorganisms present on the skin.

To satisfy the demand for better detergents, more than 1000 different cation- or anion-active compounds have been synthesized and tested during recent years. Many of these synthetic detergents have been found to possess antiseptic or even disinfectant properties. In general, cation-active detergents, such as the alkyl-dimethyl-benzyl-ammonium chlorides, are most effective in alkaline solutions, are inhibited by anion active detergents and phospholipids, and are more active against Gram-positive than they are against Gram-negative bacteria. Anion-active detergents, such as triethanolamine lauryl sulfate, are more effective in acid solutions, but like the cation-active substances are more antagonistic toward Gram-positive than they are toward Gram-negative bacteria.

Quaternary ammonium salts have been found to possess detergent action and to function as antiseptics or disinfectants. Many compounds of this type have been synthesized recently and are being tested under varying conditions to determine their efficacy. Preliminary studies indicate that the quaternary ammonium bases having alkyl side chains containing 12 to 16 carbon atoms are especially germicidal. These substances function as cation-active detergents.

2. *Alkalies.* The main effect of alkalies is dependent upon their ability to dissociate in aqueous solutions and thereby liberate free OH^- ions. This causes the reaction of the liquid to which they are added to become so alkaline that the activities and growth of microorganisms are inhibited, and death may result. Strong solutions of alkalies which kill microorganisms will

finally dissolve their cells. For this purpose, NaOH, used commonly in the form of commercial lye, is very effective. For example, when used in 0.3 to 0.5 per cent aqueous solution, lye is valuable as an antiseptic for use on the rubber parts of milking machines. A 5 per cent aqueous solution of lye is commonly used in the disinfection of barns and stables, and is one of the best agencies available for this purpose. Alkalies are also effective as detergents, and help to remove materials that hold and protect microorganisms. However, *Mycobacterium tuberculosis* and other acid-fast bacteria are very resistant to the action of alkalies. The whole group of Gram-positive bacteria is more resistant to alkalies than are Gram-negative bacteria and filterable viruses.

Other substances which yield strongly alkaline solutions when dissolved in water, and which have considerable antiseptic activity, are lime (CaO), trisodium phosphate, sodium carbonate, and sodium metasilicate. One or more of the last three substances may be incorporated in the alkaline washing powders used in dairy plants and in bottle washing equipment.

3. *Alcohols.* Ethyl alcohol, in concentrations of 50–70 per cent, may be germicidal. It is believed that it causes coagulation of the proteins of the cell's protoplasm. In concentrations lower than 50 per cent its antiseptic properties are diminished; the opposite extreme, absolute alcohol (100 per cent alcohol), has very little antiseptic action. Ethyl alcohol is widely used as a skin disinfectant and owes some of its effectiveness to its ability to act as a detergent. Ethyl alcohol is a better antiseptic than methyl alcohol. Other alcohols, such as propyl and butyl have not been studied extensively, but isopropyl alcohol is reported to have greater disinfectant power than ethyl alcohol. Glycerol (glycerine) is known to be a fairly effective antiseptic when used in a concentrated form, and is supposed to act by dehydrating microbial cells.

4. *Aldehydes.* Formaldehyde is an effective antiseptic and disinfectant, but its use is limited because of its poisonous nature and its sharp, disagreeable odor. It is particularly useful in killing molds, but is also effective on bacteria and viruses. A common formaldehyde solution is formalin—an aqueous solution of 37–40 per cent formaldehyde and a little methyl alcohol. A 5 to 10 per cent aqueous solution of formaldehyde is highly germicidal, even in the presence of organic matter. A 0.1 to 0.5 per cent aqueous solution of formaldehyde is antiseptic for most microorganisms. Another important use of formaldehyde involves its action on toxins, such as diphtheria toxin. It has the ability to destroy the poisonous properties of the toxin; thereby changing it to a toxoid, which, when injected into a human being or animal, will stimulate the formation of specific antitoxin without pro-

nounced ill effects. Formaldehyde probably acts by combining with free amino ($-NH_2$) groups of the proteins of the cell's protoplasm, or of toxins. This alteration results in inhibition of the activities, or even death, of the cell and in a decrease in toxicity of toxins.

Other aldehydes, such as furfural, appear to be antiseptic for certain fungi, but they are not widely used at present.

5. *Acids.* Strong mineral acids are harmful to skin, metals, and fabrics, and are poisonous; hence they are used very little for practical disinfection despite the fact that they are good disinfectants. Their action is due to dissociation in aqueous solution, with the consequent formation of free H^+ ions. A small concentration of free H^+ ions is antiseptic, while a larger concentration may be germicidal. Boric acid, a weak acid, used in saturated, aqueous solution, is mildly antiseptic toward bacteria, and is widely used because it has very little harmful effect on the skin or mucous membranes.

Organic acids, such as acetic, propionic, lactic, benzoic, and salicylic are used as antiseptics. Their activity, while caused in part by free H^+ ions, is largely due to the undissociated molecules and varies a great deal with the different acids. Propionic and acetic acids are particularly effective against molds, while benzoic and salicylic acids are inhibitory for bacteria. Lactic acid, formed in the fermentations involved in the manufacture of sauerkraut, pickles, olives, silage, and some kinds of cheese is antiseptic for many protein-decomposing bacteria, particularly the aerobic spore-forming species. Undecylenic acid, $CH_2: CH \cdot (CH_2)_8 \cdot COOH$, a white, crystalline, organic acid, has been shown to exert fungicidal action on certain fungi which cause skin infections.

6. *Phenols and Cresols.* Phenol (carbolic acid), used commonly in a 5 per cent aqueous solution, is the standard disinfectant with which all others are compared. It is a stable compound which is effective against vegetative cells of bacteria and fungi, but relatively ineffective against spores and viruses. It is poisonous, irritating, has a penetrating odor, is relatively expensive, is inhibited by low temperatures, and has other properties which limit its use. But at one time it was the most commonly used disinfectant, and still is widely used in hospitals because its properties and limitations are well known. It probably kills microorganisms by coagulating the proteins of their protoplasm. The germicidal activity of phenol is decreased in the presence of proteinaceous materials, alkalies, soaps, oils, and glycerol.

Hexylresorcinol, an aqueous solution containing 30 per cent glycerol and 0.1 per cent hexylresorcinol, is sold under the trade name of S.T. 37. The structure of hexylresorcinol, compared with that of phenol, is given below:

OH   OH

CH_2—CH_2—CH_2—CH_2—CH_2—CH_3

Phenol   Hexylresorcinol

Hexylresorcinol is a powerful disinfectant, but, like phenol, is relatively ineffective against bacterial spores. Its action may be due in part to the low surface tension which it produces. Although less poisonous and less irritating than phenol, it is comparatively expensive.

The cresols are effective against the same kinds of microorganisms as phenol, but are most highly germicidal. Like phenol, however, they are relatively ineffective against viruses and bacterial spores. Cresol disinfectants usually contain a mixture of the three cresols:

Ortho cresol   Meta cresol   Para cresol

They are mixed with soap and a little alkali which serve as emulsifying agents and must be present because the cresols are not very soluble in water. One of the commercial cresol preparations on the market is called Lysol. In general, cresols retain their germicidal activity in the presence of organic matter, but are inhibited by soaps and strong alkalies.

Creosote, obtained by destructive distillation of wood, and coal-tar creosote, manufactured by destructive distillation of coal, are effective preservatives for wood because of their fungicidal properties.

7. *Chlorine and Chlorine Compounds.* These substances are the most widely used of all disinfectants. Chlorine gas, when added to water, probably reacts in this manner:

a. $Cl_2 + H_2O \longrightarrow HCl + HOCl$ (Hypochlorous acid)
b. $HOCl \longrightarrow HCl + O$

The nascent oxygen liberated is a powerful oxidizing agent which is capable of killing microorganisms by oxidation. In the presence of NH_4OH the following reaction occurs in water:

$NH_4OH + HOCl \longrightarrow 2 H_2O + NH_2Cl$ (Monochloramine)

The chloramine is also germicidal, although it acts more slowly than free hypochlorous acid.

Calcium hypochlorite (also known as bleaching powder, chlorinated lime, or chloride of lime) is manufactured from lime and chlorine in this manner:

$$CaO + Cl_2 \longrightarrow CaOCl_2 \text{ (Calcium oxychloride)}$$

In solution, $CaOCl_2$ changes to $Ca(OCl)_2$, which is calcium hypochlorite.

Sodium hypochlorite is represented by the formula NaOCl, and is made from Cl_2 and NaOH, or by electrolysis of NaCl in an alkaline solution. In aqueous solution, both NaOCl and $Ca(OCl)_2$ yield HOCl. The HOCl decomposes to yield nascent oxygen.

Chloramine-T (sodium-paratoluene—sulphon-chloramide) is represented by the formula $CH_3 \cdot C_6H_4 \cdot SO_2 \cdot N \cdot NaCl$. Dichloramine-T is para-toluene-sulfon-dichloramide: $CH_3 \cdot C_6H_4 \cdot SO_2 \cdot N \cdot Cl_2$. Halozone is para-dichlor-sulphonaminobenzoic acid: $HOOC \cdot C_6H_4 \cdot SO_2 \cdot N \cdot Cl_2$. These are the more important of the so-called **chloramine** compounds used as disinfectants. All of these substances give up their chlorine rather slowly, while the hypochlorites are less stable and liberate with comparative rapidity the chlorine which they contain.

Chlorine kills microorganisms in two ways: by oxidation, due to nascent oxygen formed in its reaction with water; and by direct chlorination of the proteins of the cell.

The strength of a chlorine solution is expressed in terms of "available chlorine"—a value based on the oxidizing ability of the solution. This means that if the strength of chlorinated lime is given as 35 per cent available chlorine, the compound does not contain 35 per cent by weight of chlorine, but the total oxidizing power of the compound is equal to that of a 35 per cent solution of free chlorine. This does not measure the full disinfecting power of the solution because it does not take into consideration the direct chlorination which it may cause; it does, however, serve as a basis for comparing different chlorine solutions.

On standing, hypochlorites and organic chlorine compounds decrease in strength at a rate influenced by temperature, pH, and sunlight. At high temperatures and in sunlight, the decomposition goes on rather rapidly. The presence of alkalies, such as an excess of CaO, $Ca(OH)_2$, NaOH, Na_3PO_4 or Na_2CO_3 retards this decomposition; whereas acids hasten the process. Unfortunately, the addition of large quantities of alkali, though serving to stabilize the compounds, makes them less effective when mixed with water because in alkaline solutions they do not liberate their chlorine as rapidly as in neutral or acid solutions. It is necessary for the manufacturer of chlorine compounds to adjust the pH of the product to such a point that it will be relatively stable, but will give up its chlorine rapidly when dissolved in water.

Chlorine compounds are hindered in their action on microorganisms by the presence of organic matter; particularly by proteinaceous substances. Utensils or other objects to be treated with any chlorine disinfectant should be as chemically clean as possible, and water to be chlorinated should first be freed of organic matter.

Acid-fast bacteria are comparatively resistant to chlorine disinfectants; and the spores of spore-forming bacteria are more resistant than vegetative cells. From the small amount of work which has been done, it appears that viruses are only slightly more resistant to chlorine compounds than are the vegetative cells of bacteria.

Chlorine is added to drinking water in quantities varying from 0.025 to 2 or more parts of available chlorine per million parts of water, and if the time allowed for it to act is long enough, is a very effective disinfectant. A large number of microorganisms, as well as the presence of even traces of organic matter or other oxidizable substances, requires the addition of the higher concentrations of chlorine.

Chlorine compounds are used in the disinfection of utensils, vats, pipelines, bottles, and many other pieces of equipment in dairies, breweries, and other food-handling establishments. Solutions freshly prepared from hypochlorites or chloramines that contain an abundance of available chlorine are effective disinfectants when used on clean equipment. Weak chlorine compounds or solutions that have been allowed to stand for a considerable period of time are unreliable. Chlorine compounds dissolved in solutions of high alkalinity are of comparatively little value as disinfectants because the chlorine which they contain is not readily set free.

Chlorine compounds are of great value as disinfectants for medical and veterinary purposes because they are relatively nonpoisonous and noninjurious to living tissues.

8. *Iodine and Iodine Compounds.* Iodine is probably the most widely used skin disinfectant. It is usually employed in the form of a 2 per cent tincture of iodine—made by dissolving 20 grams of crystalline iodine in 500 ml. of water, in which 50 grams of sodium iodide have previously been dissolved, and then adding sufficient 95 per cent ethyl alcohol to bring the final volume to one liter. Although poisonous if taken internally, irritating to the skin, and capable of destroying delicate tissues, it is "the old stand-by" for disinfecting abrasions and in preparing the site of an operation. Bacteria vary but little in their resistance to iodine; the spores of bacteria are more resistant than the vegetative cells, but are killed in time. Iodine is also effective in killing fungi and viruses.

Aqueous solutions of iodine, the most commonly used of which is Lugol's solution (dissolve 10 grams of KI in 80 ml. water, then dissolve 5 grams of crystalline iodine in this solution; add water to bring the final volume to 100 ml.), are also fairly effective disinfectants, and are less irritating than tincture of iodine.

Iodoform, CHI_3, is an insoluble, crystalline substance which has some antiseptic action when applied to wounds. In contact with living tissues it decomposes slowly with the liberation of iodine, to which its antiseptic properties are due.

9. *Heavy Metals and Their Salts.* In aqueous solutions, the ions of metals will, when present in very small quantities, stimulate the growth of microorganisms; but when present in greater concentrations, metallic ions will act either as antiseptics or disinfectants. This is known as the oligodynamic action of metals. The germicidal activity of metallic ions is probably due to their reaction with the proteins of the cell's protoplasm, and the subsequent precipitation of the metal proteinates that are formed.

a. Compounds of mercury: Simple compounds of mercury (of which mercuric chloride, $HgCl_2$, is most widely used) ionize in aqueous solution with the resultant formation of Hg^{++} ions. A 0.1 per cent (also expressed as 1-1000) aqueous solution of $HgCl_2$ is a highly effective disinfectant, but its use is limited because it is poisonous, irritating and injurious to tissues, corrosive to metals, and precipitated by proteins. Another simple compound of mercury—yellow oxide of mercury, HgO—is an antiseptic substance commonly used in ointments. Unlike $HgCl_2$, it is not irritating or corrosive, but its disinfectant action is not great.

Attempts have been made to reduce the poisonous, irritating, and corrosive action of mercury, while retaining its antiseptic and disinfectant powers, by incorporating it in complex organic compounds which ionize very slowly if at all. Perhaps the best known of these is mercurochrome (the disodium salt of 2-7 dibromo-4 hydroxy-mercuri-fluorescein). Although commonly used as a skin disinfectant in the form of a 2 per cent aqueous solution, it is but mildly antiseptic and not as reliable as tincture of iodine for this purpose. Tincture of mercurochrome, sometimes called surgical mercurochrome, is a 2 per cent solution in 50 per cent alcohol that contains one per cent acetone; it is more germicidal than an aqueous solution of the same concentration. Mercurochrome is relatively nonpoisonous, nonirritant and noncorrosive, but should be considered as an antiseptic rather than a disinfectant.

Merthiolate (sodium-ethyl-mercury-thiosalicylate) is even less poisonous than mercurochrome; and from the limited amount of work which has been done on it, appears to be more germicidal. It is particularly effective when used as a tincture.

Metaphen (4 nitro-3, 5 biacetoxy-mercuri-2 cresol), a yellow powder, which is relatively insoluble in water, but can be dissolved in a dilute solution of NaOH of pH9, or in 95 per cent ethyl alcohol, is a fairly effective antiseptic, and is somewhat germicidal.

Phenyl-mercuric-nitrate is an effective antiseptic when employed in dilute aqueous solutions. It is relatively nonpoisonous and nonirritating.

The manner in which complex organic compounds containing mercury act upon microbial cells is not well understood. It is possible that since they do not ionize, the whole molecule combines with the proteins of the cell's protoplasm.

b. Compounds of silver: Relatively simple salts of silver are widely used as antiseptics and disinfectants. In aqueous solution they dissociate to form Ag^+ ions which combine with the proteins of a microorganism's protoplasm. Silver nitrate, $AgNO_3$, although expensive, irritating, astringent, and corrosive, is the most commonly used; but ammoniacal silver nitrate, $Ag(NH_3)_2NO_3$, which is employed in dentistry, and silver citrate, $Ag_3C_6H_5O_7$, are also of importance. These substances exert antiseptic action in solutions of 0.01 per cent (1-10,000) strength; more concentrated solutions are germicidal. Putting one or two drops of a 1 per cent solution of silver nitrate into the eyes of infants at the time of birth is a practice commonly followed—in many states it is required by law—as a prophylactic measure against gonorrheal infection of the eyes.

Colloidal silver compounds, such as argyrol, protargol, silvol, neosilvol and argyn, are silver-proteinates in which metallic silver or silver oxide is combined with some protein substance. These substances are relatively nonirritant, noncorrosive, and nonastringent and hence are used on delicate tissues. They are antiseptic, but may be germicidal if used in great enough concentration and allowed to act for a considerable period of time. It is believed that the activity of these compounds is due to slow ionization and the consequent liberation of the silver they contain.

c. Compounds of copper: Metallic copper, dissolved in minute quantities in water free from organic matter, is antiseptic as is a dilute solution of copper sulfate, $CuSO_4$. Copper ions, formed by the ionization of $CuSO_4$, are particularly effective against algae, and this compound is widely used in reservoirs and lakes. The $CuSO_4$ is added to a lake in small quantities in order to avoid killing fish and other forms of life. A concentration of approximately 1 part of $CuSO_4$ in 1,000,000 parts of water is sufficient to prevent the growth of algae. Although added in small quantities throughout the summer months, the total amount of $CuSO_4$ used is often great; for example, the City of Madison added a total of approximately 30,000 pounds of this chemical to Lake Monona during the summer of 1938.

d. Compounds of zinc: Zinc oxide is a mild antiseptic used in ointments.

Zinc chloride is an astringent employed in mouth washes, and exerts slight antiseptic action. The zinc salt of undecylenic acid is used as a fungicide in combating fungus infections of the skin (such as "athlete's foot").

10. *Compounds of Arsenic.* These substances are of importance mainly because they are antiseptic and germicidal for disease-producing spirochetes as well as for trypanosomes and some other protozoa. The number of these compounds available for use is apparent from the fact that Ehrlich manufactured 605 of them before making number 606 (Salvarsan), which was found to be particularly effective against *Treponema pallidum,* the cause of syphilis. Since Ehrlich's time, additional arsenic compounds have been synthesized in an attempt to find more effective disinfectants of lower toxicity to man. At present, arsphenamine, neoarsphenamine, and mapharsen are the most widely used arsenicals.

11. *Dyes.* Several of the coal tar dyes are capable of inhibiting the activities and growth of some microorganisms, but are not effective disinfectants. They have been studied extensively because they are relatively nonpoisonous and nonirritant when used on delicate tissues. The so-called basic dyes, such as crystal violet, methylene blue, basic fuchsin, and acriflavine have an affinity for acidic constituents of microbial protoplasm; acid dyes, such as acid fuchsin, combine with basic constituents of protoplasm. Such combinations result in the inhibition of metabolism and growth of the microorganisms, but a complete explanation for the antiseptic action of dyes is lacking. In general Gram-positive bacteria are more susceptible to dyes than are Gram-negative species; basic dyes are more effective in neutral or alkaline media, while acidic dyes exert their greatest effect in an acid medium; acid-fast bacteria and viruses are comparatively resistant to the action of dyes. The dyes are rather specific in their action and some species of microorganisms are not affected by their presence. For this reason it is necessary to test the action of a dye on the specific microorganism to be inhibited, and to make the test under conditions similar to those which will be encountered in practical usage.

12. *Sulfonamides.* In 1935, prontosil, which is 4 sulfamido-2, 4-diamino-azo-benzene-hydrochloride, was suggested as an agent which could be injected intravenously to combat infections caused by certain streptococci. Two years later, it was shown that the active part of the prontosil molecule is sulfanilamide, which is para-amino-benzene-sulfonamide:

$$NH_2 \langle \underline{\quad} \rangle SO_2 \cdot NH_2$$

Since the introduction of prontosil and sulfanilamide as chemotherapeutic agents, many derivatives of the latter have been prepared in attempts to synthesize compounds which would be effective under different conditions, and which would act upon various kinds of microorganisms. Some of the principal sulfonamides which have been studied extensively are the following:

Sulfanilamide   Sulfapyridine   Sulfathiazole

Sulfadiazine   Sulfaguanidine

These compounds are inhibitory to bacterial growth, rather than strongly bactericidal, in their action. In the body of a human being or animal the sulfonamides inhibit or stop growth of certain pathogenic microorganisms, and thus make it possible for the bodily defenses to destroy or remove the invading pathogens. In general, these compounds are most effective when administered in the early stages of an infection when the invading microorganisms are growing rapidly. All of the sulfonamides are more or less toxic and must be administered with care under the supervision of a competent physician.

Sulfanilamide is particularly effective against beta-hemolytic streptococci. Sulfapyridine has given good results in the treatment of pneumonia caused by *Diplococcus pneumoniae*. Sulfathiazole is particularly effective against staphylococci, and also has been used with success in the treatment of gonorrhea. Sulfadiazine has been found to be effective against infections caused by pneumococci, meningococci, beta-hemolytic streptococci, gonococci, and some of the causative agents of gas gangrene. Sulfadiazine has also been used effectively in prophylaxis against meningococci. Sulfaguanidine appears to have some value against certain Gram-negative bacteria which can cause infections of the intestinal tract.

These are but a few of the many sulfonamides which have been prepared and which are now under study. New compounds are reported almost monthly; hence it is not possible to list here all of the sulfonamides available to the physician or veterinarian for clinical use.

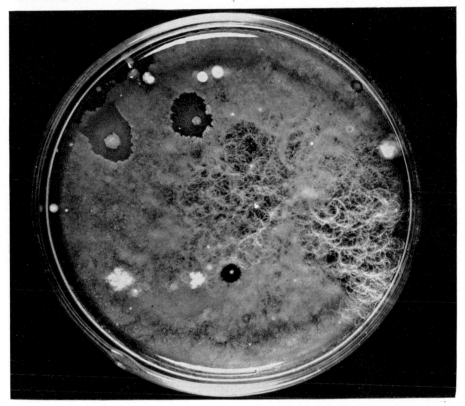

FIGURE 37. Examples of inhibition and of compatibility among microorganisms in a 1:10,000,000 dilution of soil. Three of the colonies visible have produced an inhibitory substance that has diffused into the medium and prevented the growth of the spreading colonies of different species; however, a number of colonies are compatible with the "spreaders" because none produces substances antagonistic toward the other. (Kelner, S.A.B. No. 143.)

It is believed that the sulfonamides act on bacteria by interfering with their normal metabolism. Woods and Fildes first showed that the action of sulfanilamide could be neutralized by para-aminobenzoic acid, which is required as an accessory growth substance by many different kinds of bacteria. Sulfanilamide is para-amino-benzene-sulfonamide, and it is believed that microorganisms which require the closely related para-aminobenzoic acid are inhibited readily by the presence of small amounts of the sulfonamide. This hypothesis of competitive inhibition is now well supported by extensive experimental evidence.

13. *Antibiotic Substances Produced by Microorganisms.* Many of the earliest studies made on microorganisms in their natural habitats showed that some of them produced substances that would inhibit or kill others. It was soon recognized that bacteria which produced lactic acid were able to inhibit the

growth and activities of protein-decomposing bacteria present in the immediate vicinity. However, it was also noted that certain bacteria and higher fungi produced substances other than easily identified acids that diffused into the surrounding medium to exert antiseptic or disinfectant action on other bacteria or fungi. Figure 37 shows a petri dish culture in which some of the colonies of bacteria are producing substances antagonistic to other bacteria. Gradually, over a period of many years, interest in microbial antagonisms, and in antibiotic substances produced by microorganisms, developed to its present pre-eminent position. Progress was slow at first, but following the discovery of penicillin by Fleming in 1929 and of tyrothrycin, gramicidin, and tyrocidin by Dubos in 1939 work in this field has progressed at a terrific pace. World War II provided additional impetus to the search for substances that would kill or inhibit pathogenic microorganisms without undue harm to the human body. As the number of wounded increased, the need for effective chemotherapeutic agencies became more apparent; the limitations of the sulfonamides in combating wound infections soon became evident. Medical men and laboratory workers of Great Britain, Canada, and the United States entered into a combined effort to produce penicillin rapidly and in quantities previously considered to be impossible. In this work they had the effective co-operation of the pharmaceutical and fermentation industries of the United States. In addition, a concerted drive was made to find new antibiotic substances, and to test their efficacy and toxicity.

During the approximately 60 years in which research on microbial antagonisms has been carried on, numerous antibiotic substances have been described. Table 3, page 123, contains a list of some of the better-known antibiotic substances, and the types of microorganisms which they inhibit or kill.

This list of some of the important antiobiotic substances is admittedly incomplete. New antibiotics are being reported almost weekly, and it is not possible to list all of those which show promise of usefulness. Also, it is not possible in the limited space available to list the names of all microorganisms which have been shown to be susceptible to various antibiotics.

A great deal of work is being done on the chemical composition and structure of antibiotic substances with a view toward the ultimate synthesis of those shown to be most valuable. At present, the structural formulas of penicillin, streptomycin, and chloromycetin have been worked out. In the meantime, the search continues for new antibiotics which will be effective against pathogenic microorganisms, including viruses, against which penicillin and streptomycin are ineffective. As this is written, penicillin, streptomycin, aureomycin and chloromycetin are the only antibiotics in full-scale industrial production. Figure 38 shows crystals of the potassium salt of pure penicillin G.

TABLE 3. Some of the Important Antibiotic Substances

Microorganism Producing the Antibiotic	Name of Antibiotic	Types of Microorganisms Inhibited or Killed
True Bacteria:		
Pseudomonas aeruginosa	pyocyanase	Gram-positive and some Gram-negative bacteria
Pseudomonas aeruginosa	pyocyanin	Gram-positive bacteria
Bacillus brevis	tyrothricin	Gram-positive bacteria
	tyrocidin	Gram-positive bacteria
	gramicidin	Gram-positive bacteria
Bacillus polymyxa	polymyxin	Gram-positive bacteria
Bacillus subtilis	bacitracin	Gram-positive bacteria
	subtilin	Gram-positive bacteria
Actinomycetes:		
Streptomyces antibioticus	actinomycin	Gram-positive and Gram-negative bacteria and some fungi
	actinomycin A	mainly bacteriostatic
	actinomycin B	bacteriostatic and bactericidal
Streptomyces lavendulae	streptothricin	Gram-negative and Gram-positive bacteria
Streptomyces griseus	streptomycin	Gram-positive and Gram-negative bacteria; possibly certain acid-fast bacteria
Streptomyces aureofaciens	aureomycin	Same groups of bacteria affected by streptomycin; possibly certain viruses
Streptomyces venezuelae	chloromycetin	Same groups of bacteria affected by streptomycin; in addition, certain rickettsiae and viruses
Streptomyces rimosus	terramycin	Same groups of bacteria affected by streptomycin; also certain rickettsiae and viruses
Molds:		
Penicillium notatum or *Penicillium chrysogenum*	penicillin	Gram-positive and some Gram-negative bacteria
Penicillium chrysogenum	notatin	Active only in presence of glucose on same types affected by penicillin
Aspergillus clavatus	clavacin	Gram-negative bacteria
Aspergillus fumigatus	fumigacin	Gram-positive bacteria
Gliocladium fibriatum	gliotoxin	Gram-positive and Gram-negative bacteria

All of the antibiotics possess some degree of toxicity for human beings or animals, and hence must be administered only under the supervision of a competent physician or veterinarian. Methods for the assay and evaluation of antibiotics are at present empirical and inadequate. There is a great need for procedures that will predict with some degree of accuracy the efficacy of an antibiotic under practical conditions of use.

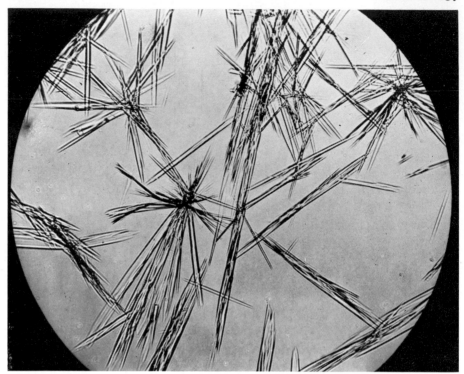

FIGURE 38.   Enlarged crystals of the potassium salt of penicillin G. (Courtesy of Commercial Solvents Corporation, Terre Haute, Ind.)

14. *Miscellaneous Chemical Agencies.*   (a) Volatile oils: Many volatile oils are used in proprietary compounds and ointments as well as in the pure state. Most of these oils are mild antiseptics. Thymol and emulsified pine oil, however, when used in great enough concentration for sufficient periods of time, are germicidal. Oil of cinnamon, oil of clove, and menthol are definitely antiseptic, whereas oil of peppermint, camphor, turpentine, and eucalyptus have some antiseptic properties.

(b) Sulfur: When sulfur is burned, SO_2 is formed which, when dissolved in water, forms sulfurous acid (H_2SO_3), an antiseptic. At present sulfur is burned and used as a fumigant in the treatment of wine casks, of dried fruits, and of musts produced in the manufacture of wine.

While crystalline sulfur has little if any antiseptic properties, colloidal sulfur is a fairly effective germicidal agent which is used in combating bacterial and fungus infections of plants.

(c) Oxidizing agents: Although chlorine is the most widely used disinfectant which acts as an oxidizing agent, hydrogen peroxide (H_2O_2) and potassium permanganate ($KMnO_4$) find considerable use for this purpose.

Commerical hydrogen peroxide contains approximately 3 per cent of H_2O_2. If allowed to act directly upon microorganisms it is germicidal. In the presence of blood or living tissues, however, the catalase which is present decomposes it to H_2O and O_2, neither of which has lethal effect. For this reason it is not a reliable skin disinfectant.

Although potassium permanganate in solution is germicidal to some microorganisms, others are relatively resistant to its action. Because it stains tissues and is corrosive when used in concentrations greater than 0.1 per cent, it is not commonly employed at present.

Ozone (O_3) is an oxidizing agent used in one method of water purification.

(d) Effects of various salts on microorganisms: Salts that in small quantities are used as food by microorganisms may in larger quantities become antiseptic or even disinfectant. This lethal effect is not caused by an increase in osmotic pressure; it is due to the effects of the ions of these salts upon the permeability of the cell membrane, upon the protoplasm and enzymes of the cell, and upon the ionization of other salts in solution. Microorganisms vary widely in their resistance to cations (ions which carry a positive charge, such as Na^+, Ca^{++}, Fe^{+++}, etc.), and to anions (ions which carry a negative charge, such as Cl^-, SO_4^{--}, PO_4^{---}, etc.). Ions which exert an antiseptic effect in one medium may have no effect in another. The toxic effect of one kind of ion on a microorganism may be neutralized by another kind of ion. The effect of different salts on microorganisms varies so widely with different kinds of organisms, and with the conditions under which the salt is allowed to act that it is next to impossible to make a general statement describing the influence of salts on microorganisms.

(e) Fumigation: Fumigation of rooms or dwellings with gaseous hydrocyanic acid kills insects, rats and other vermin, but has little or no effect on microorganisms. Sulfur dioxide, produced when sulfur is burned, is used as a fumigant in wineries, but is of little or no value for use in the home. Fumigation with formaldehyde, at one time widely practiced, has been discontinued in most progressive localities because it is uncertain and inefficient. Fumigation has been abandoned in favor of cleanliness and of disinfection of contaminated substances.

(f) Aerosols. Clouds of finely divided particles are called aerosols. Triethylene glycol or propylene glycol can be caused to form aerosols, and in this state will kill many different kinds of air-borne microorganisms. Disinfectant aerosols have been employed on a large-scale experimental basis to combat air-borne disease-producing bacteria. Under carefully controlled conditions, and when used in low concentrations, these substances do not appear to be harmful to human beings.

REFERENCES

McCulloch, E. C., *Disinfection and sterilization* (2nd ed.). Philadelphia, Pa., Lea and Febiger, 1945.

Ratcliff, J. D., *Yellow magic, the story of penicillin*. N. Y., Random House, 1945.

Rosebury, T., *Experimental air-borne infection*. Baltimore, Md., Williams & Wilkins, 1947.

Waksman, S. A., *Microbial antagonisms and antibiotic substances*. N. Y., The Commonwealth Fund, 1945.

Waksman, S. A. (ed.), *Streptomycin, its nature and practical application*. Baltimore, Md., Williams & Wilkins, 1949.

PART III

Cultivation, Observation, and Classification of Microorganisms

While no attempt will be made to describe all of the many procedures employed in the cultivation and observation of microorganisms, some of the fundamental methods of microbiology will be outlined, and the results which may be secured through their use will be discussed briefly. There are available numerous manuals and books which contain descriptions of and directions for laboratory work in microbiology; the more widely used sources of such information are listed as references at the ends of the chapters.

It is necessary for a student of microbiology to work in the laboratory in order to understand the problems encountered, the methods which can be used in an attempt to solve such problems, and how to interpret the results secured through the use of these procedures. A written description of methods and their uses and applications can therefore serve only as an aid in laboratory work, and never as a substitute for it.

11. CULTURE MEDIA

Any substance in or on which microorganisms can be grown in the laboratory is called a **culture medium.** The thousands of different media which have been devised range in complexity from living tissues down to simple mixtures of inorganic salts. In general, media are employed for three main purposes: to grow and maintain cultures of bacteria; to study the action of microorganisms upon some substance in the medium; and to favor the production by microorganisms of some particular product or combination of products. A medium to be used for any one of these purposes must, as pointed out in Chapter 8, contain the foods and in some cases, the accessory growth substances required by the microorganisms to be grown. In addition, it must supply other conditions favorable to growth as described in Chapter 9. That is, it must supply moisture; have a suitable osmotic pressure, oxidation-reduction character, hydrogen-ion concentration, and surface tension; and be free from substances that will inhibit growth of the microorganisms to be cultivated.

Natural Media

Naturally occurring substances may be used as culture media; in fact, some parasitic microorganisms will grow only on or in living tissues or on secretions or extracts of such tissues. Thus the vaccinia virus may be cultivated on the chorio-allantoic membrane of a growing chick embryo; sterile blood serum containing bits of sterile liver tissue can be used for growing some of the pathogenic spirochetes.

Sterile blood or blood serum is employed as a culture medium for some of the pathogenic bacteria. It is also possible to prepare a solid medium from blood serum, or from egg yolk, by autoclaving tubes of such material in a slanting position so that the serum or yolk proteins will coagulate upon heating to form solid slopes upon which the microorganisms may be grown.

Milk is another natural substance which is widely used as a culture medium. As a rule, skim milk is employed for this purpose because few microorganisms utilize butter fat, and because it is easier to sterilize and to inoculate fat-free milk.

Pieces of potatoes or carrots may be used as culture media if they are immersed in water during sterilization. The excess water is poured from the tube before the sterilized plant tissue is inoculated.

ARTIFICIAL MEDIA

Artificial media may be compounded from a wide variety of materials. If the chemical composition of the ingredients is known, the medium is termed synthetic. If substances of unknown composition are employed, the medium prepared is nonsynthetic. For purposes of description, synthetic or nonsynthetic media may be classed as liquid, liquefiable solid, and solid.

1. *Liquid Media.* Probably the most widely used liquid medium is a nonsynthetic one called **nutrient broth**—an aqueous solution containing 0.5 per cent peptone and 0.3 per cent beef extract. **Peptone** is a dry, powdery material prepared by digestion of some proteinaceous substance such as lean meat with the enzyme, pepsin. The pepsin catalyzes hydrolysis of the complex, insoluble proteins of the meat to a mixture of soluble polypeptides, dipeptides, and amino acids, known collectively as "peptone." Although the exact chemical composition of peptone is not known, its properties may be kept more or less constant by carrying on the digestion under carefully controlled conditions. When the digestion has reached the desired point, the manufacturer neutralizes the acids present and carefully dries the solution. The resulting peptone is a dry, brownish powder which is readily soluble, in the concentrations used, in warm water. A similar product, called "tryptone," is prepared in much the same manner from casein.

Beef extract is prepared by concentrating—by evaporation—an aqueous extract of lean beef. It contains in concentrated form the water soluble components of cooked beef and is easily dissolved in warm water.

Nutrient broth is but one example of the hundreds of different kinds of broths which may be prepared from meat, fish, or plant extracts or products of partial enzymatic digestion of complex foods.

Many different kinds of synthetic liquid media may be prepared from substances of known composition. One example of this type of liquid medium is the following:

Ammonia medium for nitrifying bacteria

(NH₄)₂SO₄	2.0 gr.	NaCl	0.4 gr.
K₂HPO₄	1.0 gr.	FeSO₄	0.01 gr.
MgSO₄	0.5 gr.	CaCO₃	5.0 gr.
		Distilled water	1000 ml.

This medium is used for the cultivation of bacteria responsible for the oxidation of ammonium salts to nitrites.

2. *Liquefiable Solid Media.* A liquefiable solid medium is one which is solid at room temperatures of approximately 20° C., but can be liquefied by the application of heat. Such media are used in order to induce colony formation by bacteria and yeasts and to provide a solid substrate for the cultivation of molds. It is possible to prepare liquefiable solid media from any liquid medium by adding to it some solidifying agent of suitable properties. Originally, such liquefiable solid media were prepared by dissolving from 12 to 15 per cent of gelatin in the nutrient liquid. **Gelatin** is a protein manufactured by boiling bones, joints, and tendons in water and carefully evaporating the resulting water extract until the gelatin can be obtained in powder or sheet form. Media containing approximately 12 per cent of gelatin liquefy at temperatures above 26° C., and must be kept at about 20° C. if they are to remain solid. But gelatin, since it is a protein, may also become liquid through hydrolysis by the proteinases of many microorganisms; this type of liquefaction is irreversible. Because it liquefies at 37° C., which is the temperature at which many cultures of bacteria are incubated, and because it may be liquefied by the proteinases of microorganisms, gelatin has been largely supplanted by agar as a solidifying agent in culture media.

As pointed out in Chapter 3, **agar** is a galactan obtained by extracting with water certain algae of the genus *Gelideum.* When 1.5 per cent of air-dried agar is added to a nutrient broth, the liquid must be heated to 97°–99° C. in order to bring the agar into solution. After the agar is dissolved, the solution may be cooled to approximately 40° C. before it gels. When completely gelled, it may be heated as high as 97° C. before it again becomes liquid. This wide range between the melting and the solidifying point of agar makes it a very useful substance in the bacteriological laboratory. It permits the cooling of a melted agar-containing medium to temperatures low enough to permit mixing bacteria or other microorganisms with the medium without injuring them seriously; after the medium has gelled, it will remain solid while being incubated at any temperature up to

97° C. In addition, agar is not hydrolyzed by the majority of micro-organisms; comparatively few species produce enzymes that will catalyze its hydrolysis and consequent irreversible liquefaction.

3. *Solid Media.* Solid artificial media may be prepared by heat coagulation of solutions containing blood serum or eggs, or by addition of some material such as plaster of Paris or a mixture of silicates which will "set" or gel upon standing. The so-called silica-gel media are particularly valuable for growing certain autotrophic bacteria which are inhibited by even the traces of soluble organic matter present in agar-containing media.

REFERENCES

Levine, M., and Schoenlein, H. W., *A compilation media for the cultivation of microorganisms.* Baltimore, Md., Williams & Wilkins, 1930.

Society of American Bacteriologists, Committee on Bacteriological Technique, *Manual of methods for the pure culture study of bacteria.* Geneva, N. Y., Biotech Publications.

Wadsworth, A. B., *Standard methods of the division of laboratories and research of the New York State Department of Health* (3rd ed.). Baltimore, Md., Williams & Wilkins, 1947.

12. STERILIZATION

Sterilization is a procedure which involves freeing a substance of all living things. A discussion of the different agencies employed in sterilization and of the factors which govern the effectiveness of these agencies has been given in Chapter 10. The use of different means of sterilization in laboratory practices is the chief topic of this chapter.

STERILIZATION OF LIQUIDS

1. *Filtration.* Water and many liquid culture media may be freed from microorganisms, excepting viruses and filterable forms of bacteria, by suitable filtration. Several types of "bacteria-proof" filters are available for such procedures. These include filters made of unglazed porcelain (Pasteur-Chamberland filters), diatomaceous earth (Berkefeld or Mandler filters), asbestos pads (Seitz filters), sintered glass, and reinforced collodion membranes. The filter and receptacle into which the filtered liquid will fall are sterilized in the autoclave (usually at 120° C. for from 30 to 60 minutes) after being wrapped in heavy paper or plugged with cotton so as to prevent contamination following sterilization. The liquid to be filtered may be forced through the filter by pressure, but more commonly it is drawn through by negative pressure or "suction." Upon passing through the filter, the liquid is collected in the sterilized receptacle without exposure to contamination from external sources.

If the positive or negative pressure used is too great, or if the filter is used for too long a time, bacteria will be forced through its pores and will contaminate the filtrate. Liquids containing substances in suspension, colloids, or fats are difficult or almost impossible to filter because these materials clog a filter very quickly. Liquids containing large numbers of micro-organisms are usually filtered first through a coarser, larger-pored filter before being passed through the final "bacteria-proof" filter; this procedure removes most of the cells and makes the final filtration more rapid and more reliable.

Liquids which have been sterilized by filtration must be handled in such a manner that contamination from external sources will be prevented.

After a filter is used it must be disinfected and then thoroughly cleaned before again being sterilized. Since different filters vary in composition a cleaning procedure suitable for one kind may be unsuitable for another. In general, unglazed porcelain and diatomaceous earth filters may be cleaned by forcing clean water through them in the opposite direction to that followed by liquids being filtered. Following this step a 5 per cent aqueous solution of NaOH is drawn or forced through the filter to remove proteinaceous materials; finally, distilled water is passed through the filter to wash out the alkali. The filter must then be carefully and thoroughly dried before being sterilized. Since alkalies tend to dissolve glass, sintered glass filters, after a preliminary rinsing with distilled water, may be cleaned by passing hot, concentrated sulfuric acid through them. The final step in cleaning such filters involves drawing distilled water through them until the filter is free from acid. Like other filters, those made of sintered glass must be dried slowly and completely before being sterilized.

Although filtration may be used to sterilize liquids of almost any kind provided they are free from suspended matter or colloids which would clog the filter, it is used mainly on liquids such as sugar solutions which might be harmed by sterilization with heat. Filtration is a slow and relatively expensive means of sterilization and is used only when more rapid methods are impracticable.

2. *Steam Sterilization.* Water and culture media are usually sterilized with steam. If steam at atmospheric pressure is used, its temperature will be 100° C. at sea level and will decrease with increases in altitude. Flowing steam must be applied either for a long period of time or intermittently on successive days in order to effect sterilization of a liquid. In general, a temperature of 100° C. will kill the vegetative cells of microorganisms in 15 minutes, but a much longer time at this temperature will be needed to kill bacterial spores. This does not mean that putting a flask of water or culture medium in a steamer, where it is exposed to flowing steam for 15 minutes, will kill the vegetative cells that are present. The important point to recognize is that all of the liquid in the flask must reach 100° C. and be held at this temperature for at least 15 minutes. It may require an hour for the heat

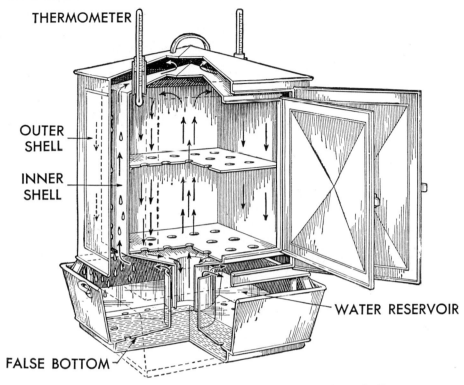

THERMOMETER

OUTER SHELL

INNER SHELL

WATER RESERVOIR

FALSE BOTTOM

FIGURE 39.   The Arnold sterilizer for sterilizing materials with flowing steam. (From *A Textbook of Medical Bacteriology* by D. L. Belding and A. T. Marston, D. Appleton-Century Co., Inc., 1938.)

from the steam to penetrate a large mass of medium and to bring every bit of it to 100° C. Sterilization of liquids by continuous exposure to flowing steam is not practicable because it takes too long and may cause undesirable chemical changes in the liquid if it contains organic materials.

It is possible to sterilize media with flowing steam by heating them to 95°–100° C. for 30 minutes on each of three successive days. This is called intermittent or discontinuous sterilization. It is based on the facts that the first exposure kills vegetative cells; incubating the liquid for 24 hours following the first heating allows germination of the spores present; the second heating kills the vegetative cells formed by germination of the spores; the second period of incubation permits germination of the spores which failed to germinate during the first incubation; and the final heating kills the vegetative cells thus formed. Intermittent sterilization is time-consuming, results in injury to organic materials present in media, and is used infrequently. Figure 39 shows a working diagram of an Arnold sterilizer, which employs flowing steam.

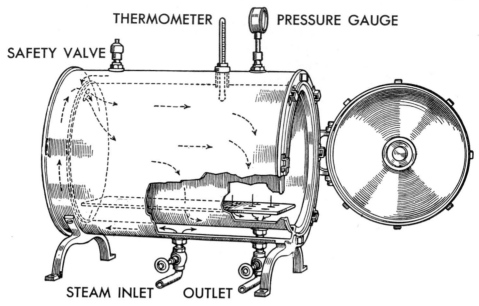

THERMOMETER   PRESSURE GAUGE

SAFETY VALVE

STEAM INLET   OUTLET

FIGURE 40.   The autoclave sterilizer for sterilizing materials with steam under pressure. (From *A Textbook of Medical Bacteriology* by D. L. Belding and A. T. Marston, D. Appleton-Century Co., Inc., 1938.)

The most satisfactory method available for sterilizing water and culture media involves the use of steam under pressure in an instrument known as an autoclave or sterilizer. The containers of liquid are placed in the autoclave, the door is closed, and steam is admitted to the chamber. While the steam fills the chamber an air exhaust valve is kept open until all of the air present has been displaced by steam. The air exhaust valve is then closed and the pressure in the chamber allowed to rise to the desired point, usually 15 pounds steam pressure per square inch. Steam at this pressure has a temperature of 121° C.—heating liquids to this temperature renders them sterile in a relatively short time. It must again be emphasized that the temperature of the liquid, not the temperature of the steam, is the immediate cause of sterilization; hence sufficient time must be allowed for all of the liquid to come to 121° C. and to remain at that temperature for a period of time long enough to effect sterilization. As a rule, 121° C. for 20 minutes will sterilize a liquid, but the actual time of autoclaving may be much longer than this depending upon the bulk of liquid and its resistance to the penetration of heat. A working diagram of an autoclave is shown in Figure 40. At a lower temperature a longer time of exposure will be needed to sterilize a liquid, while at a higher temperature a shorter exposure will accomplish the same result.

Different temperatures may be secured in the autoclave as follows:

TABLE 4. Temperature of Steam at Different Pressures at Sea Level

Pounds of Steam Pressure per Square Inch	Temperature ° C.	° F.
0 (Flowing steam)	100	212
5	108	226.4
10	115	239
15	121	249.8
20	126	258.8

After the liquid has been sterilized, the steam inlet and air exhaust valves of the autoclave are closed and the temperature and pressure within the chamber allowed to diminish gradually. This is necessary because if the pressure were reduced rapidly by opening the air exhaust valve, the super-heated liquids in the chamber would boil violently.

When the pressure within the chamber reaches "zero" (equal to external atmospheric pressure) the door is opened and the containers of liquid are removed and allowed to cool.

Before autoclaving, the openings of the containers of liquid must be plugged with cotton, or covered with several thicknesses of gauze, a loose-fitting cap, or a screw cap which is not turned down tight. Upon removal from the autoclave and subsequent cooling, the liquids are thus protected against contamination from the air by the filtering action of the sterile cotton or gauze, or by the protective lip of the cap. Too rapid cooling must be avoided because it causes a rush of air into the container with the result that the plug or cap is unable to prevent the entrance of air-borne microorganisms.

STERILIZATION OF GLASSWARE

1. *Sterilization in the Autoclave.* Glassware fabricated of glass resistant to moist heat may be sterilized in the autoclave in a manner similar to that just described for sterilizing liquids. Glassware such as cotton-stoppered flasks and test tubes, empty screw-capped bottles, and pipettes or petri dishes wrapped in paper or enclosed in metal containers may be sterilized in this manner. At 15 pounds steam pressure (121° C.) the time of auto-claving will depend upon the amount of glassware being sterilized and how tightly it is packed; more time is needed to heat a large bulk of glass to 121° C. than is needed for a smaller amount. Also, because glass is a poor conductor of heat, a longer time of heating at the sterilizing temperature is needed than when liquids are being autoclaved. As a rule, glassware

THERMOMETER   DAMPER

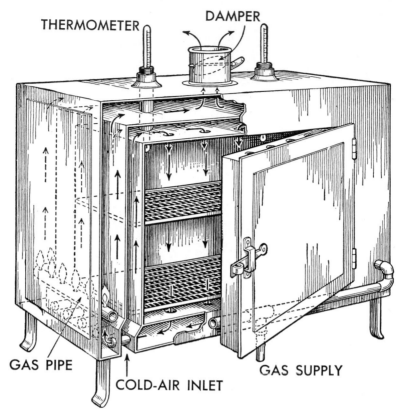

GAS PIPE   GAS SUPPLY

COLD-AIR INLET

FIGURE 41.   A hot-air sterilizer (gas) for sterilizing glassware with
heated air. (From *A Textbook of Medical Bacteriology* by D. L. Belding and A. T. Marston, D. Appleton-Century Co., Inc., 1938.)

must be heated to 121° C. for at least 60 minutes in order to effect its
sterilization.

2. *Sterilization in the Oven.*   Dry glassware may be sterilized in a hot-air
oven. This procedure is often employed in order to make sure that the
glassware will be dry when sterilization has been completed, and because
dry heat is less injurious to most kinds of glass. Petri dishes are usually
sterilized in the oven; and empty, cotton-plugged test tubes and flasks,
pipettes, and other pieces of glassware as well as dry chemicals such as
$CaCO_3$ may be sterilized in this way. Petri dishes which are to be stored for
some time prior to use must be protected against contamination by wrapping them in heavy paper or putting them in metal containers before being
sterilized. Figure 41 shows a working diagram of a gas-heated oven for
sterilizing glassware.

Although recommendations vary considerably, glassware must be heated to between 160° to 180° C. for from two to three hours in order to effect its sterilization with dry heat. Cotton stoppered tubes or flasks and petri dishes or pipettes wrapped in paper should not be heated above 180° C. because higher temperatures will char the wrapping. As in sterilization in the autoclave, the time of sterilizing will depend upon the bulk of glassware being sterilized and its resistance to the penetration of heat. In addition, it is necessary to avoid packing glassware too tightly because the efficiency of an oven depends to a large extent upon free circulation of hot air within it.

Sterilization of Miscellaneous Materials and Equipment

Culture loops and needles, metal spatulas, and similar pieces of equipment used in a bacteriological laboratory may be sterilized by heating them red hot in a flame. There is no doubt that heating the platinum-iridium, nickel-chromium, or steel of these instruments to redness incinerates any microorganisms or their spores that might be present on them. Following sterilization, the instrument is allowed to cool without subjecting it to contamination, and is then ready for immediate use. Culture loops and needles made of 24 or 26 gauge platinum-iridium or nickel-chromium wire cool in a few seconds after being sterilized, and the chances are slight for their contamination with organisms from the air during the short period required for cooling before they are used.

Hypodermic syringes and needles, gauze bandages, rubber gloves, filters, and most other pieces of equipment used in bacteriological work may be sterilized in the autoclave at 15 pounds steam pressure for at least 30 minutes. Such equipment must be wrapped in gauze or heavy paper, plugged with cotton, or placed in some sort of metal or glass container before being autoclaved, in order to prevent contamination following sterilization.

REFERENCE

Wadsworth, A. B., *Standard methods of the division of laboratories and research of the New York State Department of Health* (3rd ed.). Baltimore, Md., Williams & Wilkins, 1947.

13. ISOLATION OF PURE CULTURES

A mass of microbial cells grown in or on a culture medium is called a "**culture.**" When all of the microorganisms in a culture are of one kind it is termed a **pure culture;** but if more than one kind is present, it is called a **mixed culture.** In studying the morphology, physiology, and pathogenicity of a microorganism, the first step is to cultivate it in pure culture. This usually is not easy to accomplish because under natural conditions, mixed, rather than pure cultures are the rule, and it is often difficult to separate one kind of organism from a mixture. Counterbalancing this difficulty to some extent is the fact that bacteria reproduce asexually, and that yeasts, molds, most protozoa, and unicellular algae also may reproduce asexually, so that crossbreeding and hybridization are believed to be uncommon. Thus the nucleoplasm of a single bacterial cell or of a single yeast, protozoan, or algal cell, and the heritable characteristics which it carries are divided equally when such a cell undergoes fission or budding, and are in turn passed on to the next generation when the daughter cells divide.

Methods of Securing Pure Cultures

1. *Enrichment Procedures.* Although pure cultures are not as a rule secured by enrichment procedures alone, such methods usually serve as a starting point in the process of isolation of the desired species from a mixed culture. An enrichment procedure involves the use of media and conditions of cultivation which will favor the growth of the desired species to the extent that it will make up the majority of the microbial population in the enrichment

140

culture. When one kind of microorganism is present in a mixed culture in larger numbers than other species, its isolation becomes much easier to accomplish than when it is present in relatively small numbers. For example, the bacteria responsible for nodule formation on the roots of leguminous plants normally are present in comparatively small numbers in most soils, and it is very difficult to isolate a pure culture of them directly from the soil. But if, for example, alfalfa seeds are planted in the soil under suitable conditions for growth, they will germinate; and the alfalfa nodule bacteria present in the soil will form nodules on the roots of the young plant. The nodulated roots can then be washed free from soil, and the alfalfa nodule bacteria isolated with comparative ease from the interior of the nodules. This is an enrichment procedure in which the roots of the alfalfa plant are used as a selective medium.

In a rather similar manner bacteria pathogenic for animals may be secured in nearly pure culture from mixtures of microorganisms by inoculating such mixed cultures into a susceptible animal and isolating the particular pathogen desired from infected animal tissue.

Selective culture media of many different kinds are available for making enrichment cultures. One type of selective medium provides some particular food which will be utilized by the species or group of species of microorganisms which is to be isolated. For example, bacteria which oxidize ammonium salts to nitrites can be obtained from soil, in which they exist in comparatively small numbers, by inoculating an ammonium-mineral salts medium with a small quantity of the soil, and incubating the inoculated medium at 20° C. After these organisms have started to grow, as evidenced by the results of tests showing the presence of nitrites in the medium, a small amount of the growth is then transferred under aseptic conditions to a fresh, sterile medium of similar composition. By repeated incubation and transfer the proportion of ammonia-oxidizing organisms in the microbial population is greatly enriched. This is but one example of many which could be given for this type of enrichment procedure.

Media for enrichment procedures can also be compounded so as to contain some substance which will inhibit all but the desired kind of microorganism. It is also possible to adjust the reaction (pH) of a medium to a level that will favor the organisms to be isolated, but will inhibit the others present in the original mixture.

Incubation of a medium inoculated with a mixture of microorganisms at temperatures of from 0° to 15° C. will favor the development of psychrophilic species; incubation at 45° to 70° C. will favor the development of thermophiles. Incubation under anaerobic conditions will favor the growth of anaerobes and prevent the growth of aerobes.

The examples which have been given represent but a few of the many ways in which it is possible to select or enrich a certain species or group of species of microorganisms from a mixed culture. After the desired species is present in large enough numbers and represents the majority of a mixed population, other means can be used to secure a pure culture of it.

2. *Serial Dilution.* Pure cultures can often be secured from mixed cultures, particularly from enrichment cultures, by serial dilution of the mixed culture in a medium suitable for the species to be isolated. For example, when raw milk is allowed to sour normally at room temperature it will, at the time of curdling, contain a mixture of microorganisms with *Streptococcus lactis* usually in the majority. If 1 ml. of the sour milk is pipetted into a tube containing 9 ml. of sterile skim milk, and then 1 ml. of this mixture transferred with a sterile pipette into a second tube of sterile milk, and the procedure repeated, i.e., tube 2 to tube 3, tube 3 to tube 4, etc., until a series of ten tubes is inoculated, the chances are that a pure culture of S. *lactis* will be secured. This process of serial dilution is also called dilution to extinction because the final tubes of the series will most likely contain no bacteria, but the tube containing the greatest dilution which shows growth upon incubation will probably contain a pure culture of S. *lactis* since this organism was present in the majority in the sour milk, and because of its greater numbers was carried farthest in the dilution procedure.

3. *Isolation from Colonies.* Pure cultures can be isolated from colonies providing the colony itself is a pure culture. As pointed out in Chapter 1, a colony of bacteria may originate from a single vegetative cell, a single spore, or a clump of cells or spores in or on a semisolid medium; this is also true of yeasts and molds. If the colony develops apart from other colonies in the medium it is likely to be a pure culture. In such a case all that has to be done is to transfer, under aseptic conditions, a small bit (theoretically, only one cell must be removed, but usually the small mass of cells that adheres to the point of a sterile culture needle is taken) of the colony to a tube of some suitable sterile culture medium. Upon incubation of the inoculated tube under favorable conditions the culture which develops will be pure if the colony from which it originated was a pure culture.

Two different methods are commonly used in obtaining the growth of well-isolated colonies. The first of these involves streaking a loopful of the mixed culture on the surface of a sterile solidified agar, gelatin, or silica-gel medium contained in a sterile petri dish. In making the streak, the loop is rubbed over the surface of the medium in such a manner that most of the microorganisms will be removed from it during the first series of streaks with the result that during the making of the last streaks comparatively few cells will be deposited, and these will be far enough apart so that isolated colonies will develop. Many ingenious streaking procedures have been developed, but the principle of all of them is essentially similar to the one just described.

The second method used in obtaining colonies involves a preliminary dilution procedure which may be quantitative (as outlined on page 90) or mainly qualitative. A qualitative procedure, known commonly as "loop-dilution," may be accomplished in the following manner. Three tubes of a sterile, liquefiable solid medium are liquefied and cooled to as low a temperature as possible without solidifying the medium. The first tube is inoculated with a loopful of the mixed culture. After the inoculum has been mixed with the medium, the loop is sterilized and then used to transfer one loopful of the mixture in tube 1 to tube 2. After the mixing of the inoculum with the medium in tube 2, the loop is again sterilized and used to transfer one loopful of the mixture from tube 2 to tube 3. The inoculated medium in tube 1 is then poured under aseptic conditions into a sterile petri dish; that in tube 2 into a second sterile petri dish; and that in tube 3 into a third sterile petri dish. When the medium solidifies the petri dishes are incubated under favorable conditions to allow the development of colonies of the desired species. Pure cultures can then be isolated from the well-separated colonies which develop as a rule on the second or third plate of the series. There are other modifications of the loop-dilution technique, but the principle in all cases is the same as that of the procedure just outlined.

4. *Single Cell Technique.* The most ideal, and yet the most difficult method of securing a pure culture involves the isolation of a single cell of a microorganism and its cultivation in a sterile culture medium. This is the only method available at present for obtaining an unquestionably pure culture. The first step in single cell isolation is to obtain the culture in as pure a state as possible by one of the other procedures that have been mentioned. A suspension of the pure culture is placed on the under side of a sterile cover glass mounted over a moist chamber on the stage of the microscope. While looking through the microscope, a single cell or spore is removed from the suspension with a sterile micropipette, and transferred to a small drop of sterile medium on a sterile cover glass. Then the sterile cover glass, with its drop of medium containing the single cell, is mounted on a sterile hanging-drop slide, which is then incubated at a suitable temperature. If the single cell grows in this drop, some of the cells in the liquid are transferred to a tube of sterile medium, and upon incubation, a pure culture is obtained which originated from a single cell.

The procedure is fraught with many difficulties which can be appreciated only by those who have attempted to use it, but it stands today as the ideal method for securing a pure culture of a microorganism.

CULTIVATION AND MAINTENANCE OF PURE CULTURES

After a pure culture of a microorganism has been secured it may be grown and maintained as a pure culture in several different ways. The most common procedure is to grow the culture in or on some suitable culture medium until it reaches the maximum stationary phase of growth, and then store it at room temperature or in a refrigerator. Some cultures can be stored only a day or so; others can be kept for weeks or months; but sooner or later all cultures must be transferred to a fresh, sterile medium if they are to be kept alive. Thus by successive transfers a culture may be kept alive and free from contamination with other species for an indefinite period.

A second means for maintaining pure cultures involves freezing a young culture and desiccating it under vacuum. As a rule, the cells of a pure culture will remain viable for a longer period of time if they are mixed with sterile blood serum, sterile skim milk, or a mixture of serum and milk, before freezing and drying. The dried culture kept in the sealed, evacuated tube and stored in a cool place remains viable for long periods of time. When the tube is opened its contents are transferred aseptically to a favorable sterile medium; upon suitable incubation the organisms again become active and grow as they did before being frozen and dried. This is one of the main procedures employed by the American Type Culture Collection for maintaining its tremendous stock of pure cultures of various microorganisms.

A third method for maintaining pure cultures of microorganisms is one which is most suitable for spore-forming species. The microorganisms are grown in pure culture in suitable media and under conditions favorable to spore formation. A suspension of the organisms, most of which are in the spore state, is then transferred aseptically to cotton-stoppered tubes of sterilized, dry soil. In the dry soil the spores remain viable, though dormant, for long periods of time. When an active culture is desired, some of the soil is transferred to a favorable medium, and upon incubation the spores germinate to form vegetative cells of the pure culture.

ISOLATION AND CULTIVATION OF ANAEROBIC BACTERIA

The methods used for the isolation of pure cultures of anaerobic bacteria differ very little in principle from the procedures just described, most of which are designed for securing pure cultures of aerobic or facultative species. Various types of enrichment procedures, serial dilution, isolation from colonies, or single cell isolation may be used to obtain pure cultures of anaerobic bacteria. However, in isolating and maintaining pure cultures of anaerobes, it is necessary to grow the organisms in the absence of free oxygen or in media of such reduced oxidation-reduction potential that they can develop in contact with the air. Such media usually contain an abundance of oxidizable material together with reducible substances which can be used in the organisms' metabolism.

If it is possible to use a liquid or semisolid medium for the isolation and cultivation of an anaerobe, the problem of providing anaerobic conditions is comparatively simple. The tubes of culture medium may be heated just prior to inoculation in order to drive out dissolved oxygen, and then cooled rapidly before being inoculated. If a large inoculum is used the anaerobes can usually establish themselves under such conditions. It is also possible to add a small amount of reduced iron to test tubes which are then filled with culture medium and sterilized. If these tubes of medium are inoculated soon after autoclaving, there will be a reduced zone, free from dissolved oxygen, in the vicinity of the reduced iron at the bottom of the tubes where anaerobes will find conditions suitable for their development.

So-called "shake" cultures also provide more or less anaerobic conditions. If a tube of agar medium containing the nutrients needed by the specific anaerobe to be cultivated is melted, cooled to approximately 45° C., inoculated with the material containing the bacteria, the inoculum mixed thoroughly with the melted medium, and the agar allowed to solidify while the tube is in an upright position, those bacteria in the center and toward the base of the agar will be provided with anaerobic conditions. Upon incubation they will grow to form colonies from which pure cultures may be isolated.

A variation of the shake culture procedure involves drawing the inoculated agar of a shake culture up into a long, small-bore sterile glass tube. The "mouth" end of the tube is kept closed until the agar solidifies. Upon incubation the anaerobic bacteria form colonies in the agar. Isolation of a pure culture from these colonies is relatively easy because the glass can be broken near one of them and a small bit of the colony transferred with a sterile culture needle to a tube of sterile medium.

If it is desired to grow anaerobic bacteria in test tubes on the surface of slanted agar, or in petri dish cultures, some provision must be made for incubating such cultures in an atmosphere free from oxygen. Many ingenious procedures have been developed for creating such an anaerobic environment, but only a few of these will be described here.

1. *Evacuation.* The petri dishes or tubes may be placed in a vacuum desiccator and a nearly complete vacuum drawn with a suction pump. This method is only fairly successful because liquids boil as their dissolved gases are removed, with the result that cotton plugs in tubes become wet, and agar in petri dishes may bubble and crack. It is also difficult to maintain

a high vacuum for any prolonged period of incubation due to leaks in the joints and valves of the desiccator.

2. *Displacement of Air with an Inert Gas.* It is possible to remove the air from a vacuum desiccator and to replace it with some inert gas such as hydrogen or nitrogen, and thus provide anaerobic conditions for bacteria in test tubes or petri dishes contained in the apparatus. This method is somewhat more successful than evacuation as it avoids the boiling of liquids, and since the pressure within the desiccator can be adjusted to nearly equal atmospheric pressure there is small opportunity for leaks to develop.

3. *Chemical Removal of Oxygen.* There are several substances which will react with or absorb gaseous oxygen present in the atmosphere of an airtight container. If phosphorus is burned in a sealed container it will consume the free oxygen present to form P_2O_5 which will dissolve in water in the bottom of the chamber. A mixture of pyrogallic acid and concentrated potassium hydroxide will absorb free oxygen from the atmosphere of a sealed container. Either of these procedures may be used to secure anaerobic conditions, but their use is complicated by two main difficulties: If phosphorus is used, some of the P_2O_5 will be dissolved in the culture medium to form phosphoric acid which, if the medium is not well buffered, will make it acid in reaction; a mixture of pyrogallic acid and concentrated potassium hydroxide tends to desiccate the medium, and this in turn will inhibit the growth of the bacteria. In spite of these difficulties both methods are fairly satisfactory.

4. *Biological Removal of Oxygen.* It is possible to remove the oxygen from the atmosphere of a sealed container and replace it, to some extent, with CO_2 by purely biological means. If moistened oats are placed in the bottom of a sealed container (about one-half pint of moistened oats to each liter of air in the container) in which the cultures of anaerobes are placed, the respiration of the oats, combined with that of the microorganisms on them, rapidly removes the gaseous oxygen from the container and partially replaces it with CO_2. In such a gaseous environment anaerobic bacteria grow very well because the atmosphere is free from oxygen, it is moist, and there is an abundance of CO_2, which seems to help bacterial growth. Cultures of aerobic microorganisms, as well as other kinds of plant tissue, such as sliced potatoes, can also be used for this purpose, but oats are inexpensive and easy to use, and hence are most satisfactory.

As pointed out previously, other methods are available for securing anaerobic conditions, but those which have been given are fairly representative, and illustrate the chief principles involved in such procedures.

The maintenance of cultures of anaerobes can be accomplished by the procedures which have been outlined, but the problem is somewhat complicated by the necessity for providing anaerobic conditions during cultivation.

REFERENCES

Society of American Bacteriologists, Committee on Bacteriological Technique, *Manual of methods for the pure culture study of bacteria*. Geneva, N. Y., Biotech Publications.

Wadsworth, A. B., *Standard methods of the division of laboratories and research of the New York State Department of Health* (3rd ed.). Baltimore, Md., Williams & Wilkins, 1947.

14. CHARACTERIZATION AND CLASSIFICATION OF BACTERIA

To the student beginning a study of microbiology, the need for an exact, complete characterization of every kind of microorganism may not seem of great importance. It may also be difficult for the beginner fully to appreciate the value of giving a microorganism which has been characterized a scientific name, and of assigning it to a definite place in a system of classification. But the necessity of work of this type, which is known as determinative bacteriology, will become evident as the student works with an increasing number of different kinds of microorganisms, and investigates more of the natural changes and applied processes in which microorganisms play the principal roles.

An adequate system of classification, though admittedly artificial and man-made, is a great convenience to the microbiologist. After a microorganism has been secured in pure culture and thoroughly characterized, it is given a genus and a species name. To one familiar with the characteristics of the genus in which the microorganism has been placed, the name of the genus conveys a general description of the organism, and thereby saves the actual listing of its chief properties. The name of the genus may be purely arbitrary, or it may be descriptive of the organism. For example, the genus name, *Streptococcus,* is given to bacteria which are cocci, dividing only in one plane and typically growing in chains or pairs; the cells may be spherical, bean-shaped or almost cylindrical; they are Gram-positive and insoluble in bile; and may be aerobic, facultative or in a few cases, anaerobic.

The species name indicates the discoverer of the species or is descriptive of the organism. For example, *Streptococcus lactis* is a species of *Streptococcus* which is commonly found in milk and causes it to become sour.

Streptococcus pyogenes, another species of the same genus, is a pus-producing streptococcus as indicated by its species name. *Nitrobacter winogradskyi* is an example of a species named after its discoverer, Winogradsky. Although it is practically impossible to define exactly what is meant by a species, it may be assumed to be a group of organisms which differ one from another only in unimportant, minor characteristics. The characterization and identification of a microorganism through the use of a suitable genus and species name is a sort of scientific shorthand.

Since bacteria are the simplest of fungus plants, the problem of their characterization and classification might well be expected to be correspondingly uncomplicated. If morphology could be employed as the only basis for characterization this would be the case. But other properties of bacteria, such as their ability to cause some specific disease or the fact that they can produce some particular product, vary so widely among cultures of similar morphology, that these properties also must be used as bases for characterization and classification. At present, four main properties of bacteria are used in their characterization and classification. These are: (1) morphology; (2) cultural characteristics; (3) physiological characteristics, including both the effects of the environment upon the bacteria and the effects of the bacteria upon the environment; and (4) pathogenicity (disease-producing ability and specific diseases caused), and in some cases, immunological or serological properties. Hence the characterization and classification of bacteria is, unfortunately, very decidedly complicated.

It is the purpose of this chapter to describe some of the procedures used in studying the morphological, cultural, physiological, and pathogenic properties of bacteria, and to point out very briefly how bacteria may be identified and classified once they have been characterized.

Morphological Characteristics

Examinations of the morphological characteristics and related properties of bacteria are made with a compound microscope of sufficient magnifying and resolving power to give a clear image of spheroidal organisms as small as 0.15 μ in diameter. Space does not permit description of the optical principles of a compound microscope, but a student of microbiology should become familiar with this subject through study of books on the microscope, and through experimentation in the laboratory. Knowledge of how to use a compound microscope is a prerequisite for successful studies of the morphological characteristics and related properties of microorganisms.

It is possible to examine under the microscope either unstained, living cells of bacteria, or to study stained, dead cells.

1. *Examination of Unstained, Living Cells.* Unstained living cells may be examined in order to determine the form, internal structure, motility and cell arrangements of bacteria, and to observe the processes of reproduction, spore formation, and spore germination. Such studies are usually made on hanging-drop mounts which are prepared by placing a small drop of a liquid culture on a cover slip which is then sealed over the hollowed-out portion of a hanging-drop slide in such a manner that the drop hangs suspended from the cover glass into the circular depression of the slide. Evaporation of the drop is prevented by the seal between the cover glass and hanging-drop slide.

It is also possible to study living cells in wet mounts which are prepared by floating a cover glass on a drop of liquid culture that has been placed on a standard microscope slide. Evaporation of the liquid in such preparations may be prevented by sealing the edges of the cover glass to the slide with melted vaseline.

A third way in which to study living bacterial cells is to pipette, under aseptic conditions, a melted and partially cooled sterile agar medium into the depression of a hanging-drop slide. The surface of the solidified agar is then inoculated with a small number of bacteria, and a sterile cover glass is placed on it and sealed around the edges. As the bacteria grow on the surface of the agar and in the film of moisture between the agar and cover glass they may be examined with a microscope. This is the type of procedure usually employed in studies of the reproduction, spore formation, and spore germination of living bacteria.

It is difficult to study, and even more difficult to photograph living bacteria through the microscope because they are colorless and offer little resistance to the passage of light through their cells. Also, it is almost impossible to see the flagella on motile, living bacteria, or the capsules that surround the cells of some species. The use of dark-field illumination, which causes bacterial cells in a liquid to appear as brightly shining objects against an almost totally dark background, is of some assistance in observation of living cells.

2. *Examination of Stained Cells.* Stained preparations of bacteria and other microbial cells may be made to facilitate determinations of morphology (including cell arrangements, and such structures as endospores, granules, capsules, and flagella), and to ascertain the reaction of the cells to differential staining procedures. It is possible to employ "vital staining" techniques in which certain dyes or reagents (such as 7 per cent of iodine dissolved in a 20 per cent aqueous solution of KI) are added to suspensions of living cells. But the usual method is to fix the cells of the microorganisms on a microscope slide through the use of heat or some fixing agent such as alcohol, and then treat them with one or more stains.

"Simple" stains are made by treating the fixed preparation with a solution of methylene blue, basic fuchsin, carbol fuchsin (an aqueous solution of basic fuchsin containing phenol), crystal violet, or some other basic anilin dye. Such dyes have an affinity for proteins such as those in nucleoplasm, and for volutin, but do not stain free fats or carbohydrates. Young bacterial cells are usually stained uniformly by such dyes. In some species, older cells become granulated, and the granules that are composed of free nucleic acid or carbohydrate-nucleic acid compounds (volutin) stain more intensely than does the remainder of the protoplasm. The cells of some species which store fat upon reaching maturity show a vacuolated appearance because these dyes do not stain fat globules. The endospores of bacilli are not stained by the ordinary short-time applications of these dyes, but the vegetative portion of each spore-containing cell "takes" the stain.

It is also possible to make "negatively stained" preparations of bacteria through the use of India ink, nigrosin, or Congo red. In these preparations, the cells are not stained, and appear colorless against the dark background of the dense substance which precipitates around them.

Capsules may be demonstrated by suspending the cells in some liquid such as sterile blood serum or milk which contains proteins that will stain when treated with one of the dyes mentioned. In such preparations, the bacterial cells are stained, the capsules surrounding the cells are colorless, and the protein materials which form the background of the preparation are stained more lightly than the cells.

The staining of flagella is not an easy task. It involves first the cultivation of the motile bacteria under suitable conditions so that their cells will be flagellated, and then transferring the cells to, and fixing them on a slide in such a manner that the flagella will remain attached. Next, the preparation must be treated with a mordant which will either precipitate colloidal material on the flagella or possibly cause them to swell so that they will stain when treated with a dye such as carbol fuchsin.

Bacterial endospores may be stained by treatment for from 2 to 24 hours with cold carbol fuchsin, or by exposure to hot (steaming) carbol fuchsin for from 10 to 30 minutes. Following such treatment, the preparation may be treated with alcohol to decolorize all parts of the cell save the endospore, which, when stained, retains the carbol fuchsin tenaciously. If an aqueous solution of nigrosin is next added, and allowed to dry, the background of the preparation then appears bluish-black, the endospores a bright red, and the vegetative portions of each spore-containing cell are colorless. There are other methods for staining endospores, but this one—a modification of Dorner's technique—is reliable and yields permanent preparations.

The two differential staining procedures most commonly used are the Ziehl-Neelsen method for determination of whether or not bacteria are acid-fast (described in Chapter 7), and the Gram method. There are several modifications of the original Gram method, none of which will be given in detail at this time, but the principles of the different modifications are similar. The following is a general outline of the Gram method:

a. The fixed preparation is treated with a solution of a dye such as crystal violet. This stains the vegetative cells of all bacteria except those which are acid-fast purple in from 1 to 5 minutes. As a rule, the crystal violet is dissolved in a weak alkali to intensify its staining properties.

b. After washing off the excess crystal violet with water, the preparation is treated with an aqueous solution of potassium iodide + iodine, or an alkaline, aqueous solution of iodine. The iodine solution mordants the crystal violet in the cells of Gram-positive bacteria, but has no mordanting action in Gram-negative cells. (A mordant makes a stain relatively permanent.)

c. The preparation is next treated with 95 per cent ethyl alcohol, acetone, or a mixture of alcohol and acetone, for sufficient time to decolorize Gram-negative bacteria (usually 15 to 30 seconds). Gram-positive bacterial cells, in which the crystal violet has been mordanted by the iodine, are not decolorized by this short exposure to the decolorizing solution. Longer exposure will remove the dye from Gram-positive cells; hence the time of decolorizing must be carefully controlled.

d. After washing off the remaining decolorizing solution with water, the preparation is treated with a counterstain of some contrasting color, such as aqueous safranin or basic fuchsin. This treatment stains the Gram-negative cells pink, but the Gram-positive cells remain purple because they have retained the color imparted to them by the crystal violet.

The cells of some species of bacteria are Gram-positive, those of other species are Gram-negative, and those of a third group of bacterial species are variable in their reaction to the Gram method. The cells of Gram-variable species are, as a rule, Gram-positive when young, but become Gram-negative upon aging. There is as yet no complete explanation for the reaction of cells to the Gram staining method, but it is believed that Gram-positive bacteria contain more ribose-nucleic acid than Gram-negative bacteria, and owe their Gram-positiveness to the presence of this compound.

CULTURAL CHARACTERISTICS

A culture is a mass of cells grown in or on a culture medium. A study of the main features and distinguishing characteristics of cultures is of aid in the characterization, identification and classification of bacteria. Despite the fact that bacteria are unicellular, the masses of cells present in colonies, or in slope, stab, shake, or liquid media cultures, present many differences in appearance. Furthermore, the cultural characteristics of a pure culture are, under uniform environmental conditions, remarkably constant, and appear to be as heritable as the morphological characteristics of the cells.

1. *Colony Characteristics.* The macroscopic and microscopic examination of colonies of bacteria usually provide the first data of value in the characterization of cultures of bacteria. As previously described, colonies of bacteria may originate from a single cell or spore, or from a clump of cells or spores present in or on a semisolid medium. If the colonies are found imbedded in the medium they are called deep, or subsurface colonies; those which grow on the medium are termed surface colonies. The latter type exhibits a greater variety of distinguishing characteristics and is usually studied when a description of colony characteristics is being made.

A macroscopic examination of surface colonies is made in order to determine their size; form (punctiform, i.e., under 1 mm.; circular; irregular; filamentous; or rhizoid); elevation (flat, raised, or convex); optical characteristics (color; opaque, translucent, or transparent); and surface (smooth or rough; glistening or dull; moist or dry; concentrically ringed or radiately ridged; etc.).

A microscopic examination of surface colonies, and sometimes of deep colonies, is made in order to determine the appearance of the edge of each colony (entire, i.e., the segment of a circle; wavy; lobed; toothed; filamentous; or curled), and the internal structure (amorphous, granular, or filamentous).

2. *Characteristics of Slope Cultures.* Pure cultures of bacteria grown on slopes of agar, coagulated egg or blood serum, or some other solid or semisolid medium, exhibit characteristics of value in determinative work. Macroscopic examinations are made to determine the amount and uniformity in appearance of the mass of cells; the form (following the line of inoculation or spreading); elevation; optical characteristics; appearance of surface; and consistency when touched with a sterile loop or needle. The odor of slope cultures may also be noted along with other minor distinguishing properties.

3. *Characteristics of Stab Cultures.* Stab cultures are usually made in media containing gelatin in order to determine both the appearance of the mass of cells which will grow upon suitable incubation, and the ability of the culture to cause irreversible liquefaction of the gelatin. The purely cultural characteristics of stab cultures in gelatin media may be determined by macroscopic examination. They include, mainly, the location of the growth (surface only, surface and along the line of inoculation, or only toward the base of the line of inoculation); the appearance of the mass of cells which grow along the line of inoculation (beaded, arborescent—branched, treelike—or uniform and smooth-edged).

4. *Characteristics of Shake Culture.* Shake cultures are prepared by inoculation of melted, cooled, but not solidified, sterile agar with a pure culture.

After solidification of the tube of agar in an upright position and upon suitable incubation, colonies of the bacteria develop in or on the agar, and their appearance may be described. This technique is usually employed to determine the free oxygen needs of a pure culture, as indicated by the location of the colonies which develop, but it may also bring out cultural characteristics of some value.

5. *Characteristics of Cultures Grown in Liquid Media.* Pure cultures may be inoculated into transparent liquid media to determine whether or not growth will occur in the particular medium employed. If growth occurs, it may be on the surface (forming a ring or pellicle); throughout the medium (causing uniform clouding, or in the form of flocs); or in the form of a sediment, which may be dispersed by shaking to yield a uniform clouding of the broth, flocs of cells; or a stringy, viscous mass. Very often cultures in liquid media exhibit a combination or succession of the characteristics just described.

PHYSIOLOGICAL CHARACTERISTICS

So many different physiological characteristics of bacteria may be studied and used in determinative work that space does not permit more than a bare outline of a few of those which are more commonly investigated.

1. *Influence of the Environment upon Bacteria.* The effect of each of the many factors that may influence the growth of bacteria may be determined in a study of the influence of environment upon the rate and extent of growth of pure cultures. These factors have been described in Chapter 9, and may be listed as follows: foods (amounts and kinds); moisture requirements and effect of osmotic pressure; temperature (maximum, optimum, and minimum); free oxygen requirements and oxidation-reduction condition of medium; hydrogen-ion concentration (maximum, optimum, and minimum pH values); surface tension; and effects of antiseptics and disinfectants. Factors influencing survival of bacteria have been described in Chapter 10.

2. *Effects of Bacteria upon the Environment.* The physical and chemical changes which bacteria may produce in their environment are many and varied. They may be the result of the action of extracellular, hydrolytic enzymes which catalyze the hydrolysis of relatively complex organic compounds; of respiration processes; or of synthetic activities of bacteria. In the characterization and classification of a pure culture its ability or inability to utilize complex organic compounds (which depends upon the ability of the bacteria to produce the necessary extracellular enzymes); its ability to make use of simple, soluble substances in its respiration processes (which depends upon the nature of its intracellular enzymes which catalyze the oxidations

and reductions of the respiratory processes); the physical (such as light and heat) and chemical by-products of respirations and other intracellular processes; and its ability or inability to reduce such dyes as methylene blue or litmus may be determined. These are but a few of the many changes which bacteria may produce in their environment. The following outline presents in a very abbreviated form some of the physiological characteristics which may be studied.

I. Changes which depend upon the ability of bacteria to produce certain extracellular, hydrolytic enzymes
  1. Decomposition of cellulose, hemicelluloses, pectins, gums, starch, and other polysaccharides, and disaccharides; proteins such as casein, albumen, globulin, and gelatin; fats and oils—chemical and physical changes resulting from such decompositions may also be noted
II. Ability to utilize relatively simple, soluble, nonnitrogenous organic compounds such as simple sugars, alcohols, and organic acids in respiration processes
  1. Determination of disappearance of such compounds from media correlated with
    a. Growth of culture (both rate and extent of growth)
    b. Increased respiration of culture
  2. Detection of by-products of respiration, such as acids, alcohols, aldehydes, ketones, gases, and other products
III. Ability to utilize relatively simple nitrogenous compounds
  1. Nitrogen fixation (use of free N_2 as only source of nitrogenous food—indicated by growth and actual increases in the nitrogen content of the cells in nitrogen-free media)
  2. Nitrification (oxidation of ammonium salts to nitrites and of nitrites to nitrates)
  3. Nitrate utilization (use of nitrates as sole source of nitrogenous food)
  4. Nitrate reduction (reduction of nitrates to nitrites)
  5. Denitrification (reduction of nitrates with formation of gaseous N_2)
  6. Use of certain amino acids as sole source of nitrogenous food
  7. Formation of by-products such as ammonia, H_2S, indol, skatol, melanins, amines, and toxins, as a result of utilization of organic nitrogenous foods
IV. Utilization of free sulfur or of inorganic compounds containing sulfur
  1. Oxidation of free sulfur to sulfuric acid
  2. Oxidation of H_2S to free sulfur or to sulfuric acid
  3. Sulfate utilization as sole source of sulfur
  4. Sulfate reduction with production of H_2S
V. Ability to reduce certain dyes such as methylene blue, janus green, or litmus
VI. Possession of certain enzymes such as catalase

Pathogenicity for Plants, Animals, or Humans, and Immunological Studies

The ability of a pure culture to produce a specific disease when inoculated into, or transported by natural means to a plant, animal, or human being, is an outstanding characteristic of certain bacteria. The detailed technique of such inoculations and of the pathological studies involved in the determination of their effects cannot be described here for want of space.

It is also impossible for the same reason to describe and discuss the many methods of immunology and serology which may be employed in the characterization, identification, and classification of bacteria. These methods may be employed in the study of nonpathogenic as well as of pathogenic bacteria. Various serological methods are described in the Manual of Methods for the Pure Culture Study of Bacteria, to which reference is made at the end of this chapter.

CLASSIFICATION OF BACTERIA

After a pure culture of bacteria has been characterized it is given a genus and species name. Three basic rules are followed in the assignment of scientific names to bacteria: (1) The scientific name of a bacterium (as of any plant or animal) is made up of two words with Latin endings. (2) The first word, which is the name of the genus, is always a proper noun, and is capitalized. (3) The second word, which is the name of the species, is usually an adjective or a noun in the genitive case modifying the genus name; occasionally it is a noun in apposition with the name of the genus. If the name of the species is an adjective it must agree in gender with the name of the genus. The name of the species is not as a rule capitalized, but it may be if it is a proper noun. When printed, scientific names of bacteria are italicized; when typed or written, they are underlined.

At present no system of classification is accepted as standard by all bacteriologists, but the classification given in the 6th edition of *Bergey's Manual of Determinative Bacteriology,* and which is presented in a modified, outline form in Appendix B, is the most widely used at this time. This classification is based upon the four main groups of characteristics that have been described. The historical developments leading up to this system of classification of bacteria have been discussed by Buchanan, and by Bergey, *et al.* (See references at end of chapter.) For the student interested in a survey of general bacteriology, as well as for bacteriologists who are interested mainly in applied bacteriology, this system of classification may be used as a means for grouping together in orderly fashion those bacteria which exhibit more or less closely related properties, and for providing suitable names for these groups. As new species, genera, families, or orders of the class *Schizomycetes* are discovered and characterized the classification must be altered to allow their inclusion.

Bacteria are often given other names than those found in the system of classification. Thus, *Mycobacterium tuberculosis* is spoken of as "the tubercle bacillus"; various species of the genus, *Rhizobium,* are called "root-nodule bacteria"; *Mycobacterium phlei* is frequently described simply as "the grass bacillus." These are names which have developed through common usage. They have no place in a system of classification, but are of considerable practical value, and are widely used. Space does not permit the listing of all these common names of bacteria and their scientific equivalents. This is a task which the student of bacteriology must perform for himself just as a student of botany must learn the scientific names of such plants as alfalfa, timothy, and corn.

Certain pure cultures of a species are found to be "atypical"; this is an indication that the system of classification is inadequate, or that the particular culture of the species is a variant form.

Constancy and Variability of Bacteria

The morphological, cultural, physiological, pathogenic, and immunological characteristics of bacteria are remarkably constant. As a pure culture of bacteria grows in or on a culture medium or in living tissues, succeeding generations of cells are produced which are amazingly similar to the original cell or cells from which they have been formed. Such constancy might well be expected since bacteria reproduce by asexual fission, and there is little possibility for the addition to their cells of new germ plasm which might contain different heritable characteristics.

However, the main characteristics of bacteria doubtless do vary to some extent, and such variation must be taken into consideration in their characterization and classification. Any one of a pure culture's morphological, cultural, physiological, or pathogenic properties may be lost; or, in some cases, a property may be gained. If the property lost or gained is a major one in the characterization of the organism, it may be necessary to classify it in a different species. However, if the property lost or gained is of minor importance in characterization, the culture is considered as a variant within the species, and is set apart as a variety of that species.

An enormous number of papers on the subject of bacterial variation may be found in bacteriological literature, and studies on variation constitute one of the main fields of research in microbiology at present. Some of the well-established examples and theories of variability will be described briefly.

Temporary (Reversible) Variation

The changes in morphology which occur during the normal growth history of a pure culture (see Chapter 9) are one example of this type of variation.

Old cells in a pure culture often look quite different from the young cells considered as typical of the species, but if these old, often peculiarly shaped cells are placed in a suitable environment, their progeny will exhibit the morphology typical of the species.

Some bacteria can be cultivated in certain media or under such conditions that they fail to produce capsules, but when placed under different conditions, form capsules readily.

When cultivated in media rich in available nitrogenous foods, species of *Azotobacter* fail to fix appreciable quantities of atmospheric nitrogen; but when grown in nitrogen-free media the property of nitrogen-fixation is regained.

Clostridium botulinum, when grown in a medium rich in available carbohydrate and relatively low in organic nitrogenous food, produces little or no botulinus toxin; but when cultivated in the presence of suitable nitrogenous food and the proper quantity of available carbohydrate, it again produces toxin.

These are only examples of the many temporary, reversible variations that may occur in pure cultures of bacteria; they are usually caused by changes in environment.

Permanent (Irreversible) Variations or Mutations

Bacillus anthracis, when cultivated continuously at 42° C., loses, in time, its ability to form endospores. Cultivation of the nonspore-forming variant at 37° C. does not bring back its ability to form endospores.

When *Salmonella typhosa* is cultivated continuously in broth containing phenol, it loses permanently its ability to form flagella. The nonflagellated variant fails to develop flagella when cultivated in media free from phenol.

Whether these variations, and others of somewhat similar nature, are due to selection or to an irreversible change in the heritable characteristics of all of the cells in a culture, is difficult to say. The characteristics of a pure culture are usually determined by those of the majority of cells in it. If the conditions of cultivation are such that the "normal" forms continue to make up the majority of the population of the culture, its characteristics will remain constant. If, however, the conditions of cultivation are varied sufficiently, the growth of the few variant individual cells in the original population may be favored with the result that they become the dominant forms. In time, continued cultivation under such conditions may result in the death of the few "normal" individuals which remain, and the population will then be made up entirely of the progeny of the variant.

Rigid experimental proof remains to be given in order to determine whether temporary and permanent variations are due to selection or to "training," i.e., an induced change in the heritable characteristics of all the cells in the population.

Dissociation

A single bacterial cell or several cells obtained from a colony which is apparently a pure culture will as a rule, when placed on a suitable agar medium, form a colony or several colonies similar in all respects to the parent colony. This has been accepted as a normal occurrence. But it has also been demonstrated that the progeny of a single cell, or several cells obtained from a single colony, may produce different types of colonies as follows: (1) a smooth, glistening, moist, regular, smooth-edged colony, known as the smooth, or S, type; (2) a very moist, smooth, glistening, regular, smooth-edged, rather viscous colony known as the mucoid, or M, type; (3) a relatively rough-surfaced, rough-edged, dull, dry irregular colony, known as the rough, or R, type. The formation of one of these different types of colonies from an inoculum obtained from a pure culture of another type is known as dissociation. Colonies with all the possible properties intermediate between smooth, mucoid, and rough colonies may also be formed; that is, a culture dissociates from a typically smooth to a typically rough type by stages. In a fast-growing culture these intermediate stages may easily be overlooked. Figure 42 shows photographs of normal and dissociative variant colonies of *Lactobacillus bulgaricus*. Pure cultures isolated from variant colonies are called dissociative variants. Some of the important characteristics of such dissociative variants are as follows (these descriptions are general, and exceptions to them no doubt exist):

Smooth, or S, type. Cells normal in size, shape, and structure (if the S type is the normal colony form of the species); cause uniform clouding when grown in broth; sensitive to bacteriophage; usually virulent or toxic if a pathogen (if the S type is the normal colony form of the species); active in producing chemical changes.

Mucoid, or M, type. Cells usually normal in size and shape, but heavily capsulated; may form visible strings of growth in broth cultures.

Rough, or R, type. Cells may form filaments; capsules, if formed, are smaller and undoubtedly of a different chemical constitution from those of the other types; no flagella present; granular or flocculent growth in broth; relatively avirulent even if a pathogen (unless R type is the normal colony form of the species); less sensitive to bacteriophage than the S type of the same species; relatively inactive in the production of chemical changes.

The causes of dissociation and of the differences in characteristics of the dissociative variants isolated from the different types of colonies are un-

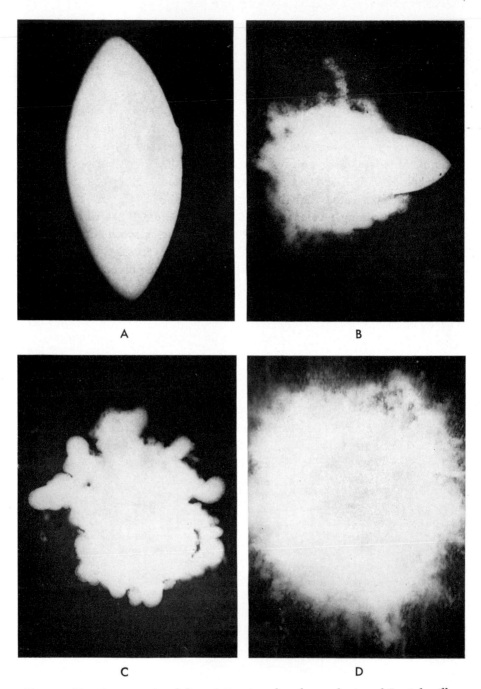

FIGURE 42. An example of dissociation in subsurface colonies of *Lactobacillus bulgaricus*. **A.** Smooth colonial type. **B** and **C.** Intermediate colonial types. **D.** Rough colonial type. Plating any one of these colonies will give rise to all 4 types of colonies in varying proportions.

doubtedly environmental; changes in pII, in the oxidation-reduction condition of the medium, and the presence of antiserum or such a substance as lithium chloride in the medium will bring about dissociation of some species experimentally. Whether dissociation occurs in nature, or only under laboratory conditions, is another problem under investigation at present. Most of the studies on bacterial dissociation have been made on pathogenic bacteria, but many different pathogens remain to be studied, and the great majority of the nonpathogenic bacteria have not been investigated with the object of studying their dissociative behavior. Dissociation is found to occur regularly when investigations are made, and it is entirely possible that in the future dissociation may be shown to occur in all species. Dissociation, and the properties of dissociative variants, must be considered in the characterization and classification of bacteria. The description of a species should make allowances for normal variation and dissociation within the limits established for the species.

REFERENCES

Allen, R. M., *The microscope*. N. Y., Van Nostrand, 1940.

Breed, R. S., Murray, E. G. D., and Hitchens, A. P., *Bergey's manual of determinative bacteriology* (6th ed.). Baltimore, Md., Williams & Wilkins, 1948.

Buchanan, R. E., *General systematic bacteriology*. Baltimore, Md., Williams & Wilkins, 1925.

Cold Spring Harbor Symposia on Quantitative Biology, *Heredity and variation in microorganisms*, Vol. XI. The Biological Laboratory, Cold Spring Harbor, N. Y., 1946.

Dubos, R. J., *The bacterial cell*. Cambridge, Mass., Harvard University Press, 1945.

Gage, S. H., *The microscope* (16th ed.). Ithaca, N. Y., Comstock, 1936.

Lederberg, J., "Problems in microbial genetics." *Heredity* (1948), 2:145–198.

Society of American Bacteriologists, Committee on Bacteriological Technique, *Manual of methods for pure culture study of bacteria*. Geneva, N. Y., Biotech Publications.

PART IV

Microorganisms in Industry

Industries have been developed in which microorganisms are produced for use in other industries, in the home, in agriculture, or for medical purposes. A second group of industries makes use of the abilities of microorganisms to cause physical and chemical changes that are necessary in the manufacture of fermented foods, beverages, and other substances such as flax and hemp fibers. A third group of industries uses microorganisms to produce chemical products, such as alcohols, acids, gases, antibiotics, and enzymes, which are then removed from the medium in which they were produced and used for various industrial, agricultural, or medical purposes.

15. INDUSTRIAL PROPAGATION OF MICROORGANISMS

Production of Yeast

In the United States, yeast has been manufactured on a large scale by two methods. At present, most yeast is grown in a molasses-mineral salts medium, but may be manufactured by use of a grain medium if warranted by economic conditions.

Yeast from Molasses

The most extensively used of the various methods for the manufacture of yeast employs molasses as a source of sugar; it is, therefore, the chief constituent of the culture medium in which the yeast is grown. Molasses from sugar cane or sugar beets varies in composition with the process used in its manufacture.

Ordinary "blackstrap" molasses is the sirup that is left after the recovery of crystalline sucrose from concentrated sugar-cane or sugar-beet juice. Blackstrap molasses usually contains from 48 to 55 per cent of sugars, mainly sucrose, but with smaller and variable amounts of glucose and fructose. So-called "high-test" molasses is an evaporated sugar-cane juice that contains all of the original sugar of the juice, but much of this sugar has undergone hydrolysis during the evaporation process, and hence high-test molasses contains relatively more glucose and fructose than is found in blackstrap. High-test molasses usually contains from 75 to 80 per cent total sugars. Molasses also contains many of the inorganic foods needed by yeast. But nitrogenous foods and other food elements required by the yeast usually must be added to a molasses culture medium if maximum growth is to be obtained. A satisfactory molasses-mineral salts culture medium for the industrial propagation of yeast from molasses may contain:

Sugar: molasses, which contain sucrose, glucose and fructose—final concentration of sugars, 7 to 9 per cent
Nitrogenous foods: ammonium sulfate, ammonium phosphate, or other ammonium salts; urea, barley sprouts, or some other source of organic nitrogenous food —final concentration of nitrogenous foods, 0.2 to 0.4 per cent
Inorganic salts: phosphates and small amounts of other minerals in molasses, or added in soluble form—final concentration of phosphates, 0.1 to 0.3 per cent
Accessory growth substances: extracts of vegetables, grain or yeast or small quantities of vitamin precursors, vitamin concentrates, or purified vitamins

This medium is acidified to pH 4.3 to 4.5 with mineral acids such as HCl or H_3PO_4, and is clarified to remove as much coloring matter as possible from the molasses.

The inoculum of yeast added to the large quantity of molasses-mineral salts culture medium in the vat or "fermenter" in which the yeast is to be grown must be developed by means of a "build-up" process in a molasses medium similar in composition to that employed for the final, large-scale cultivation of the yeast. Stock cultures of *Saccharomyces cerevisiae* that are maintained in an active, viable condition by frequent transfer on molasses-mineral salts agar medium serve as the initial inoculum or "seed." A small flask of sterile molasses-mineral salts medium is inoculated with yeast from such an agar slant culture. Following incubation at 25° to 30° C. (77° to 86° F.) until the maximum stationary phase of growth is reached, yeast from the flask culture is transferred aseptically to a larger flask of sterile molasses-mineral salts medium. This process is repeated, with each successive transfer being made to a larger volume of molasses-mineral salts medium, until the final culture is inoculated into a large tank or vat of the culture medium. During growth of the yeast in the last two stages of "build-up" the culture medium is aerated in order to obtain a maximum yield of cells. The yeast cells obtained from the final culture vat are separated by centrifugation from the liquid, and the heavy suspension thus secured is used as the inoculum for a large volume of molasses-mineral salts medium. In this manner, sufficient numbers of active yeast cells are obtained to provide an inoculum that will grow rapidly in the large volume of culture medium in the final vat, and reach the maximum stationary phase of development in the shortest time possible. As a general rule, the culture medium in the vat in which the yeast is to be grown is inoculated at a rate of 3 to 5 pounds of moist yeast cells per 100 gallons of medium.

At the time of inoculation, the molasses-mineral salts medium is adjusted to a temperature of 30° C. (86° F.) and a reaction of pH 4.3 to 4.5, and is aerated at a rapid rate with filtered air. Aerobic conditions are maintained in order to make it possible for the yeast to derive the maximum amount of energy from the sugar of the culture medium.

$$C_6H_{12}O_6 + 6\ O_2 \xrightarrow[\text{aerobic conditions}]{\text{yeast under}} 6\ CO_2 + 6\ H_2O + 689{,}800 \text{ calories}$$
glucose

This is a theoretical equation. Under actual plant conditions, the yeast also produces small amounts of alcohol and organic acids. This is evidence that it does not oxidize completely all of the sugar which it utilizes. However, under aerobic conditions most of the sugar is oxidized and much better growth of the yeast occurs than would take place under anaerobic conditions, where the yeast would secure less energy from the sugar, and would grow very slowly.

$$C_6H_{12}O_6 \xrightarrow[\text{anaerobic conditions}]{\text{yeast under}} 2\ C_2H_5OH + 2\ CO_2 + 31{,}200 \text{ calories}$$
glucose

The nitrogenous materials, phosphates, and other minerals in the medium are used by the yeast as food for growth, i.e., for synthetic purposes. The accessory growth substances of the medium, particularly the vitamin B complex, are incorporated into the yeast cells.

Under optimum conditions in the final large vat or tank culture, the maximum yield of yeast is obtained in about 8 to 10 hours. During this time the mass of yeast cells increases from approximately 3 to 5 pounds per 100 gallons of medium to approximately 16 to 20 pounds per 100 gallons; a net gain of from 11 to 17 pounds of moist cells per 100 gallons of medium.

When the yeast in the vat has reached the peak of its growth curve, the liquid in the vat is immediately run through a centrifugal separator. The yeast-free liquid, which contains about 0.3 to 0.5 per cent of ethyl alcohol, may be discarded or used in the manufacture of vinegar. The "yeast cream," which is a heavy suspension of yeast cells obtained from the separator, is put through a filter press in order to remove excess liquid from the mass of cells. These cells may then be mixed with a small amount of edible oil or with starch and oil, pressed into cakes, wrapped, and stored at 0° to 5° C. (32° to 41° F.). The cakes of compressed yeast are then delivered as rapidly as possible, and under constant refrigeration, to bakers and grocers.

Preservation of Compressed Yeast

Compressed yeast is perishable. The cells which make up a cake of compressed yeast are removed from the culture medium when at the maximum stationary phase of their growth. They contain from 65 to 70 per cent of moisture, and will carry on an endogenous respiration, i.e., a respiration in which reserve foods in the cells are utilized, at temperatures above freezing. Respiration of this type soon results in death of the cells, and death is followed by autolysis. When the cells autolyze, the cake of yeast becomes soft and develops a stale taste and odor. Endogenous respiration and autolysis of yeast may be retarded by storage at temperatures of 0° to 5° C. (32° to 41° F.); at higher temperatures the yeast spoils more rapidly.

Molds, film yeasts, actinomycetes, or bacteria may grow on the surface or throughout an entire cake of yeast, and their growth may be extensive enough to cause spoilage. The first step in the prevention of spoilage due to such contaminants is asepsis all along the line of production and handling of the yeast. It is easy to prescribe rigid asepsis, but quite another matter to actually accomplish prevention of contamination under plant conditions. When one considers the possibilities that exist for contamination of yeast during its manufacture, he can only marvel at the vigor and hardiness of the yeast and its ability to outgrow other microorganisms which may enter from the air, from the raw materials used, and from the vats, pipes, separators and other pieces of equipment. Filtration of air which is blown into the fermenters and culture tanks, thorough cleansing and practical sterilization of all equipment and utensils used, and sterilization of wrapping materials are employed in attempts to reduce contamination.

The second step in the prevention of spoilage of compressed yeast due to contaminating microorganisms is storage at 0° to 5° C. (32° to 41° F.), in order to prevent or retard the growth of the contaminants.

Preservation of Yeast by Drying

Yeast to be used in baking or as a food may be preserved without refrigeration if it is dried immediately following manufacture. Yeast to be used for livestock feed or as food for human beings usually is preserved by drying it to a powder which contains approximately 2 to 4 per cent moisture. Like dry milk, dry yeast will keep indefinitely if protected from moisture. The yeast cells in dried yeast of this type are dead.

If dried yeast is to be used in baking, it is necessary to dry it in such a way that the cells will not be killed. At the same time, the moisture content of the yeast must be reduced to a level that will not permit active respiration of the cells or growth of contaminants. Drying of the yeast must be carried on at temperatures below the thermal death point, and special care must be used to prevent contamination during the drying process. The yeast cells in dried preparations will live for long periods of time at room temperature, but their numbers decrease in time. Storage of viable dried yeast at high temperatures hastens death of the cells. As a rule, greater quantities of dried yeast (on a dry-weight basis) must be employed to cause the same rate and degree of leavening action produced by fresh compressed yeast. Older types of dried yeast must be added to a sugar solution which is then incubated at 26.7° to 32.2° C. (80° to 90° F.) for 6 to 12 hours before the cells become sufficiently active and numerous to serve as satisfactory leavening agents; newer types of dried yeast may be used directly without preliminary treatment.

Yeast from Grain

The older of the two methods for the industrial production of yeast involves the use of a culture medium prepared by the malting of a mixture of grain and barley sprouts; hence the designation "yeast from grain."

In the United States, corn has been used as the main source of carbohydrate food. The corn is ground, mixed with water, and cooked by means of steam under pressure. The cooked corn usually makes up about 40 per cent of the dry matter of the grain mixture which is used.

Dried barley sprouts from malted barley are the chief source of soluble nitrogenous organic foods. The sprouts also supply a small amount of sugar.

The barley malt is the chief source of amylase, proteinases and polypeptidases which catalyze the hydrolysis of starch, proteins, and polypeptides, respectively, in the mashing process. The malt serves also as a source of starch, sugars, proteins, and partially hydrolyzed proteins.

In the "mashing" process, water is added to the grain-malt mixture to give the desired concentration of solids. The reaction is adjusted to approximately pH 5.0, and the temperature is raised to 60° to 65° C. (140° to 149° F.), and held at that point for approximately three hours. During the mashing process the amylase of malt catalyzes hydrolysis of starch to maltose; proteinases of the malt catalyze hydrolysis of proteins to polypeptides, and polypeptidases catalyze hydrolysis of polypeptides to amino acids. Mashing is necessary because the yeast is unable to use starch as a source of carbohydrate food, or proteins for nitrogenous food. The mashing process changes a large proportion of the starch in the grain mixture to maltose, and the proteins and polypeptides to amino acids.

Following the mashing process the mash is acidified to pH 4.3 to 4.5 either by the addition of mineral acids such as HCl or H_3PO_4, or by fermentation. If fermentation is to be used, the mash is cooled to 45° to 50° C. (113° to 122° F.) and inoculated with an active culture of *Lactobacillus delbrueckii* which has been cultivated in sterilized wort. This organism ferments the maltose in mash, with lactic acid the chief product. The acid developed in mash, or added to it, serves two main purposes: first, it preserves the mash against the activity of protein-decomposing and starch-fermenting bacteria which would cause spoilage, and second, it changes the reaction to a point (about pH 4.5) which is optimum for the growth of yeast.

From the mash tub, the mash flows into a filter tub which has a perforated false bottom on which the barley sprouts in the mash accumulate and form a mat. As the liquid passes through this mat the spent grain is removed from it, and the filtrate, which is called "wort," then contains only substances in solution and a small quantity of colloids. The mat in the filter is washed several times with water to remove from it all soluble foods that may be used by the yeast.

Small amounts of the wort obtained from the filter are used as a medium for the cultivation of the inoculum of yeast. Most of the wort is run into the "fermenter," which is a large, open vat provided with perforated pipes, filtrose plates, or some other air-diffusing apparatus, and coils through which water may be run for the purpose of temperature regulation.

The wort contains maltose and glucose, amino acids, peptides, phosphates and other necessary minerals, and accessory growth factors. Its reaction is pH 4.3 to 4.5, and its temperature is adjusted to approximately 30° C. (86° F.). Under these conditions it is an ideal medium for the growth of yeast.

The inoculum of yeast to be added to the wort in the "fermenter" is developed from a pure culture of *Saccharomyces cerevisiae* which has been cultivated on an agar slant of wort medium. The inoculum is "built up" in a manner similar to that described for the preparation of the inoculum for the molasses-mineral salts process, except that wort is used as the culture medium.

The inoculation of the wort in the "fermenter," conditions of growth, time of growth, separation of the yeast, and final processing and preservation are similar to the same procedures and conditions involved in the manufacture of yeast from molasses.

The main problems of the yeast industry are: to obtain as high a yield of yeast as possible; to manufacture a yeast that is an active leavening agent, i.e., one which produces CO_2 rapidly in bread dough; and to manufacture yeast of satisfactory keeping quality. These problems are particularly difficult to solve because they are closely interrelated. For example, a high yield of yeast which is an active leavening agent can be secured only when relatively large amounts of readily available nitrogenous foods are present in the wort or molasses medium. However, the addition of too much nitrogenous food results in the production of yeast of unsatisfactory keeping quality. If too little available nitrogenous food is supplied, the yield is reduced and the activity of the yeast is lowered, although its keeping quality may be excellent.

Yeasts from Other Materials

It is also possible to manufacture yeast from sugar-containing materials produced by the hydrolysis of wood or other cellulosic substances, or of starchy foods such as potatoes. The procedures and conditions described for the manufacture of yeast from molasses or from grain must be adapted to these processes. In addition, it is necessary to use a variety of yeast which will grow rapidly in the culture medium produced, and to build up the inoculum in that medium. At present, yeast to be used in baking is not manufactured from these substances in the United States. In Europe, some leavening yeast is produced from these materials, and considerable quantities of yeast for food are manufactured from waste cellulosic or starchy substances.

PRODUCTION OF CULTURES OF ROOT-NODULE BACTERIA

The need for and use of cultures of root-nodule bacteria for the inoculation of seeds of leguminous crops will be discussed in Chapter 21. At present, cultures of these bacteria are produced on a large scale by a number of industrial concerns and by a few Federal and State supported institutions. Nearly all of these manufacturers prepare a separate culture for each of the different bacterial-plant groups; e.g., one culture for alfalfa and sweet clover, another for red, white, alsike, and mammoth clovers, etc. A few manufacturers prepare cultures for one species or variety of leguminous plant within a bacterial-plant group; e.g., one culture for use on alfalfa, another for sweet clover; one culture for Thomas Laxton peas, another for Alaska peas, etc. A small number of manufacturers go to the opposite extreme, and prepare cultures which contain root-nodule bacteria for two or more bacterial-plant groups, e.g., for alfalfa and peas, or for peas, beans and lupines.

Three types of cultures are prepared: liquid cultures, solid base cultures, and agar cultures. Few liquid cultures are produced at present. They are made by growing the desired species of root-nodule bacteria in a suitable liquid medium; the resulting liquid culture is then bottled and shipped to the user. Manufacture of liquid culture is uncommon because they are bulky, difficult and expensive to ship, and easily contaminated with undesirable microorganisms. Although the methods and media used by different concerns and institutions in the production of solid base and agar cultures vary considerably, the following outline illustrates the general production procedures in use at present.

Outline of Industrial Propagation of Cultures of Root-Nodule Bacteria

Agar Cultures	Solid Base Cultures
Pure, agar-slant test tube cultures of one or more strains of desired species of *Rhizobium*	Pure, agar-slant test tube cultures of one or more strains of desired species of *Rhizobium*
↓	↓
Several agar-slant bottle cultures	Small flask of liquid culture medium
↓	↓
Aqueous suspension of *Rhizobium* cells prepared from bottle cultures	Large flask of liquid culture medium
↓	↓
Large number of agar-slant bottle cultures inoculated with suspension; incubated at 20° to 25° C., then sealed for shipment	Small tank of liquid culture medium; aerated during incubation
	↓
	Large tank of liquid culture medium; aerated during incubation
	↓
	Liquid culture of *Rhizobium* added to solid base of dried peat, finely divided carbon, or sand; moisture content adjusted to 40 to 50 per cent; packaged for shipment in paper, cardboard, or tin containers

In the production of agar cultures, pure culture technique must be employed throughout the entire procedure; the final bottle cultures must contain only the desired strain or strains of one species of *Rhizobium*. In the final bottle cultures, the bacteria are found on the surface of the agar. These cultures should be used as soon as possible after the bacterial population has reached its maximum. Storage at 10° to 15° C. (50° to 59° F.) will prolong the viability of the cells in these cultures; storage at higher temperatures will cause the bacteria to die more rapidly. Rhizobia for the alfalfa, clover, pea, and bean bacterial-plant groups are more hardy and will survive storage better than rhizobia for the soybean, lupine, and cowpea bacterial-plant groups.

Pure-culture technique must also be employed in the production of solid base cultures. The solid base to which the bacteria are added is either completely or partially sterilized with heat before the addition of the bacteria. Contamination of these cultures is bound to occur when the bacteria are mixed with the solid base and packaged in the final containers, but in most instances the contaminants cause no serious deterioration of the cultures.

The bacteria in solid base cultures will remain viable for comparatively long periods of time if the cultures are stored at $10°$ to $20°$ C. ($50°$ to $68°$ F.). Storage at higher temperatures will hasten death of the cells. As in the case of agar cultures, solid base cultures should be used as soon as possible after preparation to insure best results.

Propagation of Microorganisms for Medical Purposes

Viruses, rickettsiae, and bacteria are produced in large quantities for use by the medical and veterinary medical professions. These viruses and microorganisms are employed as vaccines: weakened, modified, partially neutralized, or killed viruses or cells which can be injected into a human being or animal to induce an active immunity against some specific infectious disease. The nature and use of vaccines will be discussed in Chapters 29, 31, and 32.

Propagation on a large scale of viruses, rickettsiae, and bacteria to be used as vaccines involves control of many fundamental and special problems. Obviously, the microorganisms grown must be cultivated in pure culture, and protected against contamination at all times. Furthermore, the microorganisms propagated for this purpose must be cultivated in such a manner that they will serve as effective immunizing agents. In addition, all of the microorganisms to be employed as vaccines are potential disease-producers; hence they must be cultivated, handled and treated so that they will not produce disease.

Viruses and rickettsiae are strict parasites, and must, therefore, be cultivated in susceptible living tissue. For example, vaccinia virus, employed in vaccination against smallpox, is cultivated on the skin of a calf or in embryonated eggs; modified yellow fever virus is grown in the developing chick embryo, as are the rickettsiae which cause typhus fever.

Pathogenic bacteria, such as those which cause typhoid fever, may be grown on ordinary culture media in test tubes, flasks, and special culture tanks. This procedure may also be employed for the cultivation of avirulent strains of *Brucella abortus*, the causal agent of Bang's disease in cattle.

The viruses, rickettsiae, or bacteria which have been cultivated in the manner best suited to maintain their value as immunizing agents are then harvested aseptically and made into suspensions in physiological salt solution (0.85 per cent NaCl) or some other suitable liquid. They may be employed in their original condition if they are incapable of producing disease, but in some cases they must be modified by the addition of formalin, chloroform, or some other agent which will produce the desired change. It is also possible to modify or kill certain viruses, rickettsiae, or bacteria in vaccines by use of ultraviolet light, or by controlled use of high temperatures.

Vaccines which contain living viruses, rickettsiae, or bacteria are perishable, and hence must be packaged in containers and stored under conditions that will maintain viability of the microorganisms for a maximum period of time. Suspensions of modified or killed cells of viruses, rickettsiae, or bacteria must be packaged in sealed containers and stored at low temperatures, just above freezing, to maintain their potency as immunizing agents. All vaccines deteriorate upon storage even under the best possible conditions, but loss of immunizing value is more rapid at high temperatures and in the presence of direct sunlight.

Production of Cultures Used in the Dairy Industry

The different kinds of microorganisms employed and the purposes for which they are used in the dairy industry will be discussed in Chapter 27. Production of cultures of these microorganisms is the function of a small but important industry. Nearly all of the different microorganisms employed in the dairy industry are grown in milk and sent to the user in the form of milk cultures. *Lactobacillus acidophilus, Lactobacillus bulgaricus* and *Streptococcus thermophilus* are grown in sterile skim milk at 37° C. (98.6° F.). The viability of *L. bulgaricus* and *S. thermophilus* may be prolonged if they are grown in association with certain species of film-forming yeasts.

Streptococcus lactis, S. cremoris or mixtures of these bacteria with the aroma-producing *Leuconostoc citrovorum* and *Leuconostoc dextranicum* may be grown in sterile skim milk at 21.1° C. (70° F.). Another practice is to grow these organisms at 21.1° C. (70° F.) in whole milk that has been pasteurized at 82.2° C. (180° F.) for 30 minutes.

Milk cultures of lactic acid-producing bacteria give best results when used immediately after they have been prepared. When stored at room temperatures of 21.1° C. (70° F.) or above, the bacteria in milk cultures die rapidly. Cultures of *S. lactis, S. cremoris,* or mixtures of these organisms with aroma producers, may be preserved for short periods by storage at 0° to 5° C. (32° to 41° F.). Cultures of S. *thermophilus* and lactobacilli are best preserved for short periods by storage at 10° to 15° C. (50° to 59° F.). Dried cultures of lactic acid-producing streptococci and lactobacilli may be prepared, but are not widely used in the dairy industry at present.

Penicillium roqueforti is grown on bread crumbs. The spore-laden crumbs are then dried, crushed, and packed in tin containers. While dry, the spores remain viable for long periods of time.

PRODUCTION OF CULTURES USED IN OTHER INDUSTRIES

Cultures of yeasts used in the manufacture of beer and ale, wine, brandy, and distilled liquors are maintained in specialized laboratories under carefully controlled conditions. Before a fermentation in which the yeast is to be employed is started, the culture must be "built up" in such a manner that it will possess maximum activity and a sufficiently large number of cells to cause the desired change. During the building-up process, the purity and desirable characteristics of the culture must be maintained.

In industries which employ bacteria, actinomycetes, or molds to produce physical or chemical changes in a product, or to manufacture some chemical, the same general procedures of culture maintenance and preparation are involved. In the maintenance and development of cultures of bacteria and actinomycetes, the additional problem of protection against bacteriophage contamination is encountered. This problem may be dealt with in two ways: (1) by prevention of contamination of cultures with bacteriophage; and (2) by selection and use of bacteriophage-resistant varieties of the pure culture employed.

It must be remembered that many of the procedures and media employed in the industrial propagation of microorganisms are patented. In addition, many "trade secrets" are involved in this branch of industrial microbiology. For these reasons, the procedures which have been described are general, and point out principles of manufacture rather than exact methods.

REFERENCES

Frey, C. N., "History and development of the modern yeast industry." *Ind. Eng. Chem.* (1930), *22*:1154–1162.

Frey, C. N., Kirby, G. W., and Schultz, A., "Yeast. Physiology, manufacture and uses." *Ind. Eng. Chem.* (1936), *28*:879–884.

Gershenfeld, L., *Biological products.* N. Y., Romaine Pierson, 1939.

Prescott, S. C., and Dunn, C. G., *Industrial microbiology* (2nd ed.), N. Y., McGraw-Hill, 1949.

16. USE OF MICROORGANISMS TO PRODUCE PHYSICAL AND CHEMICAL CHANGES IN SUBSTANCES

The ability of microorganisms to cause specific physical and chemical changes in certain organic compounds is used by various industries in the manufacture of a number of products. The microorganisms may be used for the production of definite chemicals, for one or more of the treatments in a process necessary to the manufacture of a product, or for the change of the original substance to another and desired product. The production of chemicals, such as organic acids and solvents, by fermentation will be discussed in the next chapter (Chapter 17).

It will be noted that the lactic acid fermentation by bacteria and the alcoholic fermentation by yeasts are most often concerned in industrial fermentations, especially those for the production of foods or beverages. The use of lactic acid or other fermentations in the production of sauerkraut, cucumber pickles, green olives, silage (Chapter 24), "starter" butter, fermented milks, and cheese (Chapter 27) serves not only to aid in the preservation of these foods; but causes the production of new foods, which differ from the original foods in taste, odor, and other characteristics. These, then, are industrial fermentations in which the original substance has been changed by microbial action to another and desired product. The fermentations involved in the production of bread, wines, beer, distilled liquors, vinegar, and oriental foods, which will be discussed in this chapter, fall into this same group of industrial fermentations. It will be observed that alcoholic fermentation is involved in the manufacture of these products.

BREAD

The fermentation of sugar by yeasts with the production of alcohol and carbon dioxide has been discussed in Chapters 8 and 15; and the preparation of yeast cultures has been described in Chapter 15. It will be recalled that when the yeast acts on glucose, the more aerobic the conditions, the more carbon dioxide will be produced and the less alcohol will be formed. The primary function of the yeast in bread-making is the leavening or raising of the sponge (leavened dough) by means of the carbon dioxide it forms. This gives a porous spongy texture to the bread as compared to the tough body and close texture of unleavened bread. At the same time the yeast may contribute some of the flavor of the bread, and may assist in causing "ripening" of the dough or changes in the flour protein or gluten and hence in the relative elasticity and toughness of the bread. Modern methods of bread-making, especially in large bakeries, involve the use of a fresh, active yeast culture and hence rapid rising of the sponge and a comparatively short time for growth of microorganisms before the baking process. Consequently bakers' bread usually is low in flavor compared with home-made bread, salt-rising bread or sour-dough bread in which the yeasts have been active longer and bacteria have had a chance to grow and produce special flavors.

In the manufacture of bakers' bread the dough is inoculated with the relatively pure culture of bakers' yeast prepared as described in Chapter 15. A small quantity of sugar often is added with the flour so that the yeast, which cannot attack starch, may have sufficient fermentable carbohydrate for growth and carbon dioxide production. Most flour contains a little sugar, due to action of the diastase (amylase) of the wheat (or other grain) on the starch, and this diastatic action continues during that part of bread-making previous to baking. The flour also contains nitrogenous food for the yeast in the form of a protein called gluten and small amounts of simpler nitrogenous compounds. Sometimes, however, a so-called "yeast food" or "improver," consisting chiefly of ammonium salts and phosphates, is added to aid the growth of the yeast. The carbon dioxide produced by the yeast causes the rising of the sponge; and the alcohol, which is formed in relatively small amounts, is driven off by the baking process.

In the making of home-made bread the raising and kneading processes usually take long enough to permit prolonged action of the yeast and growth of bacteria in the sponge, with the production of more flavor than found in bakers' bread. Self-rising or salt-rising bread is leavened, not by added yeast, but by microorganisms already in the dough. Gas-forming microorganisms, chiefly bacteria (usually of the coliform group), leaven the dough by means of the carbon dioxide and hydrogen they form, and during the long period of rising act with other bacteria to give a characteristic flavor to the dough and, consequently, to the bread. The making of sour-dough bread probably involves the development of similar leavening agents in the dough, but in this case the new dough is inoculated with leavening microorganisms by introduction of a piece of dough from a previous batch. The products produced by these mixed culture leavens of bacteria, or of bacteria and yeasts, include carbon dioxide and hydrogen for raising the dough, and acids, chiefly lactic and acetic, which give the "sour" flavor. Overproduction of acid in the dough causes the defect of bread known as "sourness."

Bread or other dough may be leavened by chemical agents instead of yeasts or bacteria. So-called baking powders are combinations of chemical compounds which release gas when mixed into the dough. One type of baking powder is a mixture of two parts of cream of tartar (potassium acid tartrate) and one part of baking soda (sodium bicarbonate); carbon dioxide is released when this baking powder is moistened:

$$HKC_4H_4O_6 + NaHCO_3 \longrightarrow NaKC_4H_4O_6 + CO_2 + H_2O$$

Self-rising flour contains added baking powder.

Because of its low moisture content, bread is most likely to be spoiled by molds. Occasionally, however, bread stored under moist, warm conditions becomes brown and sticky within the loaf and emits a sour, disagreeable odor. This defect, known as ropiness or "rope," is so named because at certain stages the sticky material can be pulled out into long strings. The cause of the spoilage, *Bacillus subtilis,* is a capsulated, aerobic, spore-forming bacterium. Spores of this organism are present in small numbers in most samples of flour, and have been reported to be present in some samples of yeast, dry milk, and other ingredients of bread; occasionally large numbers of the spores may be introduced into the dough through one of the ingredients. Since the temperature of the interior of the loaf of bread does not exceed 100° C. during the baking process, spores of the ropy-bread bacillus survive readily; and grow, form capsules, and thus cause ropiness in the finished product, if environmental conditions are favorable. This defect occurs in home baked more often than in commercially baked bread, and usually can be remedied by a change of flour, rapid cooling of the loaves after baking, and storage in a cool place, together with thorough cleaning and disinfection of all equipment and utensils which have been used in the bread making. Most bakers now use sodium or calcium propionate as a preventive of ropiness and mold spoilage, adding these salts to the mix. Older methods, some of which still are used by home bakers, involve acidification of the dough by acid fermentation, by the use of acid ingredients, or by the addition of lactic, acetic or propionic acids. Acetic acid, added as vinegar, has been most widely used for a home remedy; enough is added to make the *p*H of the baked bread about 4.5, that is, acid enough to prevent the germination of the spores of the rope organism that have survived the baking process. Red or "bloody" bread, due to the growth of *Serratia mar-cescens,* a bacterium producing a red pigment, is rare in occurrence. More common are the yellow, green, pink, red, brown, or black discolorations due to pigmented molds.

WINES AND OTHER FERMENTED FRUIT JUICES

It has been pointed out that a moist, acid medium containing fermentable carbohydrate is likely to undergo alcoholic fermentation by yeasts. Most fruit juices fulfill these conditions, and at temperatures of 20° to 30° C. are most likely to support the growth of yeasts and consequently undergo al-coholic fermentation. Different species and even different varieties or strains of yeasts may vary considerably in the amount of alcohol and amounts and kinds of other products they form, and consequently may produce different flavors in fermented products. Hence, a naturally fermented fruit juice may be satisfactory in quality, or it may be decidedly inferior. For this reason most wines and other fermented fruit juices are prepared commercially by use of a tested and tried culture of yeast, usually one of the *Saccharomyces cerevisiae* var. *ellipsoideus* type, able to produce fairly high amounts of alcohol and a pleasing flavor. Since this type of yeast is not inhibited by sulfur dioxide as much as are undesirable wild yeasts or acid-forming bac-teria, this chemical sometimes is added to the fruit juice as such or as po-tassium metabisulfite at the rate of about 120 p.p.m. of sulfur dioxide, in order to insure the occurrence of the desired fermentation.

Wines

The term wine should be applied to the product resulting from the alco-holic fermentation of grape juice, but other fermented fruit juices and even fermented plant juices are called wines. Thus there are different berry wines, as well as pear, citrus fruit and other fruit wines, and even dandelion wine. The product of the alcoholic fermentation of dilute honey is termed **mead.**

True wines vary with the type of grape and the conditions for its growth, the yeast used, the method of fermentation, the amount of sugar, etc. **Dry wines** are those in which the sugar has practically all fermented as com-pared with **sweet wines,** which have a considerable residue of sugar. A **for-tified wine** is one to which brandy (distillate of wine) has been added to raise the content of alcohol. Most natural wines contain from 7 to 16 per cent of alcohol, whereas fortified wines usually contain 20 to 22 per cent.

In wine-making the grapes are ripened until they have a high sugar content, then are crushed; this "**must**" is then inoculated with a pure culture of yeast of the *Saccharomyces cerevisiae* var. *ellipsoideus* type. The temperature is kept near 24° C. (75° F.) during the fermentation; for too high a temperature (90° to 95° F.) will inhibit the added yeast and favor the growth of wild yeasts or of acid-forming bacteria and result in spoilage of the product; too low temperatures (50° F. or below) will slow down the fermentation and may permit the growth of bacteria, molds, and wild yeasts. The addition of sulfur dioxide, as mentioned above, helps the yeast in its competition with acid-forming bacteria and wild yeasts. When most of the sugar has been used, the juice is run off the skins, seeds, and stems and is stored in tanks to complete the fermentation. These well-filled tanks are equipped with valves, which permit the escape of carbon dioxide yet keep out oxygen; for if aerobic conditions are permitted, acetic acid bacteria may oxidize some of the alcohol to vinegar and thus spoil the wine. After the wine has been properly aged, it is bottled and stored, and may be pasteurized. **Spanish sherry** is an interesting wine because a film yeast growing on the must is believed to be responsible for the special flavor of the wine and to aid in its aging.

"Diseases" or troubles in connection with wine-making are numerous. Most of these defects are due to microorganisms. Wild yeasts may outgrow the desired yeast and cause poor alcohol production, off flavors, cloudiness, inhibition of later growth of the wine yeast, and a high volatile acid content. Molds and film yeasts may be responsible for cloudiness, off flavors, and a reduction in the acidity of the product. Acid-forming bacteria of various sorts, especially those producing lactic, acetic, butyric, or propionic acid, may be responsible for sourness and turbidity. Certain lactobacilli may cause bitterness due to the formation of mannitol, and may cause turbidity and undesirable flavors. Capsulated bacteria may cause sliminess or ropiness. As has been stated, most of these troubles can be avoided by the use of proper manufacturing methods. A high volatile acid content is especially undesirable; federal regulations set a limit for red wine of 0.14 gram in 100 ml., and for white wine of 0.12 gram of volatile acids, expressed as acetic acid.

Other Fermented Fruit Juices

The preparation of other fermented fruit juices is, in general, similar to that of grape wines. Apple juice is known as **cider** and fermented apple juice as **hard cider;** certain varieties of apples are best for cider production. Juices from most kinds of berries are deficient in sugar and therefore some must be added before a satisfactory fermented product can be prepared.

BEER AND ALE

Mashes made by the addition of water to different kinds of crushed grains or mixtures of grains are used in the manufacture of industrial alcohol, of distilled liquors, and of various fermented beverages. The starches of these grains must have been hydrolyzed to sugars before the yeasts can utilize them.

Beer

Malted barley, as used in beer manufacture, is made by the germination of the barley, removal of the germ after drying, and crushing of the remaining grain. The malted barley is mixed with some other grain, such as crushed corn or rice, and the mixture treated with hot water at 60° to 65° C. (140° to 149° F.) so that the amylase from the malted barley converts the starch of the grains into maltose, dextrins, and soluble starch. The filtrate from this mixture is called the **wort**. The wort is boiled with hops; the heat stops the action of the amylase and pasteurizes the wort, while the extraction of the hops provides constituents which are flavor-producing and preservative. Then the wort is cooled and a starter of *Saccharomyces cerevisiae* is added. A "bottom yeast" usually is used in beer manufacture and a "top yeast" for ale. A top yeast is one in which the cells gather in clumps and are carried to the top of the fermenting liquid by gas caught in the clumps, while the cells of a bottom yeast stay fairly well separated and settle toward the bottom. The primary fermentation of the beer wort occurs at about 5° to 14° C. (41° to 57° F.) and ordinarily takes from seven to nine days. Then comes the secondary or "lager" (cellar) fermentation at 0° to 4° C. (32° to 39° F.) for six to eight months. The beer is then clarified or filtered, carbonated, and barrelled, bottled, or canned. Bottles or cans of beer ordinarily are pasteurized.

Ale

A top fermentation at 10° to 25° C. (50° to 77° F.) is used in the manufacture of ale. The primary fermentation is more rapid than that of beer and takes five to seven days. The secondary fermentation takes place in casks or vats. Ale often contains more alcohol than beer and is commonly a more highly flavored product because more hops are used.

Beer and ale are subject to many of the same diseases as wines. Wild yeasts may cause turbidity, bitterness, and other off flavors, and off odors. Lactic acid, acetic acid, and butyric acid bacteria may form their characteristic acids and "sour" the product. Other bacteria may cause turbidity, ropiness, putrefaction, gas, or off tastes and odors. A beer of good quality is crystal clear, even at refrigerator temperatures, and the brewer is especially careful to avoid, as far as possible, any cloudiness in his product.

Sake is a yellowish-white, wine-like fermented Japanese beverage made from rice. The starch of the rice first is converted to sugar by the action of a mold, *Aspergillus oryzae*, on a rice mash. The extract of the mash is fermented by a mixture of yeasts with the production of about 12 to 15 per cent of alcohol.

Kefir and **kumiss,** two fermented milks in which a mild alcoholic fermentation has followed the lactic acid fermentation, will be mentioned in Chapter 27.

DISTILLED LIQUORS

Distilled liquors ordinarily are made by distillation of fermented grain mashes: **Bourbon** or **corn whiskey** from malted and fermented corn mash, **rye whiskey** from malted and fermented rye, etc. The grain mashes are saccharified, that is the starch is converted to sugar by enzymes or by chemical hydrolysis, and may be acidified by the addition of acid or by a lactic acid fermentation. They are then subjected to fermentation by a distiller's yeast, a strain of *Saccharomyces cerevisiae*. **Brandy** is made by the distillation of a fermented fruit juice. Thus grape brandy is distilled from wine, and apple brandy or apple jack from hard cider. **Rum** is distilled from fermented molasses or cane sugar sirups.

VINEGAR

When fruit juices are allowed to spoil naturally, alcoholic fermentation by yeasts usually takes place first. Then if these products are exposed to the air, an acetic acid fermentation is most likely to follow due to the growth on the surface of the liquid of one or more of the many species of the genus *Acetobacter*, such as *A. aceti* and *A. orleanense*. These acetic acid bacteria oxidize alcohol to acetic acid and in this way obtain energy for their life processes. This same succession of fermentations is used in the manufacture of **vinegar,** which is primarily a solution of acetic acid, together with various flavoring substances.

First, some liquid containing a sugar fermentable by yeasts, and other yeast foods, is inoculated with a yeast, preferably of the high alcohol-producing ellipsoideus type, and incubated until a maximum amount of alcohol is produced. This fermentation is, of course, anaerobic to encourage alcohol production. A simple expression of the reaction is as follows:

$$C_6H_{12}O_6 \xrightarrow{\text{yeast}} 2\ C_2H_5OH + 2\ CO_2 + \text{energy}$$

glucose   ethyl alcohol

Second, aerobic conditions are provided and bacteria of the genus *Aceto-bacter* are encouraged to develop or are added from a culture. The acetic acid bacteria grow over the surface of the liquid to form a tough, heavy film which is known as "mother of vinegar" and which usually contains yeasts as well as acetic acid bacteria. These bacteria oxidize the alcohol to acetic acid as follows:

$$C_2H_5OH + O_2 \xrightarrow{\text{\textit{Acetobacter}}} CH_3 \cdot COOH + H_2O + \text{energy}$$

alcohol   acetic acid

This reaction and the one for formation of alcohol goes on in several steps rather than in the one step indicated in each of the equations.

In the home, vinegar usually is made from cider or other fruit juices. Commercially, vinegar may be made from any substance which contains enough sugar or alcohol and which is in no way objectionable, or it may be made from synthetically prepared acetic acid. Thus vinegar is made from fruit juices, malted cereals, sugar solutions such as sirups, molasses, honey, maple skimmings, etc., and from dilute alcohol solutions like the "beer" or liquid left after the manufacture of commercial yeast or dilute alcohol from any commercial process. Grains must first be malted, that is the starch must first be converted to sugar by means of enzymes or the starch must be hydrolyzed chemically. Some of the sugar solutions must have additional food, chiefly nitrogenous, added for the yeasts, before they will ferment satisfactorily. Much of the American vinegar is made from apple cider, especially that for table use. Vinegar in France is mainly from grapes and in England from malted liquors (that from ale could be termed **alegar**).

In the home, vinegar ordinarily is made in casks or barrels. These are placed on their sides and are partially filled with the hard cider or other fermented fruit juice to be used, and the juice is inoculated with "mother of vinegar" or with fresh, unpasteurized vinegar. The container is provided with holes above the level of the liquid for ventilation, for it must be remembered that the oxidation of alcohol to acetic acid is entirely an aerobic process. When these casks are provided with facilities for the removal of vinegar from the container and introduction of more alcoholic fruit juice, the process is made more or less continuous and is known as the "Orleans method" of vinegar manufacture. It has the disadvantage of being comparatively slow, although it is more rapid than the usual domestic method. The film, which grows on the surface of the liquid, occasionally may drop to the bottom and a new film must form before acetification can proceed. Removal of vinegar or addition of new alcoholic liquor should be done without disturbing this surface film.

The so-called "quick method" of vinegar manufacture, used for most commercial vinegar-making, involves increased aeration during the process and intimate contact of small portions of alcoholic liquor with the slimy growths of *Acetobacter schuezenbachii* or other species of *Acetobacter*. A cylindrical tank or "generator" is loosely filled with beechwood shavings or similar materials which will give a large surface. The alcoholic liquor is allowed to trickle down over these shavings, which soon become covered with a slimy

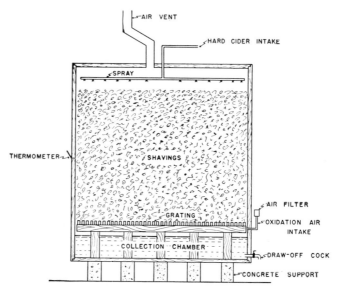

FIGURE 43.   A diagrammatic drawing of a quick method vinegar generator.

growth of acetic acid bacteria, or cultures of *Acetobacter* may be added. The tank is equipped with openings at the bottom for the entrance of air and at the top for its exit. Thus conditions favorable to the rapid oxidation of alcohol to acetic acid are provided; this reaction may take place so rapidly that the temperature may become too high for the bacteria and may even kill them unless precautions are taken to reduce it. Modern generators are run continuously with recirculation of the liquor until the desired concentration of acetic acid has been produced. These generators must be equipped with cooling coils to prevent overheating of the liquor. In older types of generators the alcoholic liquor was fed intermittently and tanks were run singly or in tandem. Figure 43 is a diagrammatic drawing of a "quick method" vinegar generator. Under favorable conditions a yield of 50 to 55 parts of acetic acid is obtained from 100 parts of glucose. According to the federal standard, legal vinegar must contain at least 4 per cent of acetic acid by weight; this would be a "40 grain" vinegar.

Spoilage of vinegar may result from fermentations other than the desired acetic acid one. Thus lactic or butyric acid fermentations may take place when there is a shortage of oxygen. The *Acetobacter* bacteria, themselves, may destroy the acetic acid they have produced, if there is a shortage of available alcohol or sugar as a source of energy. Molds and film yeasts may grow on the surface of the vinegar and reduce the acidity of the product as well as injure its flavor and appearance. The vinegar eel, *Anguillula aceti,* a nematode worm, may grow in the vinegar, break the surface film of *Acetobacter,* and support the growth of bacteria able to use dead bodies of the eel, with a resulting deterioration in the flavor and appearance of the product. To insure against the development of defects in the finished product, most commercially prepared vinegar is clarified and then pasteurized in the container.

ORIENTAL FERMENTED FOODS

Many fermented foods of the Orient are made from grains. Pure cultures of microorganisms rarely are used, but the mixed cultures from previous fermentations may be carried over and used as a "starter." In the manufacture of most of these fermented foods molds of the *Aspergillus flavus-oryzae* group are important in the first part of the fermentation, when, by action of their enzymes, they bring about decomposition of starch into sugars, proteins into simpler nitrogenous compounds, and fats into fatty acids and glycerol. In some foods the molds are reported to cause some production of alcohol, but in most cases yeasts carry on this part of the fermentation. A mixture of bacteria usually is present and must play a part in the production of the final flavor and physical character of the products.

Soy Sauce

Soy sauce is the chief one of these Oriental fermented foods imported into the United States, where it is used as a sauce on chop suey and similar foods and as a constituent of other sauces. In the manufacture of soy sauce, a mash of crushed soybeans and roasted wheat is inoculated with spores of *Aspergillus oryzae* or more commonly with a starter called **koji** or **chu** the preparation of which will be described later. The mash is spread on trays, where it is fermented by *A. oryzae* and possibly other similar molds. This is followed by a second fermentation in salt brine, in which yeasts (of the genus *Zygosaccharomyces*) and bacteria are concerned, but in which enzymes from the starter are considered the most important in causing changes during the fermentation. The first fermentation takes only a day or two, but the second may take months or even years.

The koji (chu) or starter is made from a mash of crushed soybeans and roasted wheat, to which barley and peas sometimes are added. The mash is inoculated with some of a previous lot of koji; in this way a number of microorganisms are introduced, of which *Aspergillus oryzae* and *Mucor rouxii* are considered to be the most important. The mash is allowed to ferment until a maximum amount of enzymes has been produced by the microorganisms. It is then dried and extracted with water. This extract makes up the koji or starter, which is used chiefly for its enzymes, which include amylases, proteinases, invertases, maltases, phosphatases, lactases, lipases, etc.

Other Oriental fermented foods are made with rice, with similar mixtures of molds, yeasts, and bacteria concerned in the fermentation.

Most of the fermented products described thus far in this chapter have been the result of the action of microorganisms on a substance in order to produce a new and desirable product. In the industrial fermentations to be discussed below, microorganisms are used, for the most part, during one or more of the treatments of a substance included in the manufacture of a product. These treatments may involve the removal of material or some change in the substance.

Retting of Flax and Hemp

The bast fibers in the stems of flax plants are used in the manufacture of linen thread and cloth; bast fibers in hemp are employed in the making of rope. In the flax and hemp plant these fibers, which are composed mainly of cellulose, are cemented together, and to other cells in the plant's stem, by pectins and salts of pectic acid. It is practically impossible to remove these fibers from the stems of mature plants by any simple mechanical operation, and chemical methods for the removal of the pectin binding material are likely to injure the fibers. The present method for destruction of the pectin binding, so that the bast fibers can be removed, is a process called "retting."

Dew Retting

In the process of dew retting, bundles of flax or hemp are spread on the ground where they are kept moist by dew and rain. The process requires from a week to a month or more, during which time the many kinds of molds and bacteria which grow on and in the stems of the plants decompose the pectin binding substances. Unfortunately, this mixed flora of microorganisms often decomposes some of the bast fibers of the plants, and it is difficult to control the process so as to prevent such destruction. Very little is known about the kinds of microorganisms which participate in the process of dew retting.

Following retting, the bundles of flax or hemp are dried and the bast fibers removed by mechanical means.

Water Retting

Water retting can be controlled more readily than dew retting. In the older of the two processes of water retting, the bundles of flax are thrown into a stream, canal, or pond, where they are allowed to remain until the bast fibers may be removed easily without breakage. This requires from two to seven days, depending upon the temperature of the water, the number of pectin-decomposing bacteria it contains, and the amounts of available nitrogenous and inorganic foods present for use of the bacteria. Two species of bacteria—both of which are anaerobic, but are able to grow with some oxygen present—are mainly responsible for the retting process; these are *Clostridium pectinovorum* and *Clostridium felsineum*.

Recently, in regions where flax production and the manufacture of linen are important, tank retting has been introduced, and is used to some extent. In this process, the bundles of flax are placed in tanks of water and inoculated with a starter of *C. felsineum* and *C. pectinovorum*. The starter is prepared by growing the clostridia in water containing sliced potatoes, and is used when the organisms are well within their logarithmic phase of growth. Tank retting may be accomplished in two or three days with little or no change to the bast fibers.

As in dew retting, the bundles of water-retted flax are dried, and the bast fibers removed by mechanical means.

Tanning

As in other industries, microorganisms may be very useful in the tanning industry, but may at times be harmful. To prevent microbial action, hides are preserved by drying, by salting, or by a combination of salting and drying. Imported hides may be disinfected to destroy anthrax spores.

The hides first are soaked to remove blood, salt, and dirt and to soften them. Proteolytic bacteria are likely to be active during this process, but their action is not considered desirable. Change of water and even addition of antiseptics have been recommended to prevent proteolysis as much as possible.

Next, the hair is removed from the hide. Sheep's wool may be removed by

a "sweating" process in which bacteria are active, but usually wool is removed by chemical methods. Most hides are dehaired by soaking in a liquor
made up of water and slaked lime (calcium hydroxide). It has been observed that old lime liquors are more efficient in removal of hair than are
fresh liquors. This increased efficiency is attributed to the action of bacterial
enzymes and products.

The lime is then neutralized and removed from the skin, and some proteolytic action is encouraged. Old methods involve immersion of the hides
in water suspensions of dung of various sorts, depending upon the type of
leather desired. Manure from birds or dogs has been used widely. The mixture of bacteria thus introduced causes an acid fermentation and hence
neutralization and removal of the lime from the hides. At the same time
some proteolytic action goes on, and the hides become soft and pliable. Pure
cultures or mixtures of bacteria have been used to replace those introduced
by the dung. Modern methods, however, involve the neutralization of the
lime by the addition of weak organic or inorganic acids, and proteolysis by
added pancreatin, proteases from molds of the *Aspergillus flavus-oryzae*
group, or proteolytic enzymes from other sources.

Next comes the tanning process in which the hides are treated with tannin. Bacteria, especially those of the acid-forming type, may be able to grow
in the more dilute tanning solutions, but apparently are not important in this
process.

Microorganisms may grow during the handling and processing of the
hides and reduce the quality of the finished leather. Chromogenic, halophilic
bacteria may cause red spots on the hides; molds may cause damage here
and later during the tanning processes, and bacteria may cause too much
proteolysis and consequent discoloration and weakening or pitting of the
skins.

TOBACCO

There has long been a controversy as to whether the curing of leaf tobacco is due to enzymes of the tobacco plant alone or to these enzymes plus
those of bacteria. Recent work has indicated that growth of aerobic, spore-
forming bacteria and of cocci characterizes the normal fermentation of tobacco and tends to limit the development of undesirable molds and to help
in the production of a cured tobacco of acceptable quality.

TEA

Green tea is prepared without a fermentation, while black tea has undergone a fermentation believed by most workers to be due almost entirely

to the action of its own enzymes. It is claimed by some, however, that bacteria may play a part in the improvement of the flavor of black tea.

COFFEE

When the "wet method"—which involves soaking overnight in water—is used, bacteria may be concerned in the loosening of the skins about the coffee berry. It is claimed that fermentation of the coffee beans by bacteria before the roasting process improves the flavor and aroma of the roasted product, and patents for such a process have been granted. Recent work has indicated that a lactic acid fermentation is involved.

COCOA

Cocoa is made from cacao beans, which grow in large pods. The beans, when removed from the pod, are covered with a slimy or fruity pulp, which is removed by fermentation. Both microorganisms and the enzymes of the seeds are concerned in this process, which usually generates heat to such an extent that the germ of the seed is killed. At the same time the astringency of the bean is reduced, and changes in color and aroma take place. An alcoholic fermentation by yeasts usually is the first to occur, followed by an acetic acid fermentation. Following the fermentation, the beans are dried and then roasted.

GARBAGE FERMENTATION

Patents have been granted for various processes for the disposal of garbage by fermentation followed by drying of the residue for use as fertilizer. Most of these methods involve neutralization of the garbage and aeration during the fermentation.

The chief purpose of this chapter has been to describe the activities of microorganisms that are desirable in certain industries; but incidentally undesirable activities of microorganisms in these industries have been mentioned. Other undesirable activities not discussed above include: the rotting of wood, textiles and textile fibers, leather, and paper; slime production in sugar refineries and paper mills; decomposition of scraps of hide, flesh, and sinews used in gelatin and glue manufacture; and numerous other troubles in the industries.

The foregoing discussion of the use of microorganisms in industries is, of necessity, incomplete, because of the secrecy in regard to many of the methods now in use.

REFERENCES

Blanck, F. C., "Fermentations in the food industries." *Ind. Eng. Chem.* (1930), 22:1166–1168.

Cruess, W. V., *The principles and practices of wine making.* N. Y., Avi Publishing Co., 1934.

Cruess, W. V., *Commercial fruit and vegetable products* (3rd ed.). N. Y., McGraw-Hill, 1948.

Hind, H. L., *Brewing science and practice,* Vol. I (*Brewing materials*). N. Y., Wiley, 1938.

LeFevre, E., "Making vinegar in the home and on the farm." *U. S. Dept. Agric. Farmers' Bulletin No. 1424* (1924).

Nowak, C. A., *Modern brewing* (2nd ed.). St. Louis, Mo., published by the author, 1934.

Prescott, S. C., and Dunn, C. G., *Industrial microbiology* (2nd ed.). N. Y., McGraw-Hill, 1949.

Prescott, S. C., and Proctor, B. E., *Food technology.* N. Y., McGraw-Hill, 1937.

Reid, J. J., McKinstry, D. W., and Haley, D. E., "Studies on the fermentation of tobacco." *Penna. Agric. Exp. Sta. Bulletin No. 356 and 363* (1938).

Tanner, F. W., *The microbiology of foods* (2nd ed.). Champaign, Ill., Garrard Press, 1944.

Vogel, E. H., Jr., Schwaiger, F. H., Leonhardt, H. G., and Merten, J. A., *The practical brewer.* St. Louis, Mo., Master Brewers' Association of America, 1946.

17. USE OF MICROORGANISMS TO PRODUCE CHEMICALS

A number of chemical compounds are now being prepared on a commercial scale by means of microorganisms: various organic acids such as lactic, acetic, citric, gluconic, and gallic; alcohols, including ethyl and butyl; gases such as carbon dioxide and hydrogen; acetone, antibiotics, vitamins, and various enzymes. Biological processes for the preparation of many additional compounds are known, and some of these methods have been tried out on a pilot-plant scale. Normally the new processes are put into commercial use as soon as there is sufficient demand for any of these compounds, provided that they can be produced more cheaply by microbiological than by chemical methods. In an emergency, however, as in time of war, when mass production is essential, biological methods that normally are uneconomical may be used for production of a chemical.

The use of a microorganism to produce a chemical substance involves: (1) selection of an efficient culture; (2) concoction of a satisfactory culture medium (commercially called a "mash"); (3) establishment of the best conditions for growth of the organism and more especially for production of the chemical; and finally (4) development of an efficient method for recovery of the desired product from the medium. It is obvious that a considerable amount of laboratory and plant research is necessary before a process can be placed upon a commercial basis.

1. *The Culture.* After different species and different strains of the best species have been tested, a particular strain is chosen that produces the desired product efficiently, and is stable in its characteristics (see Chapter 14). When an unstable culture must be used in order to obtain maximum yields, special precautions must be taken to avoid changes in the culture. The

highest-yielding mold culture for the production of penicillin, for example, is known to be unstable; therefore most manufacturers prepare a large enough supply of spores from a good culture to last for years, instead of trusting to serial transfer to maintain the culture.

The building up of the large inoculating culture from a small stock culture has been described in Chapter 15. The volume of the inoculum is usually from 1 to 10 per cent of the volume of mash in the large fermenter. Therefore the preparation of the inoculum is in itself a large scale procedure; for example, a 5 per cent inoculum for 60,000 gallons of mash would be 3000 gallons and would require four or five stages from the test tube culture to the final seed tank. Not only must this final seed culture be large in volume, but it must be pure and active. A mistake in the preparation of the culture would mean a large financial loss to the producer.

2. *The Culture Medium or "Mash."* The medium must be suited to growth of the organism and to efficient production of the desired product under the conditions provided for the action of the organism. The ingredients of the medium should be cheap and readily available in quantity, especially that constituent which provides the main food for energy and therefore makes up a large percentage of the solids present. The composition of the medium is varied with the process used as well as with the organism. Whenever possible the medium is made selective, i.e., more favorable for the added organism than for its competitors. For example, an acidified mash is used for growth of yeast or the production of citric acid by molds. Most media, however, must be sterilized or at least pasteurized before inoculation in order to eliminate competing contaminants.

3. *The Microbiological Process.* The factors that influence the growth and activity of microorganisms are taken into consideration during the process of production of the desired products. **Food** and **moisture** are provided by the culture medium, and its p**H** is adjusted and controlled during the fermentation if necessary. An optimum **temperature** for production of the product is maintained. If the process is **aerobic,** oxygen is provided: (a) by growth of the organism on thin layers of the medium; (b) by trickling the medium over loose materials like shavings, stone, or coke; or (c) in tank processes, as in penicillin production by the submerged method, by bubbling sterilized air through the medium at an optimum rate. **Anaerobic** conditions are provided for the acetone-butyl alcohol fermentation. Most processes also provide vigorous stirring of the medium. Neutralization or removal of **inhibitory substances,** either in the original medium or resulting from microbial action, may be performed.

Some products can be made by a continuous process, in which the medium is being introduced constantly as the final products are being removed. In other cases, the products are manufactured by the batch process.

Microbiological and chemical control measures are used throughout the process to ascertain whether or not the chemical changes are proceeding in a normal manner and the desired microorganism is free from competition from harmful contaminating organisms.

4. *Recovery of Products.* No microbiological process can be successful unless physical and chemical methods for recovery of the desired products are available. Sometimes it is necessary to adjust the composition of the culture medium to avoid substances that would interfere with the recovery of products.

The production of organic compounds from sugars, starches, or other materials by microorganisms involves the formation of a series of intermediate compounds before the desired end product appears. Since a microorganism may produce different kinds and amounts of end products, depending upon conditions during the fermentation, it is difficult to write a balanced chemical equation that will indicate all of the changes which take place. This should be kept in mind when equations given for the various processes are considered; for these equations do not indicate the intermediate compounds, the proportions of the final products, or the percentage yield of any one of these products. The student who wishes more detail in regard to these reactions is referred to more technical dissertations, some of which are listed among the references at the end of this chapter.

ORGANIC ACIDS

Microorganisms are capable of forming many kinds of organic acids, of which only a few are produced industrially on a large scale.

Lactic Acid

In most of the lactic acid fermentations discussed in Chapter 17, 25, and 27, a high yield of lactic acid is not desired, and other products of the fermentation may contribute to the quality of the product. In the manufacture of industrial lactic acid, however, a maximum yield is sought, with the production of minimum amounts of by-products. A simplified equation for the formation of lactic acid from glucose by fermentation is as follows:

$$\underset{\text{glucose}}{C_6H_{12}O_6} \xrightarrow[\text{producing bacteria}]{\text{lactic acid-}} \underset{\text{lactic acid}}{2\ CH_3 \cdot CHOH \cdot COOH}$$

Practically all of the industrial lactic acid produced in this country is made by fermentation. *Lactobacillus delbrueckii* is usually used as the fermenting organism, but other lactic acid-forming bacteria may be employed, such as the "flat sour" bacteria mentioned in connection with the spoilage of canned foods. The "mash" for the fermentation must contain a fermentable carbohydrate, available nitrogenous food, the required minerals, and the necessary growth factors. The composition of the medium will vary with the organism being used and with the cost and availability of the constituents. The source of carbohydrate might be molasses, hydrolyzed starch from grains or potatoes, or similar material. Sprouted grains, e.g., barley sprouts, often serve to add nitrogenous food and accessory growth factors. The mash to be used in the fermentation is pasteurized or sterilized, with or without acidification, before inoculation with the lactic culture. To neutralize the lactic acid when it is formed and thus increase the yield, calcium carbonate is added periodically or continuously during the fermentation process.

Fermentation by *L. delbrueckii* or by a flat sour bacillus, is carried on at about 50° C. (122° F.), a temperature high enough to favor its growth, yet hinder the growth of most contaminating microorganisms. The method of recovery of lactic acid after the fermentation varies with the grade of lactic acid to be produced: crude or technical, edible, plastics, or U.S.P. The calcium lactate, which has resulted from the reaction of the lactic acid with the calcium carbonate during the fermentation process, may be crystallized as such or may be changed back to lactic acid by addition of sulfuric acid, with removal of the resulting insoluble calcium sulfate by filtration. Concentration may be accomplished by means of a vacuum pan. Treatment with vegetable carbon followed by filtration serves to decolorize the product. Further purification may be accomplished by extraction with solvents, by additional crystallizations of calcium lactate, by methyllation of the acid, or by vacuum-steam distillation of the acid.

Lactic acid also can be made from whey, a by-product of the dairy industry. *L. delbrueckii* cannot use lactose; consequently *Lactobacillus bulgaricus* or a similar lactobacillus is employed. A fairly high temperature, about 43.3° C. (110° F.), gives a rapid fermentation with a minimum of competition from undesirable contaminants. The batch method, with periodic addition of lime, has been used industrially, but a continuous process has been tried in which whey and calcium carbonate are fed into the fermenter continuously while the fermented whey is being removed.

Because of its asymmetric (alpha) carbon atom, lactic acid exhibits optical rotation, and two optical forms are possible: the levo-rotatory and the dextro-rotatory; D-L lactic acid is an equal mixture of the two forms and gives no rotation. Most lactic acid-forming bacteria produce predominantly one of these forms, although the proportions in which the forms are produced, and even the rotation of the acid, may vary with changing conditions of growth. For most uses lactic acid of any optical form is acceptable, but recent work has indicated that dextro-lactic acid is preferable for use as food. Consequently some effort is being made to select lactic cultures for the rotation of the lactic acid they produce, as well as for other properties.

Acetic Acid

The methods used for the production of acetic acid by bacteria have been discussed in Chapter 16 under the heading "Vinegar." Industrial acetic acid is made by synthetic methods at present.

Citric Acid

Citric acid may be obtained from the juices of citrus fruits, or may be produced by fermentation of sugars by certain molds of the genera *Aspergillus* and *Penicillium*.

For the large-scale production of citric acid by biological methods a strain of *Aspergillus niger* usually is used, although other molds are able to form considerable amounts of the acid. The medium should contain about 15 to 20 per cent of sugar, preferably sucrose or fructose, necessary mineral salts, and a nitrogenous food, usually ammonium salts or nitrates. The medium is adjusted to a *p*H of 3.5 or below with hydrochloric acid in order to suppress the formation of oxalic acid, prevent sporulation of the mold, and lessen the danger of growth of other organisms. The acidity also makes more easy the sterilization of the medium by heat. The sterile medium is poured into shallow aluminum pans, inoculated with spores of the *Aspergillus niger* mold, and incubated at 25° to 35° C. (77° to 95° F.). Within two days a continuous felt of mold mycelium grows over the entire surface of the medium. Citric acid formation begins after the fourth day, and the fermentation is complete in seven to ten days. After a yeast fermentation of the residual sugar in the medium, the citric acid is either crystallized directly or first separated as a calcium salt, from which the citric acid is freed by sulfuric acid and then crystallized. Processes for the production of citric acid in fermenters analogous to those used for the manufacture of penicillin, have been patented but have not been reported in use.

Gluconic Acid

Formerly most of the gluconic acid was made by chemical methods, but now a large part of it is produced by the action of selected cultures of species of *Penicillium* or *Aspergillus*. Rotary drum fermenters and a strain of *Penicillium chrysogenum* were used in early methods of production. Of late, however, a semicontinuous method, and a special strain of *Aspergillus niger* are being used. In this process, a medium or mash is used that contains 11.5 per cent glucose, a nutrient salts mixture, including an ammonium salt as a source of nitrogen, and calcium carbonate to neutralize the acid produced. The sterilized mash in the fermenter is adjusted to 30° C. (86° F.) and inoculated with about 3 per cent by volume of mycelium containing germinated spores; the inoculated mash is aerated with sterile air during the fermentation process. The organism is allowed to act until little sugar remains; at this point aeration is stopped, the mold mycelium permitted to float to the top, and the bottom 80 per cent of the liquid replaced with fresh, sterile mash. A number of successive fermentations are carried out in this manner; as many as 13 have been tried experimentally without loss in efficiency. According to a recent patent, the addition of a borate permits the accumulation of more gluconic acid before the product must be harvested than it is possible to obtain without that salt.

Gallic Acid

Extracts of galls from the sumac or oak contain tannin, which on hydrolysis yields gallic acid. In America most of the gallic acid is obtained by acid or alkaline hydrolysis of the tannin, but fermentation methods, widely used in Europe, are used by some American manufacturers. *Aspergillus niger* or a related species usually is used, although some species of *Penicillium* can cause the hydrolysis. The fermentation may be carried out in shallow pans or in aerated tanks. In an older and cruder fermentation method, the material which contained the tannin was piled in heaps, which were stirred occasionally. A mixture of molds developed throughout the mass and hydrolyzed the tannin to gallic acid, which was removed by leaching. Gallic acid is used in the manufacture of dyes and inks.

Other Organic Acids

Other organic acids which might be produced by means of microorganisms include: butyric, propionic, fumaric, kojic, itaconic, oxalic and succinic acids. Microbiological methods for the production of these organic acids have been investigated and will be improved and used industrially whenever demand and costs of production justify their use.

ALCOHOLS AND ACETONE

Ethyl and butyl alcohol, and acetone are produced in quantity by fermentation, and some methyl alcohol is synthesized from fermentation products.

Ethyl Alcohol

Industrial alcohol (ethyl alcohol) is produced by synthesis or by the fermentation of sugar solutions by a high alcohol-producing yeast such as *Saccharomyces cerevisiae* var. *ellipsoideus*. The raw materials to be used as sources of sugar usually are divided into three classes: (1) the saccharine materials, such as molasses, sugar cane, sugar beets and fruit juices; (2) the starchy materials, including cereal grains and potatoes; and (3) the "cellulosic" materials, such as wood and sulfite waste liquor. Wood and the starchy materials are subjected to hydrolysis to produce fermentable sugars for the yeast. Cereal starch is hydrolyzed by means of acid or by the amylases of malted grains or of microorganisms (molds); wood is hydrolyzed by hot acid. Of the materials mentioned molasses is most widely used for alcohol production in normal times, with cereal grains next in importance. Use of sulfite waste liquor and of hydrolyzed wood is increasing, however. During time of war the great need for ethyl alcohol prompts the use of more of the grains and of potatoes.

The culture medium or "mash" is adjusted to the desired sugar concentration, usually about 10 to 12 per cent, and to a pH of 4.0 to 4.5 by addition of acid. If the medium is deficient in minerals, nitrogenous food, or accessory growth factors, these also are added. The yeast "starter," built up as described in Chapter 15, is mixed with the mash in the large tank or fermenter. The acidity of the mash and the large size of the inoculum make sterilization of the mash unnecessary. The fermentation is conducted at 21° to 27° C. (70° to 80° F.) and the products are mainly ethyl alcohol and carbon dioxide. The alcohol is recovered from the fermented liquor by distillation, and is further purified and concentrated in a similar way.

Wood hydrolysate and sulfite waste liquor are inhibitory to most microorganisms, hence contaminants give little trouble when these substances are used; however, the alcohol-forming yeasts must be adapted to these media before they can be used successfully.

A continuous process for the production of alcohol from a molasses mash has proved successful and can be applied also to the manufacture of alcohol from sulfite waste liquor or from saccharified grains. Unfermented mash is introduced continuously while fermented material is being withdrawn.

Glycerol

In normal times glycerol is prepared chiefly by the saponification of fats and oils employed in the manufacture of soaps. In time of war, when there is a greatly increased demand for glycerol, synthetic methods or production by fermentation may be employed. Yeasts are known to produce small amounts of glycerol during the normal alcoholic fermentation. Under special conditions the yield of glycerol is greatly increased. During World War I the Germans produced glycerol on a large scale by their sulfite process, with *Saccharomyces cerevisiae* var. *ellipsoideus* as the fermenting organism. In an American method the medium is made alkaline by the addition of sodium carbonate. A recent German process involves the addition of a balanced mixture of sulfite and bisulfite. The sulfite combines with the intermediate compound, acetaldehyde, during the fermentation, and thus tends to favor the production of glycerol and decrease the formation of alcohol. Other constituents of the medium are similar to those used for the alcoholic fermentation. The fermentation process for the manufacture of glycerol was not used to any extent during World War II. At present, investigations on improvement of this process continue; recovery of the glycerol produced is the principal problem.

Acetone-Butyl Alcohol

The acetone-butyl alcohol industry came into being during World War I to meet the great demand for acetone. The successful process was that of Weizmann, who discovered the culture later called *Clostridium acetobutylicum*. It was a vigorous organism, able to ferment a mash of plain corn meal (6–9 per cent) in water with a yield of 30–33 per cent of the "solvents," acetone, butyl alcohol, and ethyl alcohol, in ratio 30 : 60 : 10. As can be seen, the major product is butyl alcohol (butanol) and after the war uses were found for it, mainly in the production of quick-drying lacquers, so that to all intents the industry became the "butyl alcohol industry." Commercial success was great and before long tremendous amounts of corn were used. Limitations of supply of corn forced the industry to use molasses, and consequently a series of new cultures, more efficient on molasses than was the Weizmann culture, was discovered. Just prior to World War II the shift to molasses was nearly complete, and, interestingly, it led to location of butyl plants in sugar-producing countries the world over.

A typical butyl process for molasses requires: (1) a special strain of butyl bacteria, preferably one producing the highest percentage of butyl alcohol (68–74 per cent is possible); (2) molasses mash diluted to 5–6 per cent sugar, with supplement of ammonia, usually as ammonium sulfate, for nitrogenous food; and (3) pH control during fermentation by means of calcium carbonate. Fermentations are carried out in very large tanks, often of 60,000 gallon capacity. With an inoculum of 5 per cent by volume of the mash, and at optimum temperature for the culture used (it varies between

32° and 37° C.), the fermentation is rapid and the liquor is taken for recovery of volatile solvents by distillation after 48 to 60 hours. The whole process must be carried out in pure culture because contamination by lactic bacteria or bacteriophage can result in absolute failure of the normal butyl fermentation.

Gases

In addition to the solvents, considerable amounts of carbon dioxide and hydrogen are produced during the acetone-butyl alcohol fermentation. The hydrogen and part of the carbon dioxide are used for the synthesis of methyl alcohol (methanol) by a catalytic process, and the remainder of the carbon dioxide may be compressed to liquid CO_2 or carried further to "dry ice" or solid carbon dioxide.

Utilization of the gases evolved during anaerobic decomposition of sewage in Imhoff tanks and of sludge in the sludge digesters will be discussed in Chapter 23. This mixture of gases, because of its high content of methane (CH_4), may be used as a fuel for heating purposes or for running special gas motors designed for its combustion. Similar use of gas from the anaerobic decomposition of organic matter during other processes has been suggested, but such methods are not in general use.

Antibiotics

Of the scores of antibiotics reported in recent years only a few are being produced industrially in appreciable amounts: penicillin, streptomycin, aureomycin, chloromycetin, tyrothricin, subtilin, terramycin, and bacitracin.

Penicillin

It has been mentioned in Chapter 10 that penicillin is a product of molds of the species *Penicillium notatum* and *Penicillium chrysogenum*. Early commercial production of penicillin was by a surface culture method in which the mold was grown on shallow layers of culture medium in bottles, but all manufacture now is by the tank or submerged method. Figure 44 shows a battery of tanks used for the production of penicillin by the submerged culture method. The culture medium or mash has corn steep liquor and lactose as the chief ingredients, although some manufacturers also add certain salts. The medium must be sterilized and the mold kept in pure culture. The process is aerobic and requires the bubbling of large volumes of sterile air through the mash in the deep tanks, each containing about

FIGURE 44.   Battery of 12,000 gallon tanks for the production of penicillin by the submerged culture method. (Courtesy of Commercial Solvents Corporation, Terre Haute, Ind.)

12,000 gallons of mash. The inoculum (4–5 per cent) consists of mold mycelium, the mass of which has been built up in stages as described in Chapter 15. The incubation temperature is maintained at about 23° C. (73.4° F.). Following the "fermentation," which takes about two days, the liquid is removed from the large mass of mold mycelium and is sent through a complicated process for the recovery, purification, and concentration of the penicillin. These methods involve extraction with various solvents, adsorption, and concentration. The final product is prepared by crystallization and drying.

During the early days of the industry a yield of 50 to 100 units of penicillin per milliliter of culture medium was considered satisfactory; now, due to improved cultures and fermentation procedures about 500 to 1000 units per milliliter can be obtained, and the total production in the United States well exceeds a ton of penicillin per month.

It has been found that molds produce penicillin in the form of types F, G, K, and X; however, many more types of penicillin can be made in the chemical laboratory. Type K has proved to be too labile on introduction into the body to be of much value. Differences between types F, G, and X in their effectiveness against disease-producing bacteria have been reported, but most manufacturers try to produce chiefly type G. To increase the yield of this desired type of penicillin the manufacturer usually adds to the culture medium a so-called adjuvant, such as phenylacetic acid or phenylacetamide; these substances resemble part of the penicillin G molecule, and are useful to the mold in that they serve as precursors in the formation of penicillin.

Streptomycin

The other antibiotic agent now being produced industrially in large quantities is streptomycin, a substance formed by certain strains of *Actinomyces griseus* (*Streptomyces griseus*), and first obtained by Schatz, Bugie, and Waksman. Streptomycin is effective against some pathogenic bacteria not successfully counteracted by penicillin, but is somewhat more toxic to human beings than penicillin.

Streptomycin is now produced by the tank or submerged method. The culture medium or mash is a modification of the original medium of Waksman, which contained glucose, peptone, meat extract, sodium chloride, and water. The medium must be sterilized and contamination must be prevented throughout the six steps in building up the seed culture and during growth of the organism in the large (10,000–15,000 gallon) fermenters at 25° to 30° C. (77° to 86° F.). The culture in the fermenter is aerated with sterile air and is stirred mechanically during the period of growth. As soon as the yield of streptomycin is sufficient the mycelium of the actinomycete is removed from the mash by filtration and the filtrate is treated with activated carbon to adsorb the streptomycin, which later is eluted from the carbon with an acid-alcohol solution. This is followed by a series of treatments to purify and concentrate the product. The final purified streptomycin concentrate is dried by a freezing and vacuum process.

A bacteriophage active against the actinomycete used in the production of streptomycin has been encountered, necessitating care in the selection and preparation of the seed culture and in the prevention of contamination during growth in the fermenters.

Other Antibiotics

Aureomycin and chloromycetin are antibiotic agents produced by actinomycetes: *Streptomyces aureofaciens* and *Streptomyces venezuelae*, respectively. Aureomycin has been reported effective in the treatment of some diseases not cured by penicillin or streptomycin, such as certain rickettsial and virus diseases, undulant fever, and Malta fever. Chloromycetin, now made chiefly by synthetic methods, has been used in combating various Gram-negative pathogenic bacteria. Tyrothricin, an antibiotic agent which is a mixture of tyrocidin and gramicidin, is produced by *Bacillus brevis*. It has been used to some extent in the treatment of mastitis of cows and also some in human therapy; and is effective against certain Gram-positive pathogenic bacteria. Subtilin is a product of *Bacillus subtilis*. The latter two antibiotics have found limited use in the medical and veterinary professions, and at present are employed mainly in surface or localized treatment of infected tissues.

ENZYMES

The separation and purification of enzymes of microorganisms are difficult and costly processes. Consequently most of these enzymes are used in a crude form; usually a mixture of enzymes is present in any industrially manufactured preparation. The hydrolytic enzymes are the chief type used industrially, and of these the most commonly employed are amylases and proteinases. Microbial enzymes are used industrially to a considerable extent, but the methods of production, purification, and use are, for the most part, trade secrets.

Amylases

The starch-hydrolyzing enzymes, diastases or amylases, are of two types: the **alpha-amylase** catalyzes the hydrolysis of starch, chiefly to dextrins, whereas the **beta-amylase** causes the production of maltose. Amylases from germinating grains (malts) and from molds usually contain both of these types, but the amylase prepared from some bacteria, chiefly those of the *Bacillus subtilis* group, is of the alpha type. Consequently this bacterial enzyme is useful when hydrolysis of a starch to dextrins is desired rather than the production of sugar; this is the case in the preparation of wheat for the manufacture of certain types of beer, or the treatment of starch to be used for sizing of cotton and rayon fabrics or of paper. Amylases from bacteria or molds also may be used in the desizing of textiles, the liquefaction of unmalted cereals, the clarification of beer, and in the pharmaceutical trade. Malt is widely used at present for the saccharification of starch from cereals, but, in time, microbial amylases may be used for that purpose.

In the preparation of bacterial amylase, liquid cultures of the bacteria (such as *B. subtilis*) are grown under conditions which favor the formation of this enzyme. After a fairly long incubation period, most of the bacterial cells are removed by centrifugation and the liquor is concentrated *in vacuo* or the enzyme is concentrated by chemical precipitation methods.

Extracts of molds may be used industrially because of their amylase content. Taka-diastase, an extract of the mycelium of *Aspergillus oryzae*, has been used primarily because of its content of alpha- and beta-amylase, although it is known to contain proteinases, invertase, and many other enzymes. It will be recalled that koji, the starter used in the preparation of soy sauce (Chapter 16), is a similar extract of this mold, and is used chiefly because of its content of enzymes. In the **Amylo process** for production of ethyl alcohol from grains a mold, usually of the genus *Rhizopus,* is used to supply the amylase needed to hydrolyze cereal starch to sugar fermentable by the alcohol-producing yeast.

Invertase

Invertase, the enzyme catalyzing the hydrolysis of sucrose to glucose and fructose, is prepared by the autolysis of yeasts (*Saccharomyces cerevisiae*) which have been grown under conditions favorable to a maximum yield of that enzyme. It is used in the candy industry to secure a smooth fondant and avoid crystallization of sugar when sucrose is used in the formula. It also is used for partially hydrolyzing sugar sirups to increase the stability and avoid crystallization. A new and important use of invertase is in the preparation of high test invert molasses for industrial purposes.

Pectinase

Enzyme preparations containing pectinase, which catalyzes the hydrolysis of pectins to simple sugars and uronic acids, are prepared from cultures of various species of *Penicillium* or other molds, and are used in the clarification of fruit juices.

Tannase

The use of molds in the manufacture of gallic acid by hydrolysis of tannin has been discussed in an earlier paragraph of this chapter. Extracts of *Aspergillus niger* and other molds are prepared for their content of tannase and are used in the production of gallic acid.

Proteinases

Bacterial and mold proteinases are prepared by methods similar to those described for the preparation of amylases. Proteinases are used in the textile industry in the desizing of acetate rayon and the degumming of silk, in the tanning industry for treatment of the hides after the liming (dehairing) process, and in the brewing industry for the removal of the protein haze or cloudiness that appears in chilled beer. Proteinases also may be used in the manufacture of liquid glue and in the separation of silver from photographic films by digestion of the gelatin.

MICROORGANISMS AS FOOD (FEED)

Yeasts, molds, and other fungi have been used as sources of proteins, fats, and carbohydrates, as well as of vitamins.

Food Yeast

In some areas of the world where carbohydrates are cheap and plentiful and foods high in proteins and vitamins are scarce, it has been deemed practical to grow yeast for human food. So, for example, the British have built a plant in Jamaica for the production of yeast from molasses by a continuous process. *Torulopsis utilis* (*Cryptococcus utilis*) is the yeast employed; molasses from the cane sugar industry provides the fermentable sugar for the mash and ammonium salts furnish nitrogen. The yeast is washed, centrifuged from the liquid, and dried; it may then be used in soups, stews, doughs, or other foods. Yeast produced in this manner furnishes protein as well as vitamins of the B complex and may be used to supplement a diet otherwise deficient in these substances.

Considerable amounts of food yeast were produced in Germany during World War II and widely accepted as part of the German diet. Wood sugar, made by acid hydrolysis of wood, was one of the fermentable carbohydrates used in the production of the yeast; sulfite waste liquor also was employed.

Yeast Feeds

Brewers' and distillers' yeasts long have been used for animal feed, especially as part of feed mixtures compounded by feed companies. Yeast protein is too expensive for economical use in feeding, but it is possible that when a cheap source of carbohydrate becomes available yeasts may be grown especially for feeding. Small amounts of yeast are grown for that purpose now and are incorporated in some mixed feeds.

Molds as Foods or Feeds

The mold-like *Oospora lactis* (*Geotrichum candidum*) was substituted for the food yeast in a German process used during World War II. Mycelium from molds has been tested for use as food or feed. It has not come into practical use, however, because the mold proteins do not completely fulfill the needs of animals for amino acids; they could be used, however, to furnish part of the protein in a ration.

Fats from Microorganisms

A yeast-like fungus, *Endomyces vernalis,* was used by the Germans during World War I to manufacture fat. It has been reported that the yeasts *Torulopsis pulcherrima* and *T. lipoferra* were used during World War II in Sweden and in Gemany for the production of fat. The Germans also employed special strains of *Oospora lactis.* Yeasts, as well as molds, have been shown to produce appreciable amounts of fat, but the use of microorganisms to produce fats is strictly an emergency measure and thus far has been limited to time of war.

Vitamins from Microorganisms

The use of yeast, preferably killed or autolyzed, as a source of vitamins of the B complex has been well advertised. The production of riboflavin (vitamin B_2) by *Eremothecium ashbyii* (*Ashbya gossypii*) in various media, or by *Clostridium acetobutylicum* from whey, is now on a commercial basis. Also in commercial use is the oxidation of D-sorbitol to L-sorbose which is then used in the synthesis of ascorbic acid (vitamin C). Microorganisms are known to take up vitamins from the culture medium, and certain organisms can synthesize vitamins like thiamin, carotene (provitamin A), phthiocol, and nicotinic acid. In time, industrial processes for the synthesis of vitamins other than riboflavin and ascorbic acid may be developed.

REFERENCES

Burton, L. V., "By-products of milk." *Food Industries* (1937), 9:571–575, 617–618.

Jacobs, P. B., "Alcohol from agricultural commodities." *Report No. 95* (revised), Bureau of Agric. and Indust. Chemistry, U. S. D. A., 1946.

Kelly, F. C., *One thing leads to another* (*butyl alcohol-acetone*). N. Y., Houghton Mifflin, 1936.

Peckham, G. T., Jr., "The commercial manufacture of lactic acid." *Chem. & Eng. News* (1944), 22:440–443, 469.

Porges, N., Clark, T. F., and Gastrock, E. A., "Gluconic acid production." *Ind. Eng. Chem.* (1940), 32:107–111.

Porter, J. R., *Bacterial chemistry and physiology.* N. Y., Wiley, 1946.

Prescott, S. C., and Dunn, C. G., *Industrial microbiology* (2nd ed.). N. Y., Mc-Graw-Hill, 1949.

Ratcliff, J. D., *Yellow magic, the story of penicillin.* N. Y., Random House, 1945.

Schofield, M., "The citric acid industry." *Food* (1943), 12:315–316.

Silcox, H., "Production of streptomycin." *Chem. & Eng. News* (1946), 24:2762–2764.

Smith, G., *An introduction to industrial mycology* (3rd ed.). London, Edward Arnold & Co., 1946.

Thaysen, A. C., "Production of food yeast." *Food* (1945), 14:116–119.

Wallerstein, L., "Enzyme preparations from microörganisms." *Ind. Eng. Chem.* (1939), 31:1218–1224.

Wells, P. A., and Herrick, H. T., "Citric acid industry." *Ind. Eng. Chem.* (1938), 30:255–262.

Wynkoop, R., "Butanol and acetone." *Ind. Eng. Chem.* (1943), 35:1240–1242.

PART V

Soil Microbiology

One of the farmer's main jobs is to grow the crops needed to supply food for man and for animals. His ability to grow various crops is dependent upon many factors, some of which he can control. The physical condition of the soil he cultivates must be such that it will allow penetration of the roots of plants, and at the same time provide for them a firm support. The soil must contain moisture that is available to plants; if there is too little moisture the plants fail to grow; if there is too much moisture they may be "drowned out." In addition, the moisture content of the soil is of major importance in controlling the rate at which the soil responds to changes in atmospheric temperature, and in influencing the activities of microorganisms which change organic and inorganic substances into compounds available to green plants. The temperature of the soil, as well as that of the atmosphere, must be suitable for the growth of the desired crops; soil temperature is also of great importance because of its influence upon the growth and activities of soil microorganisms. The soil must contain in available form the foods needed by green plants, and it must be free from substances that will inhibit plant growth. Finally, its reaction (pH) must be favorable to the growth of the desired crop; the pH will also influence the survival and activity of the microorganisms of the soil.

It is the farmer's job not only to provide the crops grown each year with suitable growing conditions, but to conserve the desirable properties of the soil for future use. He must replace, in one way or another, the essential plant foods which each crop removes, or which are lost by erosion or leaching. He must maintain the supply of organic matter in the soil because of its desirable effects upon the soil's moisture-holding capacity and other physical properties, and because it is a reservoir of potential plant foods. Proper management of the soil must be learned through experience, but knowledge of the physics, chemistry, and biology of the soil is of tremendous aid to intelligent management.

The purpose of the chapters to follow is to describe the nature and activities of microorganisms in the soil, the ways in which they influence its fertility, and the means available for controlling certain of their activities.

18. THE SOIL AND ITS POPULATION OF MICROORGANISMS

The upper layer of the earth's surface, which varies in thickness from a fraction of an inch to as much as 20 feet, differs markedly from the underlying rocks and minerals. This upper layer, which is the soil, is distinguished from the underlying rock not only by its physical and chemical properties, but also by its content of "organic matter." The organic matter is made up of dead plant and animal cells and tissues, of waste products of the metabolism of plants and animals, and of products resulting from decomposition of these inanimate substances. The soil is not an inert mass of minerals and organic materials. It is a constantly changing culture medium in and on which microorganisms and macroscopic forms of life live and grow. Furthermore, the life of any one kind of living thing that exists in or on the soil is either directly or indirectly influenced by the other members of the soil population. The microorganisms and molds in the soil population play an outstanding role in the control of the soil's physical and chemical properties, and of its productivity. Some of the main effects of microorganisms upon the supply of plant foods in the soil can be illustrated by means of the diagram on page 210, which shows the cycle of essential foods in nature.

The chief role of the molds and of those soil microorganisms which do not contain chlorophyll is, as shown in the diagram, to decompose the complex organic and inorganic substances present in the waste products of animals, and in the dead plant, animal, and microbial cells returned to the soil; and to produce from these substances inorganic foods and CO_2 which will be available to green plants. While performing these important tasks, the soil microorganisms aid in the formation of humus—the mass of residual and synthesized organic matter in the soil that is resistant to rapid de-

209

CYCLE OF ESSENTIAL FOODS

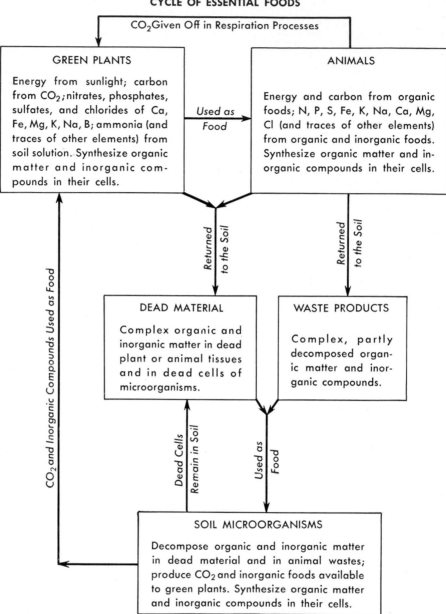

composition. They also aid in the aggregation of soil particles into small lumps that improve the physical condition of the soil and help prevent erosion. Figure 45 is an electron photomicrograph which shows aggregation of minute clay particles around the cells of bacteria in the soil. In addition, soil microorganisms prevent the accumulation on and in the soil of excessive

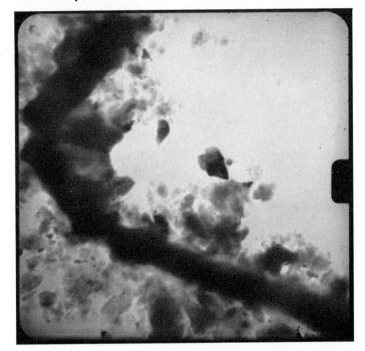

FIGURE 45. An electron photomicrograph showing the aggregation of clay particles around the cells of a common soil bacterium. (Courtesy of O. N. Allen.)

amounts of dead material and the wastes of animal metabolism; some microorganisms have the ability to fix atmospheric nitrogen; others are capable of oxidizing elements, such as sulfur, and changing them into compounds available to green plants. It is because of these activities that we are interested in the microorganisms of the soil. Those properties and conditions of the soil which control the activities and growth of the microorganisms in it, i.e., determine its value as a culture medium, are of great practical importance.

THE SOIL AS A CULTURE MEDIUM

The six principal factors that influence nutrition and growth of microorganisms have been outlined and discussed in Chapters 8 and 9. Consideration of the soil as a culture medium involves application of these concepts to conditions which may be found in soils.

1. *Foods.* The kinds and amounts of food present in the soil are important factors in determining the kinds of microorganisms which will be favored, and the rate and extent of their growth. The soil population is made up of many different kinds of microorganisms, the majority of which are hetero-

trophic, but large numbers of autotrophic species are also present; hence, there will always be at least one kind of microorganism present to utilize nearly any sort of food substance added to the soil. There are, for example, microorganisms in the soil which will utilize complex substances such as cellulose, while others are able to use methane or carbon monoxide as their principal food; some utilize proteins; others can make use of free nitrogen. Thus, when a crop is plowed under, manure is returned to the soil, or fertilizers such as ammonium sulfate or calcium cyanamid are added, the soil microorganisms are provided with food.

The soil population is a great mixture of different kinds of microorganisms which exist and grow in close association. Waste products produced in the respiration processes of one kind of microorganism may be utilized by another kind. Extracellular, hydrolytic enzymes produced by one kind of microorganism catalyze the formation of simple, soluble foods which are then available not only to the organism which produced the enzymes, but to others in the immediate vicinity.

Foods are utilized by soil microorganisms for synthetic purposes and in their respiration processes. The syntheses which occur result in the foods being bound up in microbial protoplasm, where they remain until the cells die and become decomposed by other microorganisms. By-products of respiration processes may accumulate, be utilized by green plants, be leached away, or be used by other organisms.

Protozoa which are present in the soil feed upon the bacteria, algae, and other protozoa in the soil population. When they die, their cell contents become food for molds and bacteria. The nutrition of algae is similar to that of green plants, and when they die their cells also become food for molds and bacteria.

Soils of almost any kind, from desert sands to rich, fertile loams, contain foods available to microorganisms. The total numbers, and the proportion of different kinds of organisms in the soil population, may be changed by adding different foods to the soil.

2. *Moisture.* Microorganisms must have moisture if they are to respire and grow. Molds and actinomycetes are able to carry on these activities with less moisture than is needed by other soil microorganisms, but in general, all kinds are favored by an abundant supply of available moisture. Soil moisture must be free, not bound by colloidal material, if it is to be available to microorganisms.

The moisture content of the soil has a direct influence upon two other principal factors which affect the activity and growth of microorganisms: temperature, and the supply of free oxygen. Soils which are saturated with water, or have a high moisture content, warm up more slowly in the spring, and are less subject to changes in atmospheric temperature during the growing season than comparatively dry soils. Soils which are saturated with water may become anaerobic; but in those which contain less moisture there is more opportunity for the entrance of oxygen from the air. In general, a supply of moisture suitable for the growth of most plants is ideal for the activities and growth of most kinds of microorganisms.

3. *Temperature.* The temperature of the soil is controlled mainly by the heat from the sun and the temperature of the atmosphere. As long as the soil remains unfrozen there are always some kinds of microorganisms in it which can respire and grow. Most soil microorganisms are mesophilic; hence soil temperatures of from 15° C. (59° F.) to 45° C. (113° F.) will be most favorable to their activities and growth. At lower temperatures, many of the mesophiles will grow slowly, and psychrophilic species will develop. At higher temperatures the thermophilic species will grow. When the soil is frozen, all activities and growth of microorganisms are stopped, but the cells of most species are not killed rapidly by freezing. At extremely high temperatures many microorganisms may be killed. Psychrophilic microorganisms and nonspore-forming mesophiles are more easily killed at extremely high temperatures than are spore-forming mesophiles and thermophiles.

The moisture content of the soil, the amount of organic matter which it contains, and its texture are all factors which influence its response to changes in atmospheric temperature. The covering of the soil by plants or accumulations of organic matter exerts considerable influence on the effect of the sun upon soil temperatures. In general, soil temperatures which favor the growth of green plants are most suitable to the majority of soil microorganisms, but in the population of microorganisms there are always species which will grow at temperatures from just above the freezing point to as high as 70° C. (158° F.).

4. *Hydrogen-Ion Concentration.* The hydrogen-ion concentration of the soil, which is usually expressed in terms of *p*H, affects the activities and growth of both plants and microorganisms. In general, most soil microorganisms, like most green plants, are favored by a near-neutral reaction. However, just as there are plants which will tolerate or even prefer an acid reaction, there are many molds and several kinds of bacteria which will grow in acid soils. Different kinds of soil microorganisms have been found which will grow in soils as acid as *p*H 2.0; others are known to grow in soils as alkaline as *p*H 10; but most kinds of soil microorganisms grow best, other conditions being equal, at reactions of from *p*H 6.0 to 8.0.

The respiration processes of soil microorganisms may be responsible for the production of acids. Carbon dioxide, which is produced in varying quantities in the respiration processes of all microorganisms, forms the weak acid

H_2CO_3, when dissolved in water. Heterotrophic microorganisms, particularly bacteria and molds, produce organic acids, such as formic, acetic, lactic, butyric, oxalic, and citric, as by-products of their respirations. Autotrophic bacteria are responsible for the formation of nitrous, nitric, and sulfuric acids. Buffer substances in the soil tend to inhibit changes in pH due to these acids. Other soil microorganisms decompose organic acids which are formed; green plants utilize the nitrates and sulfates formed by the reaction of nitric and sulfuric acids with basic substances. All of these agencies operate to prevent any sudden change in the reaction of the soil.

But the soil may be made more acid through the removal by plants of Ca^{++}, Mg^{++}, Na^+, and K^+ ions. In water-logged soils rich in organic matter, organic acids may accumulate. The addition of fertilizers such as ammonium sulfate provides the nitrifying bacteria with ammonia from which nitric acid is formed. Use of the NH_4^+ ion of the $(NH_4)_2SO_4$ liberates the SO_4^{--} ion, which in solution forms H_2SO_4. These are but a few examples of the different ways in which soils may become acid. In general, an acid condition may be corrected by the addition of lime (CaO) or limestone ($CaCO_3$). However, if it is desired to cause a nearly neutral soil to become acid rapidly, the best procedure available at present is to add sulfur and ammonium sulfate. The sulfur-oxidizing bacteria in the soil produce sulfuric acid from the sulfur, and, in time, enough acid is formed to overcome the buffer action of the soil with the result that it may be made as acid as pH 3.0 to 4.0.

The growth of nitrifying and of nitrogen-fixing bacteria, as well as that of most of the other desirable types of soil microorganisms is favored by a near-neutral reaction. Neutralization of an acid soil stimulates the activities and growth of these species.

5. *Supply of Free Oxygen and the Oxidation-Reduction Condition of the Soil.* The supply of free oxygen and the oxidation-reduction condition of the soil are of considerable importance in controlling the activity and growth of soil microorganisms. Most microorganisms in the soil are aerobic or facultative. Practically all of the molds and actinomycetes, and a large proportion of the bacteria and protozoa, are aerobic. There are many kinds of facultative bacteria in the soil population. Most of the anaerobic microorganisms are bacteria, but a very small number of anaerobic protozoa are known to exist in the soil.

In loose, open-textured soils, and in comparatively dry soils, there is opportunity for the entrance of an abundance of oxygen. Under such conditions, organic and inorganic substances which can be used as food by soil microorganisms are oxidized rapidly and completely. In close-textured soils, and in relatively wet soils, there is less opportunity for the entrance of oxygen, and the oxidation of microbial foods progresses more slowly. Soils which contain an abundance of organic matter, even though they may be fairly loose in texture, contain relatively little free oxygen. The carbon dioxide and other gases formed by the soil microorganisms tend to displace the oxygen in the soil atmosphere, and if the soil is sufficiently moist and contains an abundance of organic matter, there is little opportunity for the entrance and continued presence of large quantities of oxygen.

Drainage of water-logged soils enables the entrance of air, and under the resulting comparatively aerobic conditions, the soil microorganisms are again able to oxidize organic materials completely, and thus form available foods for green plants. At the other extreme, the addition of an abundance of organic matter to a loose-textured soil tends to slow down the rate of oxidation of organic matter. A supply of organic matter which is undergoing slow decomposition is most desirable because it improves the water-holding capacity of the soil, makes it easier to work, and increases its fertility. If the soil microorganisms are supplied with an abundance of oxygen, they decompose the organic matter rapidly and completely; with a limited supply the decomposition proceeds more slowly; under anaerobic conditions organic matter in the soil is decomposed so slowly by the microorganisms that it tends to accumulate in excessive amounts.

6. *Inhibitory Substances.* Soils may contain many different kinds of substances which will inhibit the growth of microorganisms. Excessive quantities of salt, alkalies, nitrates, and acids as well as substances such as oil, arsenic and arsenic compounds, and lead and lead salts, will inhibit or even kill soil microorganisms. Some microorganisms produce substances of unknown composition which will inhibit or even kill other microorganisms. For example, *Pseudomonas fluorescens*, a common species of bacterium in most soils, is known to produce soluble by-products that inhibit many other kinds of bacteria. As mentioned in Chapter 10, a species of *Bacillus* has been found which liberates, upon autolysis, a substance which will kill and even dissolve many Gram-positive bacteria. In addition, many kinds of molds and actinomycetes produce antibiotic substances which may inhibit or kill bacteria or other fungi. Figure 37 in Chapter 10 shows a petri dish culture prepared from soil; several of the colonies on this plate show antibiotic effects on other colonies. It has been demonstrated that in some cases bacteriophages may be of importance in the inhibition of bacteria in the soil. At the same time, bacteriophages and antibiotic substances that inhibit certain microorganisms may be used as food by other species in the microbial population.

In summary, the soil should be considered as a culture medium for the visible crop of plants, and for the invisible crop of microorganisms within it. The activities and growth of the invisible crop of microorganisms must be controlled if the soil is to remain fertile and capable of producing crops of economic value.

THE MICROORGANISMS OF THE SOIL

The microorganisms of the soil may be divided into two main groups: those which are typically soil microorganisms, which grow and respire under suitable conditions; and those which are introduced into the soil accidentally, and which find conditions unsuitable for respiration and growth. It is the first group, those which can grow and carry on their life processes in the soil, in which we are mainly interested.

Most of the soil microorganisms are found on or near the surface of the soil. In loose-textured, comparatively dry soils, microorganisms exist, and probably grow at greater depths than in close-textured, relatively moist soils. The same is true of cultivated soils as compared with forest soils or those which are covered with a thick carpet of sod. In general, the upper six to twelve inches of soil contain the majority of the microbial population.

It is practically impossible to list all of the different kinds of microorganisms which may be found in the soil. The microbial population is made up of bacteria, yeasts, algae, and protozoa; in addition, there are many molds present in most soils. All these organisms, with the exception of those protozoa which eat bacteria and other living cells, are saprophytic. The algae and those protozoa which contain chlorophyll are capable of carrying on a metabolism similar to that of the higher green plants. Many of the bacteria are autotrophic because they obtain their carbon from CO_2 and utilize elements or simple compounds as foods for energy and for growth. But most of the bacteria and all of the yeasts and molds of the soil are heterotrophic; their main foods are organic substances, and they utilize relatively small quantities of inorganic materials. Of the bacteria, the *Eubacteriales* and *Actinomycetales* are of greatest importance; the former are usually called "bacteria," while the latter are referred to as "actinomycetes."

The various kinds of soil microorganisms may be grouped together on the basis of the important chemical changes which they are capable of causing. Thus the nitrogen-fixing bacteria, the nitrifying bacteria, the cellulose-decomposing microorganisms, and many other similar groups may be designated on the basis of their main activities. The different kinds of microorganisms which make up these groups will be described as each type of change is discussed.

The numbers of soil microorganisms vary with the suitability of the soil as a culture medium. The range in numbers between the lowest and highest limits that have been reported is almost incredible. The following table presents the range in numbers of microorganisms which may be found in different soils as well as the numbers usually present in most soils.

TABLE 5. Numbers of Microorganisms in Soils
(Numbers per Gram of Soil)

Microorganism	Lower Limit	"Usual" Range	Higher Limit
True bacteria	1,000–10,000	1,000,000–10,000,000	1,000,000,000–10,000,000,000
Actinomycetes	100–1,000	100,000–1,000,000	5,000,000–10,000,000
Protozoa	none–100	10,000–100,000	500,000–1,000,000
Algae	none–100	1,000–100,000	200,000–500,000
Molds	1–100	1,000–100,000	200,000–500,000

It is impossible to give "average" values for the numbers of different kinds of microorganisms in soils because the variation of any one of the factors which influence the properties of the soil as a culture medium will cause a relatively sudden change in the numbers of microorganisms present. However, it may be concluded that a soil which is a good culture medium will contain a larger number of microorganisms than one which for some reason is a poor culture medium.

REFERENCES

Löhnis, F., and Fred, E. B., *Textbook of agricultural bacteriology*. N. Y., McGraw-Hill, 1923.

Lyon, L. T., and Buckman, H. O., *The nature and properties of soils* (4th ed.). N. Y., Macmillan, 1943.

Russell, E. J., *Soil conditions and plant growth* (7th ed.). N. Y., Longmans, Green, 1937.

United States Department of Agriculture, "Soils and Men." *Yearbook of agriculture, 1938*. Washington, D. C., U. S. Government Printing Office.

Waksman, S. A., *Principles of soil microbiology* (2nd ed.). Baltimore, Md., Williams & Wilkins, 1932.

Waksman, S. A., *Humus* (2nd ed.). Baltimore, Md., William & Wilkins, 1938.

Waksman, S. A., and Starkey, R. L., *The soil and the microbe*. N. Y., Wiley, 1931.

Winogradsky, S., *Microbiologie du sol*. Paris, Masson et Cie, 1949.

19. DECOMPOSITION OF ORGANIC MATTER IN THE SOIL

The principal sources of organic matter in the soil are the dead cells of plants, animals, and microorganisms, the liquid and solid waste products of animal metabolism, and organic fertilizers. Organic matter may be returned to the soil by natural processes, or it may be added by the farmer when he plows under a crop, puts barnyard manure on the soil, or applies some organic fertilizer such as tankage or urea.

There is a tremendous variety of organic compounds in the organic materials returned to the soil, but such materials have the common property of being mixtures of compounds, or single compounds of carbon. The following is a modification of a list given by Waksman and Starkey of the principal kinds of organic compounds in the organic materials which may be returned to the soil.

I. Carbohydrates (made up of C, H, and O; the H and O are in the same proportion as in H_2O)
1. Monosaccharides
   a. Pentoses: $C_5H_{10}O_5$, such as arabinose and xylose
   b. Hexoses: $C_6H_{12}O_6$, such as glucose, fructose, and mannose
2. Disaccharides: $C_{12}H_{22}O_{11}$, such as sucrose and maltose
3. Trisaccharides: $C_{18}H_{32}O_{16}$, such as raffinose
4. Polysaccharides
   a. Starch, inulin, glycogen, and dextrins: $(C_6H_{10}O_5)_x$
   b. Cellulose: $(C_6H_{10}O_5)_x$
   c. Hemicelluloses and polyuronides
      (1) Hexosans, which yield hexoses upon hydrolysis
      (2) Pentosans, which yield pentoses upon hydrolysis

(3) Pectins and gums, which yield simple sugars and uronic acids upon hydrolysis

II. Lignins (made up of C, H, and O; the empirical formula for a typical lignin is $C_{40}H_{30}O_6 \cdot (OCH_3)_4 \cdot (OH)_5 \cdot CHO$. Lignins are usually found combined with cellulose in compounds known as ligno-celluloses)

III. Tannins (made up of C, H, and O; the empirical formula for a typical tannin is $(C_6H_2 \cdot (OH)_3 \cdot COOH)_x$

IV. Glucosides (made up of C, H, O, and N; the empirical formula for a typical glucoside is $C_{20}H_{27}NO_{11}$)

V. Organic acids, such as formic, acetic, propionic, lactic, butyric, oxalic, succinic, citric, and stearic; salts of organic acids, such as calcium oxalate; esters of organic acids, such as ethyl acetate (a combination of ethyl alcohol and acetic acid). All organic acids contain C, H, and O

VI. Fats and oils (made up of C, H, and O; are glycerol esters of fatty acids); waxes (made up of C, H, and O; are esters of fatty acids and higher alcohols)

VII. Nitrogenous organic compounds (made up of C, H, O, and N, with S and P present in some compounds)
1. Proteins and nucleoproteins
2. Polypeptides
3. Amino acids
4. Amines
5. Alkaloids
6. Purines
7. Nucleic acids

VIII. Pigments
1. Chlorophyll, the green coloring matter of plants
2. Carotinoids, the yellow pigments
3. Anthocyanins, which are pigments of the leaves, fruits, and flowers of plants

Return of green plants or of manure to the soil results in the addition of most of the substances listed in this outline. It is not possible in the space available to present quantitative data showing the amounts of each kind of organic compound in the various crops or animal wastes which may be returned to the soil. Such information may be found in the books and publications on soils, to which reference is made at the end of this chapter.

The decomposition by soil microorganisms of these many different kinds of organic compounds and mixtures of compounds is an exceedingly complex process which is incompletely understood. All of the different kinds of microorganisms which may decompose each of the different compounds are not as yet known; and the chemical changes which occur in the decomposition processes have not been completely worked out. Much of the work done so far has involved the use of pure cultures and pure chemical compounds, but the mixed microbial population of the soil, acting on the many different compounds which are present in the soil, undoubtedly produces chemical changes which are quite different from those which take place in a synthetic culture medium inoculated with a pure culture of some one soil microorganism. However, the many studies which have been made on the decomposition of organic matter by soil microorganisms give some indication of the major types of reactions which occur, and it is therefore possible to describe the principal kinds of changes which take place.

DECOMPOSITION OF NONNITROGENOUS ORGANIC COMPOUNDS IN THE SOIL

For the purposes of description and discussion it is best to consider the decomposition of nonnitrogenous organic compounds apart from the decomposition of nitrogenous organic compounds. The decomposition of some of these nonnitrogenous organic compounds is described in the following outline, which presents, in the usual order of their occurrence, the principal changes caused by soil microorganisms.

I. **Hydrolysis** of complex, nonnitrogenous organic compounds.

Bacteria, molds, and actinomycetes are mainly responsible for these hydrolyses. The ability of any one kind of microorganism to hydrolyze a complex compound is governed by whether or not it produces the extracellular, hydrolytic enzyme which will catalyze the specific hydrolysis. Under anaerobic conditions, anaerobic bacteria are mainly responsible for hydrolysis; under aerobic conditions, molds, as well as aerobic bacteria and actinomycetes, are active in causing hydrolytic reactions in the soil.

1. Cellulose $+ H_2O \xrightarrow{\text{cellulase}}$ Cellobiose

2. Hemicelluloses $+ H_2O \xrightarrow{\text{cytases}}$ Monosaccharides, such as glucose, fructose, galactose, and mannose from hexosans; arabinose and xylose from pentosans

3. Pectins $+ H_2O \xrightarrow{\text{pectinases}}$ Monosaccharides and uronic acids

4. Starch $+ H_2O \xrightarrow{\text{amylase}}$ Maltose

5. Disaccharides

   a. Cellobiose $+ H_2O \xrightarrow{\text{cellobiase}}$ Glucose

   b. Maltose $+ H_2O \xrightarrow{\text{maltase}}$ Glucose

   c. Sucrose $+ H_2O \xrightarrow{\text{sucrase}}$ Glucose $+$ fructose

6. Fats $+ H_2O \xrightarrow{\text{lipase}}$ Glycerol $+$ fatty acids

The products of hydrolysis are more simple chemically and more soluble than the original compounds. When these relatively simple, soluble compounds are formed, they immediately become available to all of the microorganisms in the immediate vicinity of those cells which produced the extracellular, hydrolytic enzymes. If aerobic conditions prevail, some of these microorganisms may utilize the monosaccharides, glycerol, fatty acids, and uronic acids in their aerobic respiration processes, with the result that incompletely or completely oxidized respiratory by-products are formed. Under anaerobic conditions, however, only those microorganisms capable of carrying on anaerobic respirations are able to utilize these available foods, with the result that the by-products formed will consist largely of incompletely oxidized compounds.

II. **Decomposition** of glycerol, fatty acids and uronic acids, and monosaccharides **under anaerobic conditions.**

The microorganisms mainly responsible for the anaerobic decomposition of these relatively simple, soluble organic compounds are anaerobic and facultative bacteria, and possibly yeasts. They utilize these compounds in the intra- or intermolecular oxidation-reduction reactions involved in their anaerobic respiration processes. A partial list of the by-products of the respirations follows:

1. Acids: formic, acetic, propionic, lactic, and butyric
2. Alcohols: Ethyl and butyl
3. Gases: CO_2, H_2, and CH_4 (methane)
4. Miscellaneous products: aldehydes, acetyl-methyl-carbinol, and gums

III. **Decomposition** of glycerol, fatty acids and uronic acids, and monosaccharides **under aerobic conditions.**

Molds, aerobic bacteria, and actinomycetes are mainly responsible for the aerobic decomposition of these relatively simple, soluble organic compounds. While one species of microorganism may cause only incomplete oxidation under aerobic conditions, other species in the soil population are able to cause complete oxidation of not only glycerol, fatty acids and uronic acids, and monosaccharides, but of the organic acids, alcohols, and other products of incomplete oxidation as well. **Thus, under aerobic conditions, the final products of the complete oxidation reactions occurring in the aerobic respiration processes of aerobic microorganisms are CO_2 and H_2O.**

It will be noticed that no mention has been made of the decomposition of the lignin and ligno-cellulose which may be present in organic matter returned to the soil. The reason for this omission lies in the fact that very few microorganisms are able to decompose lignin, and that the chemistry of its decomposition is not well known. Ligno-cellulose may be hydrolyzed slowly to lignin and cellulose. The cellulose is then hydrolyzed and finally oxidized to CO_2 and H_2O in the manner which has been described. Slow hydrolysis and oxidation of lignin does occur, but the enzymes responsible, and the microorganisms which produce them are not as yet well known. However, it is believed that actinomycetes play an important role in the decomposition of lignins in the soil.

In summarizing the role of microorganisms in the decomposition of non-nitrogenous organic matter in the soil, it may be stated that complex substances are first hydrolyzed to simple, soluble compounds which can be used as sources of carbon and as foods for energy by heterotrophic microorganisms. The final products formed by these organisms, acting under aerobic conditions, are CO_2 and H_2O. Few soil microorganisms are capable of decomposing complex compounds (such as cellulose) completely. The initial hydrolysis, intermediate incomplete oxidation, and final complete oxidation of complex, nonnitrogenous organic compounds is usually caused by the successive action of several different kinds of microorganisms growing in association in the soil.

DECOMPOSITION OF NITROGENOUS ORGANIC COMPOUNDS IN THE SOIL

The principal changes which occur during the decomposition of nitrogenous organic compounds by soil microorganisms are described in the following outline.

I. **Hydrolysis** of nitrogenous organic compounds.

Bacteria, molds, and actinomycetes are mainly responsible for these hydrolyses. The ability of any one kind of microorganism to hydrolyze a nitrogenous organic compound is governed by whether or not it produces the extracellular, hydrolytic enzyme which will catalyze the specific hydrolysis. Under anaerobic conditions, anaerobic bacteria are mainly responsible for hydrolysis; under aerobic conditions, molds, as well as aerobic bacteria and actinomycetes, are active in causing hydrolysis of nitrogenous organic compounds.

1. Proteins + H_2O $\xrightarrow{\text{proteinases}}$ Polypeptides

2. Polypeptides + H_2O $\xrightarrow{\text{polypeptidases}}$ Amino acids

Many different kinds of proteins may be present in the organic matter of the soil; some are more resistant to hydrolysis than others. A proteinase which catalyzes the hydrolysis of one kind of protein may not catalyze the hydrolysis of another. The problem is further complicated by the existence of proteins in combination with other compounds. Glycoproteins are compounds containing both carbohydrate and protein; lipoproteins are combinations of lipids with proteins; nucleoproteins are combinations of nucleic acids and proteins. Different enzymes are needed to catalyze the hydrolysis of these compounds than are required for the hydrolysis of a pure protein. These facts are mentioned in order to emphasize the extremely complex nature of proteins and to explain why their decomposition is a relatively slow process. The chemistry of proteins, and of the enzymes which catalyze their hydrolysis, is incompletely understood at present.

3. Amino acids $+ H_2O \xrightarrow{\text{deaminases}}$ fatty acids, alcohols, aldehydes, CO_2, and NH_3

There are approximately 25 different amino acids. A deaminase which will catalyze the hydrolysis of one amino acid may have no effect on another. Molds and actinomycetes which hydrolyze amino acids grow only under aerobic conditions, but there are many anaerobic and facultative bacteria which can hydrolyze amino acids under anaerobic conditions. This is one method of ammonification (see II, below).

4. Nonprotein nitrogenous organic compounds
   a. Urea $+ H_2O \xrightarrow{\text{urease}} 2 NH_3 + CO_2$
      Urea is a nonprotein, nitrogenous organic compound which occurs normally in the waste products of animals
   b. Calcium cyanamide $+ H_2O + CO_2 \xrightarrow{\hspace{1.5cm}}$ Urea

      Urea $+ H_2O \xrightarrow{\text{urease}} 2 NH_3 + CO_2$
   c. Lecithin $+ H_2O \xrightarrow{\text{lecithinase}}$ glycerophosphoric acid $+$ fatty acid $+$ choline

In addition to these few examples of nonprotein nitrogenous organic compounds there may exist in the organic matter of the soil many other compounds such as nucleic acids, creatinine, guanidine, uric acids, and chitin, which contain considerable quantities of nitrogen. All of these substances are susceptible to hydrolytic decomposition by a wide variety of soil microorganisms.

II. **Ammonification** of nitrogenous organic compounds.

Both aerobic and anaerobic bacteria as well as the aerobic actinomycetes and molds are responsible for the formation of ammonia from organic nitrogenous compounds. The chemical changes involved in the liberation of ammonia from relatively simple organic nitrogenous compounds are of several different types. Hydrolysis of amino acids and of urea may, as has been described, result in the liberation of ammonia; also, the utilization by soil microorganisms of amino acids and of relatively simple, soluble, nonprotein nitrogenous organic compounds as foods for energy results in the liberation of ammonia as a by-product of microbial respiration.

1. **Decomposition** of amino acids and of certain nonprotein organic nitrogenous compounds **under anaerobic conditions.**

Anaerobic bacteria are mainly responsible for these decompositions, which are termed **putrefactions** when some of the by-products of the anaerobic respiration processes which occur are foul smelling. The products formed in such decompositions may include organic acids, alcohols, amines, mercaptans, H_2S, CO_2, and NH_3. Hydrogen sulfide, mercaptans, and such compounds as indol and skatol are responsible for the foul odors resulting from the anaerobic decomposition of amino acids and other organic nitrogenous compounds.

2. **Decomposition** of amino acids and of certain nonprotein organic nitrogenous compounds **under aerobic conditions.**

Aerobic bacteria, molds, and actinomycetes are mainly responsible for these decompositions. **Many intermediate compounds may be formed, but the final products of such aerobic decompositions are** NH_3**,** CO_2**, sulfates, and** H_2O**.** The aerobic soil microorganisms are also capable of oxidizing many of the products formed in anaerobic putrefactions, and produce NH_3, CO_2, sulfates, and H_2O as by-products of their utilization.

In summarizing the decomposition of nitrogenous organic compounds by soil microorganisms, it may be stated that complex compounds, such as proteins, are first hydrolyzed to relatively simple, soluble compounds, such as amino acids. The amino acids may be used as food for growth or as food for energy by heterotrophic microorganisms. When used as food for energy, ammonia is liberated as the chief nitrogenous by-product of respiration. Although many intermediate products may be formed under anaerobic or aerobic conditions, these may be completely oxidized under aerobic conditions with the formation of CO_2, NH_3, sulfates, and H_2O. Because ammonia is liberated in these decomposition processes, they are termed **ammonifications.** The initial hydrolysis, intermediate incomplete oxidation, and final complete oxidation of the organic nitrogenous compounds is usually caused by the successive action of several different kinds of microorganisms growing in association in the soil.

The phosphorus present in many proteins, and in some nonprotein, nitrogenous compounds, is liberated in the form of phosphoric acid. Upon reacting with bases in the soil to form phosphates, the phosphorus becomes available, if the phosphates are soluble, to green plants. The CO_2 formed in the decomposition of organic, nitrogenous compounds is also available to green plants and to autotrophic microorganisms.

The ammonia which is liberated reacts with acids in the soil solution to form ammonium salts. Some of these salts are utilized by green plants, some are leached out of the soil, and some are acted upon by soil microorganisms.

The changes produced by soil microorganisms in their action upon ammonium salts and upon H_2S will be described in the next chapter.

FORMATION OF HUMUS

The mass of residual and synthesized organic matter in the soil is known as humus. It is not a stable mixture of organic compounds because it is constantly undergoing changes caused by the action of soil microorganisms.

When organic matter, such as plant stubble, green manure, barnyard manure, or some organic fertilizer is worked into the soil, the soil microorganisms, if conditions are suitable, immediately start to decompose it. At this stage, it is termed "raw" organic matter. They act first on the relatively simple, soluble compounds which are present, such as the sugars, alcohols, acids, and urea. When the supply of these foods is exhausted they start to decompose the more complex starches, hemicelluloses, celluloses, fats, and proteins. The decomposition of these compounds proceeds more slowly, and weeks or months may elapse before their decomposition is completed. During this time, there is a tremendous growth of soil microorganisms with the result that many of the food elements in the original organic matter have been incorporated in microbial protoplasm. The lignin present in the original organic matter is not rapidly decomposed, and hence a large proportion of it remains after other components of the organic matter have disappeared. The mass of residual and synthesized organic matter which remains following the original, rapid decomposition of relatively simple organic substances is termed humus; it is dark brown in color, and much of it is in the colloidal state.

The accumulation of humus in soils is a comparatively slow process. In water-logged soils, which are relatively anaerobic, humus continues to accumulate because there is no opportunity for aerobic microorganisms to bring about its hydrolysis and oxidation. Such soils are low in fertility because the plant foods which they contain are tied up in unavailable, organic compounds of the humus.

In loose-textured, sandy soils, organic matter is decomposed rapidly and completely, and there is little opportunity for humus to accumulate. Such soils are low in fertility because they contain comparatively little humus. When humus is lacking, there is no supply of potential plant foods in the soil which can gradually be made available to plants through the action of soil microorganisms. Humus is also important because it improves the texture of the soil, and because of its tremendous adsorptive powers for plant foods and for moisture.

Humus is removed from soils by constant cultivation and by growing cultivated crops, because under these conditions, aeration of the soil is excessive, and the soil microorganisms rapidly decompose the organic matter completely. It is possible to maintain a supply of humus in the soil by turning under green manures, barnyard manure, or organic fertilizers. If this is not done, the supply of humus becomes rapidly depleted and the soil loses its productivity.

Proper management of the soil has as one of its chief objectives the maintenance in the soil of an adequate quantity of humus.

REFERENCES

Russell, E. J., *Soil conditions and plant growth* (7th ed.). N. Y., Longmans, Green, 1937.

United States Department of Agriculture, "Soils and Men." *Yearbook of agriculture 1938*. Washington, D. C., U. S. Government Printing Office.

Waksman, S. A., *Principles of soil microbiology* (2nd ed.). Baltimore, Md., Williams & Wilkins, 1932.

Waksman, S. A., *Humus* (2nd ed.). Baltimore, Md., Williams & Wilkins, 1938.

Waksman, S. A., and Starkey, R. L., *The soil and the microbe*. N. Y., Wiley, 1931.

Winogradsky, S., *Microbiologie du sol*. Paris, Masson et Cie, 1949.

20. ACTION OF MICROORGANISMS ON INORGANIC SUBSTANCES IN THE SOIL

TRANSFORMATION OF NITROGENOUS COMPOUNDS

It has been pointed out in Chapter 19 that soil microorganisms which act upon nitrogenous organic compounds ultimately produce ammonia as one of their chief by-products. The ammonia thus set free, or ammonia which has been added to the soil in fertilizers such as ammonium sulfate, may be leached out of the soil, be utilized to some extent by green plants as a source of nitrogenous food, or be acted upon by soil microorganisms. Many different kinds of heterotrophic microorganisms and some kinds of autotrophic microorganisms may utilize ammonium salts as food for synthetic purposes; such utilization results in the ammonia becoming tied up in the nitrogenous organic constituents of microbial cells. This type of microbial utilization of ammonium salts will be discussed later in this chapter. The second main type of utilization of ammonium salts by certain soil microorganisms is known as nitrification—an aerobic respiration process in which energy is liberated.

Nitrification

The oxidation by bacteria of ammonia to nitrous acid and of nitrous acid to nitric acid is termed nitrification. Three different genera of autotrophic bacteria are responsible for **nitrification.** Different species of these genera are practically always found in soils in numbers which vary from a few hundred to as many as 2,000,000 cells per gram. Species of the genus *Nitrosomonas,* and of the genus *Nitrosococcus,* oxidize ammonia to nitrous acid. Species of the genus *Nitrobacter* oxidize nitrous acid to nitric acid.

$$2\,NH_3 + 3\,O_2 \xrightarrow{\underset{Nitrosococcus}{Nitrosomonas\ or}} 2\,HNO_2 + 2\,H_2O + energy$$

$$2\,HNO_2 + O_2 \xrightarrow{Nitrobacter} 2\,HNO_3 + energy$$

All of the bacteria which cause nitrification are autotrophic. They obtain carbon from CO_2; the nitrogen which they need for synthetic purposes is obtained from ammonia (by *Nitrosomonas* and *Nitrosococcus*) or from nitrous acid (by *Nitrobacter*); other food elements needed for synthetic purposes are obtained from inorganic substances. The oxidation reactions which these bacteria cause are their sole source of energy. The nitrous and nitric acids formed react with bases and certain salts in the soil to form nitrites and nitrates, respectively.

Nitrosococcus is a small, nonspore-forming coccus; *Nitrosomonas* and *Nitrobacter* are small, nonspore-forming, cylindrical cells. Despite the fact that all species of these genera are nonspore-forming and are easily inhibited or killed by various physical and chemical agencies, they are very widely distributed in soils. Their respiration and growth are of major importance to the fertility of soils because many kinds of green plants are able to obtain nitrogen only when it is supplied to them in solution in the form of nitrates. Even those plants which can get the nitrogen which they need from ammonium salts, and the leguminous plants which, in symbiosis with root-nodule bacteria, can utilize elemental nitrogen, are able to make use of nitrates. A knowledge of the conditions which affect the activities and growth of the nitrifying bacteria, and hence the formation of nitrates from ammonium salts, is therefore of great value to the farmer. A brief discussion of these conditions follows:

1. *Hydrogen-Ion Concentration (pH).* The optimum pH for the respiration and growth of *Nitrosomonas, Nitrosococcus,* and *Nitrobacter* in the soil is from pH 6.5 to 8.0. These bacteria may respire slowly in some soils as acid as pH 3.5 and in others as alkaline as pH 10.0, but their maximum respiration and growth occur at near-neutral reactions. Nitrification proceeds best in soils which contain an abundance of buffer substances which resist a change in hydrogen-ion concentration due to the nitrous and nitric acids formed. In the absence of buffers, the acid by-products of nitrification rapidly cause the soil to become sufficiently acid to inhibit respiration and growth of the nitrifying bacteria.

2. *Supply of Free Oxygen.* All species of the bacteria which cause nitrification are aerobic. Their respiration and growth are completely inhibited by anaerobic conditions. Any practice which allows the entrance of air into the soil stimulates, if other conditions are satisfactory, the process of nitrification.

3. *Supply of Moisture.* The bacteria which cause nitrification respire and

grow most rapidly in soils which contain about 50 per cent of their water-holding capacity. Greater quantities of water tend to create anaerobic conditions; small quantities provide insufficient free moisture for the organisms.

4. *Supply of Ammonium Salts.* *Nitrosomonas* and *Nitrosococcus* must be supplied with ammonium salts if they are to respire and grow; in the absence of ammonium salts their activities cease. Ammonia may be liberated by heterotrophic microorganisms from the organic nitrogenous compounds in the soil, or supplied by the addition of $(NH_4)_2SO_4$ as a fertilizer. The nitrites formed in the soil from the nitrous acid produced by the oxidation of ammonia provide the chief food for *Nitrobacter* species, which are always found growing in association with *Nitrosomonas* and *Nitrosococcus*. Under normal conditions, nitrites do not accumulate in soils, and nitrite fertilizers are never added because large quantities of nitrites are toxic to plants. Addition of ammonium salts, or provision of conditions suitable for the ammonification of nitrogenous organic compounds, supplies the nitrifying bacteria directly or indirectly with their chief food, and therefore stimulates nitrification.

5. *Temperature.* The optimum temperature for the respiration and growth of the bacteria which cause nitrification is approximately 25° C. (77° F.). Their minimum temperature is approximately 10° C. (50° F.), and their maximum is about 38° C. (100.4° F.). Soil temperatures favorable to the growth of most plants are ideal for the respiration and growth of the nitrifying bacteria.

6. *Inhibitory Agencies.* The presence of large quantities of soluble, non-nitrogenous organic matter inhibits the activities and growth of the bacteria which cause nitrification; they are also inhibited by the presence of salt, oil, or metals in excessive quantities.

Nitrates formed by nitrifying bacteria or added to the soil in the form of nitrate fertilizers may be used by green plants and by soil microorganisms as food for growth; they may be leached away, or become reduced by soil microorganisms.

Nitrate Reduction and Denitrification

Nitrates may be reduced under anaerobic conditions by many different kinds of heterotrophic and autotrophic bacteria. If the products of reduction are nitrites, ammonium salts, or gaseous nitrous oxide (N_2O), the process is called **nitrate reduction.** If the reduction is complete and gaseous nitrogen is formed, it is termed **denitrification.** Nitrate reduction and denitrification are the result of anaerobic respiration in which intermolecular oxidation-reduction occurs. Heterotrophic microorganisms, facultative and anaerobic, use nitrates as a source of oxygen, and reduce them under anaerobic conditions in order to oxidize some oxidizable material such as a monosaccharide, glycerol, fatty acid, or amino acid. Autotrophic bacteria, facultative and anaerobic, use nitrates as a source of oxygen, and reduce them under anaerobic conditions in order to oxidize elements or simple compounds. The following are type reactions (equations are not balanced); some energy is liberated in each reaction, but the energy yield is small because some of it must be used to cause the reductions involved.

1. Heterotrophic microorganisms

   a. Nitrate reduction

$$C_6H_{12}O_6 + KNO_3 \longrightarrow KNO_2 + H_2O + CO_2 + energy$$

   b. Denitrification

$$C_6H_{12}O_6 + KNO_3 \longrightarrow K_2CO_3 + H_2O + CO_2 + N_2 + energy$$

2. Autotrophic microorganisms

   a. Nitrate reduction

$$S + H_2O + KNO_3 \longrightarrow H_2SO_4 + KNO_2 + energy$$

   b. Denitrification

$$S + H_2O + KNO_3 \longrightarrow K_2SO_4 + H_2O + N_2 + energy$$

Nitrites formed by nitrate reduction may be leached away, be reduced further to free N_2, or be oxidized to nitrates by *Nitrobacter*. Nitrites seldom accumulate in soils under usual conditions.

Free N_2 liberated by denitrification is lost from the soil, or may be utilized by nitrogen-fixing microorganisms. Both denitrification and nitrate reduction are undesirable processes because they destroy nitrates which are available to green plants, and thus lower the immediate fertility of the soil.

The conditions which favor nitrate reduction and denitrification are as follows:

1. *A Supply of Nitrates and of Oxidizable Matter in the Soil.* Since most of the anaerobic and facultative bacteria which cause nitrate reduction and denitrification are heterotrophic, these processes are favored by an abundance of oxidizable organic matter and of nitrates. An abundance of oxidizable organic matter not only provides food for energy for nitrate-reducing and denitrifying microorganisms; it may also help to create the needed anaerobic conditions.

2. *Absence of Free Oxygen.* Anaerobic conditions, which exist in water-logged soils and in soils containing large quantities of organic matter, are conducive to nitrate reduction and denitrification. In the presence of free oxygen, nitrate reduction and denitrification are inhibited or stopped completely.

3. *Supply of Moisture.* Nitrate reduction and denitrification are favored by an abundance of moisture; these processes take place most rapidly in water-logged soils. The microorganisms responsible for nitrate reduction

and denitrification are able to grow and carry on their respirations in soils that contain from one-fourth to one-half of their water-holding capacity, but under such circumstances anaerobic conditions are uncommon, and hence nitrate reduction and denitrification seldom occur in relatively dry soils.

4. *Hydrogen-Ion Concentration (pH).* A few species of bacteria can cause nitrate reduction and denitrification in soils as acid as pH 2.0; other kinds are active in soils as alkaline as pH 10.0; but most nitrate reducers and denitrifiers are favored by a near-neutral reaction. Nitrate reduction may cause the soil to become more alkaline in reaction due to the destruction of nitric acid and to the formation of small quantities of ammonia. Denitrification caused by heterotrophic microorganisms may cause an increase in alkalinity due to destruction of nitric and nitrous acids; certain autotrophic bacteria which cause denitrification, such as those which oxidize sulfur to sulfuric acid, may cause an increase in acidity, but the changes in hydrogen-ion concentration produced are seldom of practical significance.

5. *Temperature.* There are different kinds of microorganisms in the soil capable of carrying on respiration and growth from temperatures just above the freezing point to as high as 70° C., and some of the species active at any temperature within this range are able to cause nitrate reduction and denitrification. Most of the nitrate reducing and denitrifying microorganisms in the soil are mesophilic, and hence these processes go on most rapidly between 15° C. and 45° C.

Despite the facts that many different kinds of microorganisms may cause nitrate reduction and denitrification, that these organisms are nearly always present in the soil, and that their activities may occur under a wide range of conditions, nitrate reduction and denitrification are seldom of major importance in making nitrates unavailable to green plants. However, when anaerobic conditions prevail in soils, these processes are responsible for some of the loss of nitrates which occurs, and are therefore detrimental to soil fertility. In piles of barnyard manure, denitrification may occur if nitrates are present; but if stored manure is kept well packed and wet, there is little chance for nitrates to be formed from the ammonia which is present, and, therefore, no opportunity for denitrification to take place.

Utilization by Microorganisms of Ammonium Salts and Nitrates as Foods for Growth

In their foods for growth, soil microorganisms active in the decomposition of organic matter require organic compounds as a source of carbon; organic nitrogenous compounds, nitrates, or ammonium salts as a source of nitrogen; water; and a supply of phosphates, sulfates, and chlorides of Ca, Fe, Mg, K, Na, B, and traces of other elements.

The dry matter of the cells of microorganisms contains about 50 per cent of carbon. The amount of nitrogen contained in the dry matter of the cells of molds, actinomycetes, and bacteria varies considerably; it has been reported by Waksman and Starkey to be as follows:

TABLE 6.   Nitrogen Content, and Ratio of Carbon to Nitrogen, of the Dry Matter of Microorganisms

Microorganism	Nitrogen Content (per cent)	Ratio of C to N[a]
Molds	From 3 to 8; average 5	10 to 1
Actinomycetes	" 7 " 10; " 8.5	6 " 1
True bacteria	" 8 " 12; " 10	5 " 1

a Assuming that dry matter contains 50 per cent of C.

Most of the carbon in the organic matter decomposed by various soil microorganisms is liberated as CO_2, but varying quantities of carbon are incorporated into the organic compounds of microbial cells. Molds retain from 20 to 50 per cent (average, 35 per cent), actinomycetes retain from 5 to 30 per cent (average, 15 per cent), and bacteria retain from 1 to 30 per cent (average, 7 per cent) of the carbon in the organic matter which they decompose. In order to incorporate carbon into the protoplasm and other organic compounds in their cells, microorganisms must at the same time utilize other foods, the most important of which supply nitrogen, phosphorus, and sulfur. If the organic matter which the microorganisms decompose contains more than 1.7 per cent of nitrogen, enough of this element is present to serve as food for growth. However, if the organic matter contains less than 1.7 per cent of nitrogen, there is not enough nitrogenous food present to meet the needs of the cells. Under such conditions, the microorganisms must utilize ammonium salts and nitrates which are present in the soil in order to get the nitrogen they need.

For example, if enough alfalfa is plowed under to supply 100 pounds of dry matter in the soil, and if this dry matter contains 40 per cent of carbon and 3 per cent of nitrogen, it may be utilized by soil microorganisms in the following manner:

40 lbs. carbon × 0.35 (assuming that 35 per cent of the carbon is assimilated by the microorganisms and 65 per cent is liberated as CO_2) = 14 lbs. of carbon incorporated in microbial cells

If the ratio of carbon to nitrogen in the microbial cells is 10 to 1, one-tenth as much nitrogen as carbon is needed by the microorganisms:

14 lbs. carbon × 0.1 = 1.4 lbs. of nitrogen incorporated in microbial cells

Since the dry matter decomposed contained 3 pounds of nitrogen (100 × 0.03 = 3 lbs.), there is an excess of 1.6 pounds of nitrogen over the quantity required by the microorganisms. Under such conditions, little or no nitrate or ammonia in the soil will be utilized as food for growth by the microorganisms, and ammonia will be liberated by the microbial activity.

However, if enough straw is plowed under to supply 100 pounds of dry matter, and if this dry matter contains 37 per cent of carbon and 0.5 per cent of nitrogen, it may be utilized by soil microorganisms in the following manner:

37 pounds of carbon × 0.35 (assuming that 35 per cent of the carbon is assimilated by the microorganisms and 65 per cent is liberated as CO_2) = 12.95 lbs. of carbon incorporated in microbial cells

If the ratio of carbon to nitrogen in the microbial cells is 10 to 1, one-tenth as much nitrogen as carbon is needed by the microorganisms:

12.95 lbs. carbon × 0.1 = 1.295 lbs. of nitrogen incorporated in microbial cells

Since the dry matter decomposed contained only 0.5 per cent of nitrogen (100 × 0.005 = 0.5 lb.), there is a deficit of 0.795 pound of nitrogen (1.295 − 0.5 = 0.795 lb.) in the amount of nitrogen supplied by the straw. Under such conditions, the microorganisms must make use of ammonium salts and nitrates present in the soil, and incorporate them in the organic nitrogenous compounds of their cells.

The cells of microorganisms live for comparatively short periods of time, and upon their death the organic nitrogenous compounds which they contain are decomposed by other microorganisms. But their ability to tie up considerable quantities of nitrates and ammonium salts in their cells may be of practical importance. An acre-foot of fertile soil contains, as a rule, about one ton of microbial cells. The dry matter of these cells weighs approximately 500 pounds, and contains about 250 pounds of carbon and 25 pounds of nitrogen. When organic matter which contains less than 1.7 per cent of nitrogen is plowed under, the mass of microbial cells in the soil must utilize ammonium salts and nitrates, which would otherwise be available to green plants, as food for growth. This is undesirable during the growing season because it decreases the amount of inorganic nitrogenous food which is available to plants. However, this activity of microorganisms is desirable in the fall of the year because it removes soluble ammonium salts and nitrates which might be leached away during the winter, and ties them up in the insoluble organic nitrogenous compounds of microbial cells. The following spring, upon death of the microorganisms which have conserved the nitrogen in their cells during the winter, living soil microorganisms, acting in succession, first hydrolyze, then ammonify, and finally nitrify these compounds to produce ammonium salts and nitrates which are available to plants. Thus, microorganisms in the soil are not only responsible for the decomposition of nitrogenous organic matter, the liberation of ammonia, and the formation of nitrates; they may be caused to conserve the supply of nitrogen in the soil during those times of year when it may be leached away.

TRANSFORMATION OF SULFUR AND OF INORGANIC COMPOUNDS CONTAINING SULFUR

Autotrophic, nonspore-forming bacteria of the genus *Thiobacillus* have the ability to oxidize elemental sulfur to sulfuric acid, which reacts with bases in the soil to form sulfates. These same bacteria are able to oxidize II$_2$S and sulfides. In this process the *Thiobacillus* species oxidize H$_2$S to free sulfur, and then oxidize the sulfur to sulfuric acid.

Other species of bacteria may utilize H$_2$S, and produce elemental sulfur as a by-product. The sulfur thus liberated may be oxidized by *Thiobacillus* species to sulfuric acid.

Most species of the genus *Thiobacillus* are aerobic; but one is anaerobic, and is able to oxidize sulfur to sulfuric acid with oxygen which it obtains from nitrates.

Only one genus of bacteria is known which is able to reduce elemental sulfur or sulfates to H$_2$S under anaerobic conditions. The reduction of sulfate by one species of this genus, *Desulfovibrio desulfuricans,* is shown in the following reaction:

$$3 \text{ CaSO}_4 + 2 \text{ (C}_3\text{H}_5\text{O}_3)\text{Na} \xrightarrow[\substack{\text{by } \textit{Desulfovibrio desul-}\\ \textit{furicans}}]{\substack{\text{utilized in}\\ \text{intermolecular oxidation-}\\ \text{reduction reactions}}} 3 \text{ CaCO}_3 + \text{Na}_2\text{CO}_3 + 2 \text{ H}_2\text{O} + 2 \text{ CO}_2 + 3 \text{ H}_2\text{S} + \text{energy}$$

(sodium lactate)

In this reaction, the sulfate is reduced, with the formation of H$_2$S, while the lactate is oxidized to CO$_2$ and H$_2$O. The net yield of energy is low because the organism must use some of that which is liberated in order to reduce the sulfate.

Green plants and many soil microorganisms obtain the sulfur which they need as food for growth from sulfates. The sulfur present in the cells of dead plants, animals, and microorganisms, and in animal waste products which are returned to the soil, may occur in proteins, in protein decomposition products, and in sulfates; H$_2$S is also present in the wastes of animals. Heterotrophic soil microorganisms produce H$_2$S from the sulfur of organic compounds and autotrophic microorganisms oxidize the H$_2$S to sulfur, and then to sulfates. Green plants seldom suffer for want of available sulfur because most soils contain plenty of this element, and because soil microorganisms are constantly, under suitable conditions for growth, causing the formation of sulfates. Many sulfates are insoluble, and hence are not lost by leaching, but most soils contain enough soluble sulfates to supply the needs of plants and microorganisms.

TRANSFORMATION OF IRON

Iron is present in many different compounds in the soil, and is one of the elements required by green plants. Despite the fact that plants need comparatively small amounts of iron, it is often difficult to supply their wants because iron salts are relatively insoluble under the neutral or alkaline conditions which exist in many soils. Microorganisms may both directly and indirectly affect the availability of iron to plants.

The so-called iron bacteria, most of which are *Chlamydobacteriales*, but a few of which are *Caulobacteriineae*, cause the precipitation of insoluble iron compounds when they utilize soluble iron salts. A typical reaction involves the utilization by these bacteria of soluble $FeCO_3$ (ferrous carbonate), and the formation of $Fe(OH)_3$ (ferric hydroxide), which precipitates out of solution onto the bacterial cells or their sheaths.

Many heterotrophic microorganisms are able to oxidize the soluble iron salts of organic acids (such as ferric ammonium citrate) with the formation of $Fe(OH)_3$, $(NH_4)_2CO_3$, and H_2O. As the $Fe(OH)_3$ is insoluble, it precipitates out of solution.

Under anaerobic conditions, H_2S formed by the action of soil microorganisms may react with soluble iron salts to form FeS, which is insoluble and precipitates out of solution. This reaction, as well as others so far described, are undesirable as far as the availability of iron to plants is concerned.

The formation by soil microorganisms of acids (such as H_2CO_3, various organic acids, HNO_3, and H_2SO_4) aids in bringing iron compounds into solution. This is particularly true under anaerobic conditions, in which iron exists in the ferrous state. Since soil microorganisms are able to produce anaerobic conditions in localized areas in the soil, and to form acids of various kinds, they may, by indirect action, increase the availability of iron to green plants.

INDIRECT EFFECTS OF MICROORGANISMS UPON THE AVAILABILITY OF ESSENTIAL PLANT FOODS IN THE SOIL

Just as the acids formed by soil microorganisms may assist in the solution of iron salts, they may also dissolve and make available other plant food elements which are tied up in insoluble compounds in the soil. The various organic acids, as well as the H_2CO_3, HNO_3, and H_2SO_4, produced by soil microorganisms may react with many insoluble inorganic compounds to form soluble salts. The following are examples of this type of reaction:

$$(1)\quad Al_2O_3 \cdot K_2O \cdot 6\,SiO_2 + 8\,HNO_3 \longrightarrow 2\,Al(NO_3)_3 + 2\,KNO_3 + 6\,SiO_2 + 4\,H_2O$$

In the first reaction, the potassium present in the insoluble potassium aluminum silicate is changed to soluble KNO_3. Similar reactions may be caused by H_2CO_3, H_2SO_4, and some organic acids.

$$(2)\quad CaCO_3 + H_2CO_3 \longrightarrow Ca(HCO_3)_2$$

In the second reaction, insoluble calcium carbonate, the chief constituent of limestone, is changed to soluble calcium bicarbonate.

$$(3)\quad Ca_3(PO_4)_2 + 4\,H_2CO_3 \longrightarrow Ca(H_2PO_4)_2 + 2\,Ca(HCO_3)_2$$

In the third reaction, the relatively insoluble tricalcium phosphate is changed to soluble monocalcium phosphate and calcium bicarbonate.

Reactions such as these are responsible for the change of certain insoluble minerals into soluble compounds available to green plants. These reactions are also of importance in the formation of soil from rocks.

It has been estimated that the soil microorganisms in an acre of fertile soil annually produce from 1000 to 20,000 pounds of H_2CO_3, 50 to 500 pounds of HNO_3, 20 to 200 pounds of sulfuric acid, and large, uncalculated quantities of organic acids. These acids are of importance in the formation of soil, and in the solution of minerals needed by plants.

REFERENCES

Russell, E. J., *Soil conditions and plant growth* (7th ed.). N. Y., Longmans, Green, 1937.

Waksman, S. A., *Principles of soil microbiology* (2nd ed.). Baltimore, Md. Williams & Wilkins, 1932.

Waksman, S. A., and Starkey, R. L., *The soil and the microbe.* N. Y., Wiley, 1931.

Winogradsky, S., *Microbiologie du sol.* Paris, Masson et Cie, 1949.

21. FIXATION OF NITROGEN

Approximately 80 per cent of the earth's atmosphere is nitrogen; about 70,000,000 lbs. of nitrogen exist above each acre of soil. But despite the abundance of nitrogen in the atmosphere, there is seldom enough of this element in the soil in the form of nitrates and ammonium salts to meet the needs of green plants. No multicellular green plants are known which are able, through their own efforts alone, to incorporate free nitrogen in their cells. Animals also are unable to utilize the nitrogen of the air which they inhale; they must consume organic nitrogenous foods to obtain the nitrogen which they need.

At present, there are two ways in which atmospheric nitrogen may be fixed, i.e., caused to react with another element or compound to form a chemical compound which contains nitrogen: chemical fixation and biological fixation.

1. *Chemical Methods of Nitrogen Fixation.* When lightning discharges, nitric oxide is formed which reacts with water to yield HNO_3. This acid reacts with ammonia in the air to yield NH_4NO_3, and in this form a small amount of fixed nitrogen reaches the soil from the atmosphere.

A modification of this natural process is the Birkeland and Eyde method in which a high voltage alternating current is caused to arc between copper electrodes. The nitric oxide formed by the heat of the arc is dissolved in water to form nitric acid. Nitrates can then be prepared from the HNO_3 obtained.

In the Haber process, nitrogen is caused to combine with hydrogen to form ammonia. A temperature of 200° C., a pressure of 200 atmospheres, and the presence of a catalyst composed of finely divided iron are required for this reaction. Ammonium salts can be manufactured from the ammonia thus obtained.

Calcium cyanamide is manufactured by passing heated nitrogen gas over hot (1200° C.) calcium carbide. The calcium cyanamide may be used directly as a fertilizer.

Nitrides of metals are produced by passing heated nitrogen gas over hot metals, such as aluminum. Upon subsequent hydrolysis, ammonia is released from the nitrides thus produced.

All of these chemical methods of nitrogen fixation require the expenditure of large amounts of energy, and are therefore relatively expensive.

2. *Biological Methods of Nitrogen Fixation.* Certain bacteria, and at least one kind of blue-green algae, growing independently, are able to fix atmospheric nitrogen in their cells; the end products of fixation are proteins. Fixation of nitrogen by the independent action of microorganisms is termed **nonsymbiotic** to distinguish it from the **symbiotic** type of nitrogen fixation caused by the associated action of root-nodule bacteria and leguminous plants. In symbiotic nitrogen fixation the end products of fixation are proteins, most of which are found in the leguminous plant; in nonsymbiotic nitrogen fixation the proteins formed remain in the cells of the bacteria. The complete mechanism of symbiotic and nonsymbiotic nitrogen fixation is incompletely understood at present, but the biochemistry of the two processes appears to be similar in most respects.

Farmers are able to purchase ammonium salts, nitrates, and calcium cyanamide which have been manufactured out of nitrogen fixed from the atmosphere, and to use these compounds as nitrogenous fertilizers. It is also possible for farmers to enrich their soils with nitrogen through the use of soil management practices that favor the activity and growth of nonsymbiotic nitrogen-fixing microorganisms. But one of the most common and most profitable methods of nitrogen fixation is to grow leguminous crops that are infected with efficient root-nodule bacteria. When a nodulated leguminous crop is turned under, used as pasture, or fed to livestock and the manure returned to the soil, all or a large part of the nitrogen fixed by the associated action of the plants and bacteria is added to the soil.

Nonsymbiotic Fixation of Nitrogen

Aerobic bacteria of the genus *Azotobacter* and some species of anaerobic bacteria of the genus *Clostridium* are mainly responsible for nonsymbiotic nitrogen fixation in the soil. One species of blue-green algae of the genus *Nostoc* is able to fix nitrogen when grown in a nitrogen-free medium, but the importance of this organism in the soil is not well established.

The ability of *Rhodospirillum rubrum,* a purple, photosynthetic bacterium, to fix atmospheric nitrogen when growing under anaerobic conditions has been established recently. This bacterium contains pigments which enable it to utilize the energy of sunlight. It can fix nitrogen if supplied with light, and if anaerobic conditions are maintained. However, its practical importance in nitrogen fixation in soils has not been determined.

The various species of the genus *Azotobacter* are nonspore-forming, spheroidal or cylindrical cells which are aerobic. *Azotobacter chroococcum* is the type species of this genus and is more widely distributed in soils than any other.

The ability of all the different species of the genus *Clostridium* to fix nitrogen has not been determined. It is known that *Clostridium pasteurianum,* as well as a few other species of this genus, can fix nitrogen, but these should not be considered as the only nitrogen-fixing clostridia; there may be others. Bacteria of this genus are spore-forming, cylindrical in shape, and are strictly anaerobic.

The nonsymbiotic nitrogen-fixing bacteria may utilize a wide variety of foods for energy; these include certain hemicelluloses, starches, sugars, alcohols, and organic acids. *Azotobacter,* being aerobic, oxidizes its energy-yielding foods completely if given time and an abundance of oxygen. Nitrogen-fixing clostridia, acting under anaerobic conditions, ferment energy-yielding foods with the production of butyric acid as one of the main by-products. *Azotobacter* is, as a rule, able to fix from three to eight times more nitrogen per unit of energy-yielding food consumed than *Clostridium. Azotobacter* and the nitrogen-fixing clostridia grow best in the presence of large amounts of available nonnitrogenous organic matter.

These nonsymbiotic bacteria are able to use free atmospheric nitrogen, and to incorporate it in their cells in the form of proteins, but in the presence of large amounts of ammonium salts, nitrates, or soluble nitrogenous foods they fix very little free nitrogen.

The other foods essential for these bacteria are obtained from inorganic compounds dissolved in the soil moisture. Of these foods, phosphates are of great importance, particularly in the nutrition of *Azotobacter.*

The hydrogen-ion concentration of the soil has considerable influence upon the growth of *Azotobacter* and nitrogen-fixing clostridia in the soil. One species of *Azotobacter* is able to grow in soils as acid as pH 4.0, but most species grow only in near-neutral soils of pH 6.0 to 8.5. The nitrogen-fixing clostridia are not so sensitive to acid conditions and may grow in soils of from pH 5.0 to 8.5. Most species of *Azotobacter* die out rapidly in acid soils, but the nitrogen-fixing clostridia, when in the spore state, can withstand acid conditions for long periods of time.

Both *Azotobacter* and the nitrogen-fixing clostridia are mesophilic. The nitrogen-fixing clostridia can grow at higher temperatures than *Azotobacter*, but the latter are able to grow at lower temperatures than the clostridia. In general, temperatures that favor growth of plants are suitable for the growth of these bacteria.

The practical importance of the fixation of nitrogen in soils by these non-symbiotic bacteria is not great. They must compete with other soil organisms for the available foods. Being unable to utilize cellulose, lignocelluloses, or lignins, they must depend upon the existence of a supply of relatively simple foods, which are seldom present in the soil in large amounts. In the presence of available nitrogenous foods they fix relatively small amounts of free nitrogen. The amounts of nitrogen fixed by their activities range from none to as high as 40 pounds per acre per year; a fair average in fertile soils is about 5 to 10 pounds per acre per year. The nitrogen fixed by these organisms exists in their cells in the form of proteins; it is not available to plants until the cells die and become decomposed by other microorganisms in the soil. The addition of cultures of these bacteria to the soil results in little or no increase in nitrogen fixation because most soils already contain all of the *Azotobacter* and nitrogen-fixing clostridia which they can support. The practical significance of nitrogen fixation in soils by *Rhodospirillum rubrum* or by *Nostoc* has not been determined.

Symbiotic Fixation of Nitrogen

A symbiotic relationship is one which is mutually beneficial to two different forms of life which grow together in close association. The relationship between leguminous plants and the bacteria which grow in the nodules on their roots is usually symbiotic. The plant supplies the bacteria with organic and inorganic foods, and the bacteria, in some unexplained fashion, cause nitrogen to be fixed in the plant in the form of proteins. Leguminous plants which are not infected with root-nodule bacteria are unable to fix nitrogen; root-nodule bacteria growing alone, either in the soil or in culture media, are unable to fix nitrogen. The fixation of nitrogen in nodulated leguminous plants is a result of the symbiotic activities of root-nodule bacteria and the plants.

Chief Characteristics of Leguminous Plants

Leguminous plants, or "legumes" as they are commonly called, belong to the family *Leguminosae*. They are dicotyledonous angiosperms which carry their seeds in pods. The flowers of leguminous plants are typically papilionaceous (butterfly-like). The leaves of leguminous plants alternate on the stem, and each leaf is composed of leaflets which are arranged along a common stem in pairs. All leguminous plants of agricultural value have nodules on their roots if they have been infected with root-nodule bacteria. These nodules, in contrast to the fibrous nature of the roots, are relatively soft and are filled with nutrient plant juices. They are easily separated from the root because the connecting tissues are comparatively fragile. Figure 46 shows nodules on the roots of leguminous plants. Another characteristic of leguminous plants is their high protein content. One ton of alfalfa hay con-

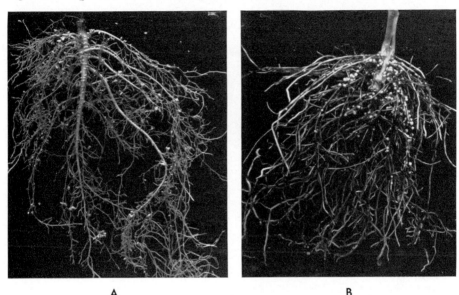

A   B

FIGURE 46.   Two views of nodules on leguminous plants. Left, sweet clover; and right, soybean. These nodules are an integral part of the roots and contain the root-nodule bacteria (*Rhizobium* species) that fix atmospheric nitrogen in symbiosis with the host plant. (Courtesy of O. N. Allen.)

tains as a rule from 300 to 350 pounds of protein; one ton of a grass, such as timothy, contains on the average from 115 to 150 pounds of protein. When grown without root-nodule bacteria, leguminous plants take all of the nitrogen which they need to manufacture their proteins from the soil in the form of ammonium salts and nitrates. When the roots of leguminous plants are infected with efficient nodule bacteria, in some cases all, but in most instances a large part, of the nitrogen in their proteins is obtained from the atmosphere.

Chief Characteristics of Root-Nodule Bacteria

The root-nodule bacteria are members of the genus *Rhizobium*. They are small, cylindrical, nonspore-forming, aerobic, mesophilic bacteria which are

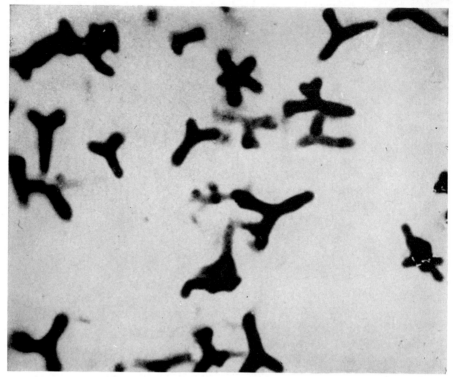

FIGURE 47. Photomicrograph of bacteroids from a nodule on a leguminous plant. These oddly shaped rhizobia are found only in the nodule and will appear as small uniform bacilli when grown on laboratory media. Enlarged about 2000X.

able to infect certain leguminous plants and cause the formation of nodules. When found in nodules, these bacteria may be rod-shaped, or exist in peculiar X, Y, T, branched, or club-shaped cells which are frequently vacuolated. These cells which show unusual shapes are called "bacteroids." Figure 47 is a photomicrograph of bacteroids from a nodule.

Different pure cultures of bacteria of the genus *Rhizobium* exhibit few differences in their morphological, cultural, or physiological characteristics. They are differentiated into species mainly on the basis of their ability to infect and to form nodules on the roots of certain leguminous plants. Any group of leguminous plants within which the root-nodule bacteria are mutually interchangeable is termed a bacterial-plant or cross-inoculation group. Those pure cultures of *Rhizobium* which form nodules on the roots of all the plants in any one bacterial-plant group, but which do not, under usual conditions, form nodules on the roots of other leguminous plants, are classified in a separate species. At present at least 21 bacterial-plant groups are recognized, but the bacteria of only six of these have received definite species designation. A list of those bacterial-plant groups in which most of the leguminous plants of agricultural importance are classified follows.

Bacterial-Plant (Cross-Inoculation) Groups of Leguminous Plants and
Root-Nodule Bacteria

  I. **Alfalfa group;** bacteria: *Rhizobium meliloti;* plants: alfalfa, sweet clover, and bur clover
 II. **Clover group;** bacteria: *Rhizobium trifolii;* plants: red, crimson, white, alsike, mammoth, and Ladino clover
III. **Pea group;** bacteria: *Rhizobium leguminosarum;* plants: garden, field, and sweet pea, vetch, broadbean, and lentil
 IV. **Bean group;** bacteria: *Rhizobium phaseoli;* plants: garden, navy and kidney bean
  V. **Lupine group;** bacteria: *Rhizobium lupini;* plants: annual and perennial lupine
 VI. **Soybean group;** bacteria: *Rhizobium japonicum;* plant: soybean
VII. **Locust group;** bacteria: unnamed species of *Rhizobium;* plants: black locust
VIII. **Cowpea group;** bacteria: unnamed species of *Rhizobium;* plants: cowpea, lima bean, lespedeza, peanut, and crotalaria

Groups V, VI, and VIII are not as distinct as the others because under some conditions, *Rhizobium japonicum* can infect and form nodules on certain plants of the cowpea group. The *Rhizobium* for cowpeas may infect and form nodules on soybeans and, occasionally, upon lupines. *Rhizobium lupini,* under certain conditions, may cause nodule formation on soybeans, cowpeas, peanuts, and some other plants of the cowpea group. There are other examples of the bacteria of one group causing the formation of nodules on plants of another bacterial-plant group, but these exceptions are not of practical importance. The importance of the bacterial-plant groups in agriculture lies in the fact that only the root-nodule bacteria of one particular group are consistently, under field conditions, able to infect, and to carry on symbiotic nitrogen fixation with the leguminous plants of that group. Root-nodule bacteria of the pea group are unable to enter into symbiosis with alfalfa; alfalfa nodule bacteria are unable to enter into symbiosis with peas, etc.

Formation of Nodules

When the seed of a leguminous plant germinates it sends a tap root into the soil. Lateral roots soon branch out from this central root. When the tap and lateral roots are young, their surfaces are covered with root hairs, which are thin-walled, hair-like extensions of cells of the surface layer (the epidermis) of roots. Root hairs may vary from a few microns to one or two millimeters in length.

If root-nodule bacteria which are able to infect the particular species of leguminous plant are present in the immediate vicinity of its roots, they will, if conditions are suitable, invade the root hairs. The manner in which the bacteria attack, and finally invade the root hairs is not known at present. It is also possible for root-nodule bacteria to invade roots through wounds.

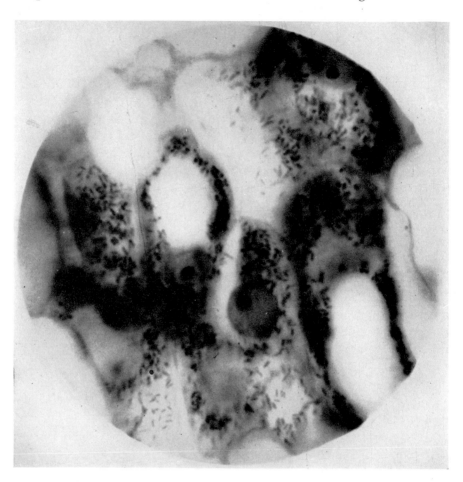

FIGURE 48.   Stained section of a root nodule showing darkly stained root-nodule bacteria inside the root cells of the leguminous host plant. In recently infected cells the rhizobia are around the periphery of the interior of each cell, in other cells the entire cell has become invaded. Enlarged 1200X. (Courtesy of O. N. Allen.)

Soon after the bacteria enter a root hair, an infection thread begins to form and to grow toward the base of the root hair. This infection thread is made up of a mass of bacterial cells around which a sheath or tube of cellulose, hemicelluloses and pectins is formed by the infected plant cells. The bacteria continue to multiply and to penetrate through successive layers of cells of the root cortex (the layers of cells just beneath the epidermis). The infection thread branches in various directions, and soon many cells of the root cortex are infected with root-nodule bacteria. In some plants, such as the pea and bean, the nodule is formed from the cells of the root cortex. In other plants, such as alfalfa, clover, and peanut, the infection thread grows through the cortex to the pericycle of the central cylinder of the root, and it is from the cells of the pericycle that the nodules of these plants are formed.

The mass of multiplying cells in the pericycle or cortex increases, with the result that the outer layers of the root cortex bulge out. The root-nodule bacteria continue to multiply and to invade the new plant cells that are formed. As the young nodule develops, vascular bundles are formed in the nodule cortex and connect with the vascular system of the root. Through the vascular bundles nutrients from the plant pass into the nodule, and the products of bacterial activity in the nodule are transported to the plant.

A mature nodule is covered with a thin layer of root cortex beneath which there is a thin layer of cells of the nodule cortex. None of the cortical cells is infected, but nearly all the cells of the inner part of the nodule contain root-nodule bacteria. In a young nodule the growing bacteria are mostly rod-shaped; in older nodules most of the bacteria exist in the different, peculiar forms of bacteroids. Each infected cell of a nodule may contain several thousand bacteria; there may be from 1,000,000 to 1,000,000,000 bacteria in the whole nodule. In young nodules most of the bacteria are alive, but in old nodules nearly all the bacteria are dead; only 0.01 to 1 per cent of the total number are alive. Figure 48 is a photomicrograph of a stained section of a root-nodule.

The formation of nodules has been described in considerable detail because it is a unique process of great fundamental importance. Nodule formation must occur before symbiotic nitrogen fixation can take place. The formation of nodules is a pathological process which is most unusual because it results in a mutually beneficial relationship between the leguminous plant and its root-nodule bacteria.

Results of Symbiosis Between Root-Nodule Bacteria and Leguminous Plants

The chief result of symbiosis between root-nodule bacteria and leguminous plants is the fixation of atmospheric nitrogen. The mechanism of the fixation process is not as yet completely understood, but there is no doubt that the nitrogen is fixed in the nodules in compounds which are then transferred to the plant. A complete review of the theories which have been advanced to explain the mechanism of symbiotic nitrogen fixation may be found in the book and review on this subject by Wilson, to which reference is made at the end of this chapter. The fixation and transfer of nitrogen continue throughout the period of active growth of the plant; the nitrogen is not fixed and stored in the nodules, and then transferred all at once to the plant.

The effects of symbiotic nitrogen fixation upon the growth, yield, and protein content of leguminous plants are of considerable importance in practical agriculture, and may be summarized as follows:

1. *Effects upon Growth.* In order to grow normally, leguminous plants must be supplied with nitrogen. If the plant has no nodules, it must obtain all of its nitrogen from ammonium salts and nitrates in the soil. If it is nodulated, it may obtain most of its nitrogen from the atmosphere, but still takes some from the soil. In nitrogen-poor soils, nonnodulated leguminous plants grow slowly, their leaves have an unhealthy, yellowish color, and they may even die of nitrogen starvation. When nodulated leguminous plants are grown under the same conditions, they grow normally, have a healthy, green color, and never die of nitrogen starvation. In soils which contain an abundance of nitrogenous foods, nonnodulated leguminous plants grow normally and as well as nodulated plants. The ability of nodulated leguminous crops to grow normally on nitrogen-poor soils, and their ability to take most of the nitrogen which they need from the atmosphere, even when grown on fertile soils, are two of the many reasons why leguminous crops are of agricultural value.

Symbiotic nitrogen fixation is of great importance during the early stages of growth of such leguminous plants as alfalfa and clover. The nitrogen content of the tiny seeds from which these plants originate is small and is soon exhausted by the growing seedling. If nodules are formed on the roots of these young plants, the resulting symbiotic fixation of nitrogen satisfies the demand for nitrogenous food. However, if no root-nodule bacteria are present in the soil around the roots, and hence no nodules are formed, the young plants are entirely dependent upon the supply of available nitrogenous foods in the soil. If the supply is inadequate, the plants grow poorly, or may even die. Success in getting a "catch" of alfalfa or clover, particularly on soils low in available nitrogen, depends to a large extent upon whether or not the young plants become infected with root-nodule bacteria which are capable of entering into effective symbiosis.

Large-seeded leguminous plants such as peas and soybeans are provided with a comparatively large amount of nitrogenous food by the seed. It is not so difficult to get these plants started, but once the supply of nitrogenous food in the seed is exhausted, they must obtain nitrogenous foods from the soil, from their nodules, or from both sources.

2. *Effects upon Yield and Protein Content of the Crop.* Nodulated leguminous plants as a rule produce greater yields and contain more protein than
similar, nonnodulated plants grown at the same time under identical conditions. This is true only when the bacteria in the nodules are able to enter
into symbiosis with the plants in a most effective manner. Differences in
yield and protein content are great on nitrogen-poor soils, but may be very
slight on nitrogen-rich soils. Not only are the yield and protein content of the
leaves and stems of nodulated leguminous plants greater than that of similar
nonnodulated plants; the yield and protein content of the seeds are also
higher. Canning peas, and in some cases soybeans, are grown for the seed
which they produce; on most soils, nodulated peas and soybeans produce
greater yields of seed that contains more protein than similar nonnodulated
plants grown under identical conditions. The food value, as well as the
value of a leguminous crop for green-manuring purposes, is usually greater
when the plants are nodulated.

Variations in Effectiveness of Root-Nodule Bacteria in Symbiosis with Leguminous Plants

When root-nodule bacteria infect the roots of leguminous plants and grow
in the nodules that are formed, the effectiveness of the symbiosis between
bacteria and plants may vary. It is possible that the symbiosis may be
highly effective, but in some cases, the plants, though infected and nodulated, may show little or no benefit from the infection. An outline of the
causes of variations in effectiveness follows.

1. *Host-Plant Specificity.* It has been shown that all pure cultures (each of
which is called a "strain") of a species of root-nodule bacteria are not identical in their ability to enter into symbiosis with all of the different genera,
species, or varieties of the leguminous plant members of the bacterial-plant
group which they may infect. For example, one strain of *Rhizobium meliloti*
is able to cause formation of nodules on *Medicago sativa* (alfalfa), *Medicago hispida* (bur clover), *Melilotus alba* (white sweet clover), and *Melilotus indica* (yellow sweet clover). The alfalfa may enter into symbiosis
with this particular strain of root-nodule bacteria more effectively than the
bur clover or sweet clover, with the result that more nitrogen is fixed in the
alfalfa than in the other nodulated plants. A second strain of *Rhizobium
meliloti* may fix more nitrogen in symbiosis with white sweet clover than
with alfalfa, bur clover, or yellow sweet clover. The host-plant specificity
may be even greater, with the result that one strain of *Rhizobium meliloti*
may fix more nitrogen in symbiosis with, for example, the Ladak variety of
alfalfa than with the Grimm variety. These same kinds of host-plant specificity are known to occur in other bacterial-plant groups.

2. *Strain Variation Within a Species of* Rhizobium. This type of variation in symbiotic relationships involves the ability of different strains of root-nodule bacteria of one species to enter into symbiosis with one variety of a species of leguminous plant. If, for example, 100 different pure cultures of *Rhizobium meliloti* are secured from nodules of alfalfa plants that have been dug at random from different fields, it may be shown that these bacterial strains vary in their ability to fix nitrogen in symbiosis with Grimm alfalfa. Possibly

FIGURE 49. The results of a laboratory and greenhouse experiment on the effect of inoculation. Ladino clover was grown under the following conditions: pot K was not inoculated; pot 205 was inoculated with an effective strain of *Rhizobium trifolii;* pot 227 was inoculated with an ineffective strain of *Rhizobium trifolii.* (Courtesy of O. N. Allen.)

25 per cent of these strains of *Rhizobium meliloti* may prove to be highly effective in symbiosis with the alfalfa; 50 per cent may be moderately effective; 25 per cent may be relatively ineffective. Yet all of these 100 strains of bacteria form nodules on alfalfa plants; they are all pure cultures of *Rhizobium meliloti.* Thus, some strains of any one species of root-nodule bacteria are effective, many are moderately effective, and some are ineffective in their symbiotic relationships. A few strains of any one species of *Rhizobium* possess outstanding ability to enter into symbiosis with certain of the leguminous plants which they infect. Other strains of the same species

of *Rhizobium* may fix little or no nitrogen when grown in symbiosis with certain of the leguminous plants which they infect. Figure 49 shows strain variation of rhizobia in symbiosis with Ladino clover.

3. *Causes for Changes in Effectiveness of Root-Nodule Bacteria.* When cultivated under suitable conditions in the laboratory, the ability of any one strain of root-nodule bacteria to enter into symbiosis with the leguminous plants which it can infect remains remarkably constant over a period of weeks, months, or even years. But it is also possible to change the effectiveness of a strain of *Rhizobium,* and even to destroy its ability to infect and form nodules on its specific host plants, by altering the conditions under which the bacteria are grown in the laboratory. For example, if the bacteria are grown in culture media which contain excessive quantities of certain amino acids, e.g., glycine, they rapidly lose their ability to enter into effective symbiosis with leguminous plants.

Another way in which the effectiveness of a pure culture of *Rhizobium* can be changed is by repeated plant passage. Thus, if a pure culture of, for example, *Rhizobium trifolii,* is allowed to form nodules on the roots of red clover plants, the result of the symbiosis in terms of total nitrogen fixed may prove to be poor. If the bacteria are isolated in pure culture from the nodules of these plants, and caused to form nodules on the roots of a second lot of red clover plants, the symbiosis may be slightly improved with the result that more nitrogen is fixed. A pure culture from this second lot of plants, caused to form nodules on a third lot, may show further improvement in symbiosis. Successive passages of the pure culture through successive lots of plants may increase its ability to enter into symbiosis with red clover to the point that it becomes an effective strain. But upon continued, repeated plant passage the effectiveness of the strain of bacteria gradually decreases till it once more becomes relatively ineffective in symbiosis with red clover. However, continued, successive plant passages may again gradually restore the effectiveness of the bacteria.

Practical application of a knowledge of these variations in the effectiveness of symbiotic relationships can be made by the farmer, and by the manufacturer of cultures of root-nodule bacteria which are used to inoculate the seeds of leguminous crops. The farmer, through his own efforts and those of governmental agencies which represent and serve him, can make sure that the cultures of root-nodule bacteria which he purchases contain effective bacteria. The manufacturer is able to test the ability of various strains of root-nodule bacteria to enter into effective symbiosis with different genera, species, and varieties of leguminous plants within each bacterial-plant group. By so doing he is able to manufacture cultures of proven nitrogen-fixing ability.

Inoculation of Seed and Soil

Inoculation is the practice of adding root-nodule bacteria to the seed of leguminous plants or to the soil. The purpose of inoculation is to place a large enough number of the right kind of root-nodule bacteria in a location which will allow them to infect the roots of some specific crop of leguminous plants.

1. *Methods of Inoculation.*   There are two general methods of inoculation: one is to transfer soil from a field upon which a nodulated crop of the same bacterial-plant group has grown; the second is to add a culture of the right kind of root-nodule bacteria to the seed just before it is sown.

a. Soil transfer method: Two general procedures may be followed in inoculation by the soil transfer method. Approximately 500 pounds of soil may be taken from the surface eight to ten inches of a field in which the nodulated crop has grown, and scattered over an acre of the new field. The soil must be evenly distributed, and turned under as soon as possible. The second method is to mix with water about four or five quarts of soil containing the desired root-nodule bacteria. This water suspension of soil is then mixed thoroughly with the seed, which is then dried before it is sown.

The soil transfer method of inoculation has several disadvantages. In the first place, one can never be sure that the soil contains a large enough number of root-nodule bacteria. Secondly, the strains of bacteria which it does contain may not be effective. Thirdly, insect pests, weed seeds, and plant-disease-producing microorganisms may be transferred. For these main reasons, the soil transfer method of inoculation is unsatisfactory, and is not often used at present.

b. Culture method: The best method of inoculation available at present is the addition of a culture of the right kind of root-nodule bacteria to the seed just before it is sown. Three main types of cultures are available for this purpose; their manufacture is described in Chapter 15.

(1) Liquid cultures. Liquid cultures contain a suspension of root-nodule bacteria. They are diluted with the amount of water recommended by the manufacturer and mixed thoroughly with the seed. The inoculated seed is then dried and sown as soon as possible.

(2) Agar cultures. Agar cultures are supplied in bottles containing an agar culture medium on which the bacteria are growing. Cold water is added to the bottle in order to wash the bacteria from the surface of the agar, and the suspension of root-nodule bacteria thus obtained is mixed thoroughly with the seed. The inoculated seed is then dried and sown as soon as possible.

(3) Solid base cultures. Solid base cultures contain sand, lamp black, or peat in which the root-nodule bacteria are evenly dispersed. These cultures are mixed with water, and the suspension thus formed mixed thoroughly with the seed. The inoculated seed is then dried and sown as soon as possible.

2. *Properties of a Good Culture.* A culture of root-nodule bacteria to be used for inoculation of the seed of a leguminous crop should have the following properties:

a. Contain effective strains: The root-nodule bacteria in the culture must be of the species which will form nodules on the leguminous crop. The bacteria must be a strain, or mixture of strains, which is effective. They must be able to enter into symbiosis with the leguminous plants which they infect in such a manner that the nitrogen fixation which results is ideal for the growth and maximum yield of the crop.

b. Contain a large number of root-nodule bacteria: A culture which contains a large number of effective root-nodule bacteria is more satisfactory, under most conditions, than one which contains a small number. So many factors enter into the determination of the numbers of bacteria required for nodule formation that it is impossible to give even approximations of the numbers required. However, a culture which contains a large number of living bacteria that are highly infective and effective is better than one which contains a small number of root-nodule bacteria.

c. Be freshly prepared: Freshly prepared cultures of root-nodule bacteria contain larger numbers of bacteria than old cultures which have been stored for some time. The bacteria in fresh cultures are more active, i.e., they have greater ability to infect the roots of leguminous plants than bacteria in old cultures.

3. *How Cultures Are Tested.* Cultures of root-nodule bacteria that are available on the market are tested annually by the United States Department of Agriculture and by several different state departments of agriculture or experiment stations. These cultures are tested under greenhouse conditions, and in some instances in the field as well, for their ability to form nodules on the leguminous plants for which they are intended. If a culture is used in a test in the manner prescribed by the manufacturer, and if nodules are formed on the test plants, the culture is considered to be satisfactory. If it fails to produce nodules under these conditions it is graded as unsatisfactory. In Wisconsin, and in several other states, manufacturers of cultures of root-nodule bacteria are licensed by the state department of agriculture. If the manufacturer's product is unsatisfactory in one year's test, his license is canceled until he is able to produce satisfactory cultures. The trend in test-

ing of cultures of root-nodule bacteria is toward determining the effectiveness, i.e., the nitrogen-fixing ability, of the culture in symbiosis with the proper leguminous plant, as well as its ability to form nodules.

4. *Is Inoculation Always Necessary?* In some fields there may be large enough numbers of effective root-nodule bacteria to make inoculation of the seed unnecessary. Such fields are the exception rather than the rule. Root-nodule bacteria which have been introduced into the soil by a preceding crop may be subjected to adverse conditions in the soil. Extreme dryness, high temperatures, lack of organic matter, an acid reaction, bacteriophages, and antagonistic molds and microorganisms all inhibit or kill root-nodule bacteria. As a result, numbers of root-nodule bacteria usually decrease rather than increase in soils under normal conditions.

Because the farmer has no tests which he can use to determine quickly whether or not the soil of any field contains large enough numbers of effective root-nodule bacteria, it is in most cases wise for him to inoculate the seed of every leguminous crop that he sows. By so doing he can be certain that effective root-nodule bacteria form nodules on the roots of each leguminous crop which is grown.

The Return to the Soil of Nitrogen Fixed by Symbiotic Activity

A crop of nodulated leguminous plants may fix from 0 to 200 pounds of nitrogen per acre in one growing season, depending upon the effectiveness of the root-nodule bacteria in the nodules, and upon the various factors that influence plant growth. On the average, a nodulated leguminous crop that is grown under suitable conditions in symbiosis with effective root-nodule bacteria, fixes from 50 to 100 pounds of nitrogen per acre per year. If the crop is plowed under, all of the nitrogen it contains is returned to the soil. The microorganisms of the soil decompose the nitrogenous organic compounds in the plant tissues and produce ammonium salts and nitrates that are available to succeeding crops.

If the leguminous crop is pastured, or made into hay or silage, and the manure from the livestock to which it is fed returned to the soil, from 50 to 80 per cent of the nitrogen of the plants is returned to the soil.

However, if the leguminous crop is harvested and the hay or seed removed, most of the nitrogen in the plants is lost to the soil. Such crops as alfalfa and clover, which have a large root system, retain about one-third of the total nitrogen in their roots. If the tops are removed entirely, there is still enough nitrogen remaining in the roots to just about balance that which the crop removed from the soil. Such crops as peas and soybeans, on the other hand, retain only about one-sixth to one-fourth of the total nitrogen of the plant in their roots. If the tops of these plants are removed entirely there is not enough nitrogen left in the roots to balance that which the crop removed from the soil.

REFERENCES

Allen, O. N., "Inoculate legumes—it pays." *Wis. Agric. Expt. Station, Bulletin 484* (1949).

Fassett, N. C., *The leguminous plants of Wisconsin*. Madison, Wis., University of Wisconsin Press, 1939.

Fred, E. B., Baldwin, I. L., and McCoy, E., "Root-nodule bacteria and leguminous plants." *University of Wisconsin Studies in Science No. 5*. University of Wisconsin Press, Madison, Wis., 1932 (supplement published in 1939).

Virtanen, A. I., *Cattle fodder and human nutrition*. London, Cambridge University Press, 1938.

Wilson, P. W., *The biochemistry of symbiotic nitrogen fixation*. Madison, Wis., University of Wisconsin Press, 1940.

Wilson, P. W., and Burris, R. H., "The mechanism of biological nitrogen-fixation." *Bact. Rev.* (1947), 11:41–73.

Winogradsky, S., *Microbiologie du sol*. Paris, Masson et Cie, 1949.

PART VI

Microbiology of Sewage, Water, and Air

Microorganisms are of great importance in the treatment and disposal of sewage. The successful functioning of the biological systems of sewage treatment and disposal is largely dependent upon the activity and growth of certain kinds of microorganisms. The purely physical or chemical treatment and disposal processes, which are employed to a limited extent, have as one of their main functions the elimination or destruction of microorganisms, or the prevention of their growth.

The suitability of water for human consumption, both from the standpoint of its flavor and its freedom from disease-producing agents, depends to a large extent upon the microorganisms it contains.

Microorganisms in the air are in many instances of no particular significance. But air-borne microorganisms may contaminate foods, sterile culture media, and equipment. It is also possible for certain disease-producing species to be transmitted through the air.

It is the purpose of the chapters that follow to point out the importance of microorganisms in sewage, in water, and in the air.

22. MICROBIOLOGY OF SEWAGE TREATMENT AND DISPOSAL

NATURE OF SEWAGE

Sewage is the used water supply of a home, community, or industry. Domestic sewage varies in quantity and composition from hour to hour and from day to day. Industrial wastes are different from domestic wastes, and the sewage of one industry differs from that of another. All sewage contains organic and inorganic substances which exist either in suspension, in the colloidal state, or in solution. These substances may serve as food for microorganisms; and, although some industrial wastes may be practically sterile, each milliliter of domestic sewage, or of mixed industrial and domestic sewage, usually contains several million microbial cells.

The following outline describes very briefly the nature of a few kinds of industrial wastes.

I. **Packing plant wastes:** wash water containing manure, blood, grease, hair, and bits of flesh; relatively high in nitrogenous organic matter and in substances which may be decomposed slowly by microbial action; contain many microorganisms.

II. **Tannery wastes.**
1. Soak wastes from dried and salted hides: relatively high in nitrogenous organic matter, grease, and hair; contain many microorganisms.
2. Lime wastes from liming pits and drums: very alkaline in reaction; relatively high in nitrogenous organic matter, grease, and hair; contain few microorganisms.
3. Tan yard wastes: acid in reaction; tannates, chromates, and bisulfites present; high in nitrogenous organic matter; contain few microorganisms; very difficult to treat because of color, high solids content, high oxygen demand, and the presence of antiseptic chemicals.

257

III. **Cannery wastes.**
  1. Vegetable canneries: wash water, water used for blanching, and cooling water; vary in composition with vegetables (from peas: high in proteins; from corn: high in carbohydrates); contain many microorganisms.
  2. Fruit canneries: wash water, and cooling water; high in carbohydrates and solids; may be rather acid in reaction; contain few microorganisms.
IV. **Malt house, brewery, and distillery wastes:** wash water from grains and from vats, bottles and pipe lines; high in carbohydrates; contain relatively few microorganisms.
 V. **Wastes from milk plants, cheese factories, creameries, condenseries, and other milk processing industries.**
  1. Milk receiving stations, milk plants, and condenseries: wash water from tanks and cans, vats, pipe lines, etc.; high in lactose, casein, and fats; contain many microorganisms.
  2. Cheese factories and creameries: whey and wash water; high in lactose, casein, and fat; may be acid in reaction; contain many microorganisms.
VI. **Paper mill wastes.**
  1. Sulfite mills: waste sulfite liquors; high in lignin and bisulfites; contain few microorganisms; difficult to treat because of color, high oxygen demand, and the presence of antiseptic chemicals.
  2. Strawboard mills: concentrated waste from beaters containing lime, soil, and organic matter; contains few microorganisms.
  3. Bleach wastes: contain fine cellulose fibers and excess of calcium hypochlorite; difficult to treat because of high organic matter content and presence of antiseptic chemicals.
VII. **Wastes from other industries.**
  1. Oil refineries.
  2. Textile mills.
  3. Coal, coke, and illuminating gas plants.
  4. Synthetic rubber plants.

A "typical" domestic sewage is nearly as difficult to describe as a "typical" industrial waste. Not only the nature of the sewage, but the volume—expressed in gallons per capita per day—varies in different cities. One hundred gallons per capita per day is a rough approximation of the average sewage flow from most of the large cities in the United States. In some cities there are ordinances that require each dwelling unit to be equipped with a grease-trap to remove soaps and fats; in other cities, grease and soaps are allowed to enter the sewers. In some cities a combined system is used to collect and treat both domestic wastes and storm water; in other cities, one system carries the storm water, and a separate system of conduits carries the domestic and industrial wastes. The latter arrangement provides for a more uniform flow and less variation in the composition of domestic sewage. The following outline describes briefly the composition of an "average" domestic sewage.

 I. **Water content:** from 99.8 to 99.95 per cent.
II. **Solids:** from 0.05 to 0.2 per cent.

1. Suspended solids: lignocellulose, cellulose, proteins, fats, and inorganic matter; cells of dead microorganisms.
2. Colloidal solids: starch, proteins, and fats.
3. Dissolved solids: sugars, glycerol, fatty acids, alcohols, sulfates, phosphates, chlorides, urea, ammonium salts, etc.

III. **Microorganisms:**
1. Total: from 500,000 to 20,000,000 per ml.
2. Kinds: largely intestinal bacteria; relatively few bacteria of soil and water origin; mostly nonpathogenic, but pathogens may be present; aerobic, anaerobic, and facultative types of both heterotrophic and autotrophic bacteria; most species mesophilic, but some psychrophiles and thermophiles are always present.

IV. **Reaction:** from pH 6.0 to 8.5, average near pH 7.0.

V. **Gases:** H_2S, CO_2, CH_4, NH_3, and H_2; usually raw sewage is free of dissolved oxygen.

In summary, it may be pointed out that sewage is mostly water, but that it contains enough organic and inorganic matter to provide plenty of food for microorganisms. A large portion of the organic matter in sewage is in the colloidal state; it cannot be removed by filtration, and it will not settle out of suspension. Much of the organic matter is complex in composition and cannot be decomposed rapidly by microorganisms. As a rule, sewage contains large numbers of bacteria of intestinal origin, most of which are able to decompose the organic matter that is present, and some of which may be pathogenic; as well as both autotrophic and heterotrophic bacteria of soil and water origin. The temperature and reaction of sewage are suitable for the growth of the majority of its microbial population.

Objectives of a Sewage Treatment and Disposal System

The chief objective of the use of any system for the treatment and disposal of any type of sewage is to remove or decompose the organic matter so that the final product of the treatment process will not support the growth of heterotrophic microorganisms. If this can be accomplished, the final, liquid product of the disposal process may be added to a river, lake or ocean, or to the soil. Another main objective is to remove or destroy pathogenic microorganisms which may be present in the sewage so as to prevent contamination of supplies of water used for drinking, swimming, or laundry purposes. A third objective, which is difficult to attain with treatment methods now available, is to produce a final effluent that is free from chemicals that will serve as fertilizers for rooted aquatic plants and for algae.

Although it is possible for many kinds of pathogenic microorganisms to be discharged in the feces or urine of infected persons, or to get into sewage from other sources, the causal agents of intestinal diseases are the ones most likely to be spread by sewage. A partial list of these organisms and the disease of human beings caused by each follows:

Salmonella typhosa—Typhoid fever
Salmonella paratyphi—Paratyphoid fever
Salmonella schottmuelleri—Paratyphoid fever
Salmonella enteritidis—Gastrointestinal enteritis
Shigella dysenteriae—Bacillary dysentery
Vibrio comma—Asiatic cholera
Entameba histolytica—Amebic dysentery

Means for prevention of the transmission of these pathogenic microorganisms are presented in Chapters 23, 30, and 31.

METHODS FOR THE DISPOSAL OF UNTREATED SEWAGE

If raw, untreated sewage is discharged into a river or lake, the microorganisms in the sewage, as well as those in the body of water, decompose the organic matter which is added. The decomposition proceeds as it does in soil. The relatively simple, soluble compounds are hydrolyzed and oxidized first; then the complex organic substances are hydrolyzed, and the soluble products formed are at first partially, and then finally completely oxidized. If the body of water is large enough, and if it is not overloaded with sewage, conditions remain aerobic, and decomposition of the organic matter is carried to completion. However, it is difficult to avoid the addition of too much sewage. When this occurs, the oxygen dissolved in the water is used up rapidly by aerobic microorganisms; and, under the resulting anaerobic conditions, anaerobic bacteria cause fermentation and putrefaction with the result that foul odors are produced. The depletion of oxygen causes death of fish and other aquatic animals, and of all green plants in the water. Such a condition ruins the recreational and esthetic values of a body of water, and renders it unfit as a source of drinking water; hence this method for the disposal of untreated sewage is unsatisfactory.

Disposal of sewage by running it onto the soil is in most cases unsatisfactory because the large areas of sandy, well-drained soil required are seldom available. In those few regions where "sewage farming" is practiced, the raw sewage is run onto a large, flat field of sandy soil until the soil is well saturated. After the excess water has drained away, crops may be grown on the fertilized field while the sewage is run onto another nearby field. By rotation of the fields, and control of the flow of sewage, the soil is kept from becoming water-logged and overloaded with organic matter. Sewage farming of this type is practiced near some European cities, and is used in some of the arid regions of the United States, but does not lend itself to widespread adoption.

The seasonal industrial wastes of canning factories in some localities are disposed of by "lagooning." In this process, the cannery wastes are discharged into large, shallow, artificial ponds. The wastes are allowed to undergo slow decomposition in these ponds or lagoons. The liquid portion of the wastes is run into a stream or other body of water during the winter months after most of the organic matter has been decomposed in the lagoons. Such a procedure may be rather odoriferous, but putrefaction can be minimized by adding sodium nitrate to the lagooned wastes. Although lagooning uses large areas of land, it is used because it reduces pollution of streams and lakes, and because any nuisance produced is seasonal.

METHODS OF SEWAGE TREATMENT AND DISPOSAL

The various methods described for the disposal of untreated sewage do not, as a rule, accomplish the objectives of proper treatment and disposal that have been set forth. A great deal of experimental work has been done to develop methods which will produce the desired results. The systems of treatment and disposal which have been put to practical use are of two main types: chemical systems and biological systems.

1. *Chemical Systems.* The procedure employed in most chemical systems of sewage treatment and disposal used at present is to add to the sewage a chemical, or mixture of chemicals, which forms a flocculent precipitate. Following the addition of the flocculating agent, the sewage is run into a large tank through which it flows slowly. Under these conditions, the flocculent precipitate settles to the bottom, and carries with it much of the suspended and colloidal material of the sewage, including most of the bacteria which it contains. The liquid portion, which flows over a baffle at the end of the tank, is then run into a body of water or onto the soil; or, if further treatment is required, it is run into a biological treatment system. The floc-forming chemicals used most frequently in chemical treatment systems are alum or iron salts, such as $FeCl_3$, or $FeSO_4$ + lime (CaO). The lime reacts with the alum or iron salts to form a flocculent precipitate of $Al(OH)_3$ or $Fe(OH)_3$. Chemical sedimentation is comparatively rapid and requires little space. However, chemical systems usually are more costly to operate than biological systems; produce a greater volume of sludge, which is difficult to dispose of; and require careful control if they are to be operated efficiently. Despite these drawbacks, chemical systems are useful in the treatment of seasonal industrial wastes and in locations where compactness of treatment facilities is necessary.

2. *Biological Systems.* In biological systems of sewage treatment and disposal, microorganisms cause the chief chemical and physical changes involved in the purification process. There are at present four main types of biological systems of sewage treatment and disposal in use: septic tank, followed by a system of tile drains or a dry well; Imhoff tank or settling tank, followed by a trickling filter; trickling filter alone; activated sludge process.

a. Septic tank + tile drain or dry well system. A longitudinal section of a septic tank is shown in Figure 50. The influent raw sewage enters the tank, which is submerged below the frost line in the soil, and passes under a baffle. Suspended solids sink to the bottom of the tank to form a sludge. Microorganisms in the sludge and in the liquids above it first hydrolyze, then ferment and putrefy the organic matter which is present. The gases CH_4,

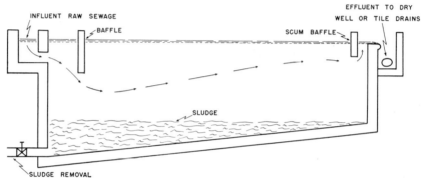

FIGURE 50.   Longitudinal section of a septic tank.

CO_2, H_2, and H_2S are produced and released from solution; hence the tank must be equipped with a vent to allow their escape. A scum collects on the surface of the liquid and helps to maintain anaerobic conditions. The tank must be equipped with a scum baffle to prevent the outflow of solids in the scum. If the tank is large enough, if the flow of sewage through it is slow, and if the temperature is suitable for growth, microorganisms which are present hydrolyze, ferment, and putrefy the less complex organic substances in the sewage with comparative rapidity. The more complex organic matter, which is resistant to decomposition, settles to the bottom of the tank and is decomposed slowly. The deeper layers of sludge, after becoming stabilized, i.e., decomposed to the point that further action of microorganisms under the conditions existing in the tank causes very little if any change, may be removed. This stabilized sludge is much like peat; it can be dried, pulverized, and used as a fertilizer. In a properly designed and operated septic tank, sludge accumulates very slowly because the microorganisms decompose all but the most resistant organic matter in the sewage, and hence the amount of residual sludge is not great.

The liquid effluent from the septic tank is comparatively free from solid matter owing to the hydrolysis, fermentation, and putrefaction which have occurred in the tank. In the liquid effluent may be found ammonium salts of organic acids, along with alcohols, amines, amino acids, glycerol, fatty acids, H_2S, and other soluble products of the hydrolysis, fermentation, and putrefaction of the organic compounds in the sewage. The effluent contains little or no dissolved oxygen, and is capable of supporting the growth of microorganisms; it cannot be added without harm to a stream or pond.

The effluent from the septic tank may be run into a dry well, which is about 6 to 8 feet in diameter and 10 or 12 feet deep; it is lined with brick, concrete blocks or loose stone, and covered with a wood or concrete lid which is fitted with a vent. The lining of the dry well is loosely laid to allow seepage of the liquid into the soil; the vent on its cover allows the entrance of air. When the effluent from the septic tank flows slowly into the dry well, the microorganisms present, acting under the aerobic conditions that exist, oxidize the dissolved organic substances, ammonium salts, and sulfides in the effluent. Thus, nonnitrogenous organic matter is oxidized by various microorganisms to CO_2 and H_2O. Nitrogenous organic matter is ammonified and then nitrified; hence nitrates, CO_2 and H_2O are produced as the final products of oxidation. Sulfides are oxidized to sulfates. The liquid which seeps into the soil from the dry well contains completely oxidized inorganic compounds which are incapable of supporting the growth of heterotrophic microorganisms.

In locations where the level of ground water is high, or where the subsoil is too compact to allow use of a dry well, a system of loosely laid tile drains may be used to carry away the effluent from the septic tank. Tile is laid near the surface of the soil in such a manner that a small space exists at the joints through which the effluent may seep into gravel, cinders or coarse soil. Under the aerobic conditions thus provided, microorganisms oxidize the soluble substances in the effluent in the same manner as in the dry well. The number of lines of tile and the length of each line are determined by the volume of effluent and by the opportunities for aeration and seepage.

Despite the fact that conditions in the septic tank and dry well or tile drains are most unfavorable for the survival of pathogenic bacteria, there is an outside chance that if pathogens are present in the raw sewage, a few might persist and gain entrance to the water supply. For this reason, the septic tank and dry well or tile drains must be so located that the oxidized effluent which seeps into the soil will not get into the supply of drinking water.

b. Imhoff tank or settling tank + trickling filter system. The microbiological principles involved in the operation of an Imhoff tank or settling tank +

trickling filter system are in many respects similar to those of the septic tank + tile drain or dry well system. The Imhoff tank or settling tank + trickling filter system is designed to treat larger volumes of sewage than the septic tank + tile drain or dry well system can handle effectively.

A cross section of an Imhoff tank is shown in Figure 51. Such tanks may vary in size, but one designed to treat about 2,000,000 gallons of sewage every 24 hours is approximately 20 feet deep, 30 feet wide, and 100 feet long. The raw sewage enters at the end and flows slowly through the "flowing-through" chambers. Although the entire tank is filled with sewage, the only liquid which is in motion is that in these chambers. Suspended solids

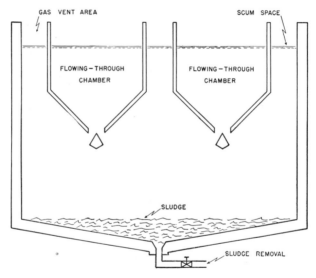

FIGURE 51. Cross section of a double chamber Imhoff tank.

settle through the slots in the bottoms of these chambers to the bottom of the tank. These slots are protected by wedge-shaped structures that keep gases which bubble up from the decomposing sludge from passing into liquid in the flowing-through chambers. The gases bubble up through the liquid in the gas vent areas. The scum which collects on the surface of these areas is composed of particles of sludge brought to the surface by the gas bubbles.

Anaerobic and facultative microorganisms in the sludge, and in the liquid in the tanks, hydrolyze, ferment, and putrefy the organic matter in the sewage. The chemical changes which they cause are similar to those which take place in the septic tank. The sludge, composed of the most resistant organic substances, is decomposed slowly, and eventually becomes stabilized. It is then removed, dried in a shallow layer on a well-drained drying bed, and used as fertilizer.

The liquid effluent from the Imhoff tank contains colloidal organic matter, along with the products of hydrolysis, fermentation, and putrefaction produced by the action of microorganisms in the tank. This liquid is devoid of dissolved oxygen, and must be given further treatment before it can be added without harm to a body of water. To accomplish the oxidation of organic matter, ammonium salts, and sulfides which it contains, and to remove its content of colloidal substances, it is sprayed onto a trickling filter.

In many sewage treatment plants a settling tank is substituted for the Imhoff tank. The settling tank is long, narrow, and about 8 to 12 feet deep. Sewage is caused to flow slowly through the settling tank so that 50 to 70 per cent of the solids will settle out of suspension. The settled solids are removed at frequent intervals from the bottom of the settling tank, and are pumped to a separate sludge digestion tank. The liquid effluent from the settling tank, similar in composition to that from the Imhoff tank, is sprayed onto a trickling filter to accomplish its further purification.

The trickling filter is a large bed of coarse rock about six feet in depth. The surfaces of these rocks, which are from one to three inches in diameter, become covered with a gelatinous film of microbial growth as the effluent from the Imhoff or settling tanks is sprayed onto the filter. Aerobic heterotrophic and autotrophic bacteria and many kinds of protozoa make up this film. As the effluent from the Imhoff tank or settling tank is sprayed onto the trickling filter, the liquid absorbs some oxygen from the air, and as it seeps slowly through the bed of crushed rock it draws oxygen from the atmosphere into the filter. The trickling filter cannot be sprayed continuously with effluent because it would become overloaded with water and organic matter, and anaerobic conditions would result. To preserve aerobic conditions, the effluent is sprayed onto the trickling filter intermittently; a "rest period" is allowed after each application of effluent in order to maintain aerobic conditions. As the effluent seeps down through the filter, most of the colloidal organic matter and microbial cells which it contains are adsorbed and held by the gelatinous microbial film on the rocks. The tremendous number of microorganisms which make up the flora and fauna of this microbial film hydroylze and oxidize the organic matter in the effluent; and oxidize its ammonium salts to nitrites and nitrates, and its sulfides to sulfates. Figure 52 shows photographs of settling tanks and of a trickling filter in operation.

The effluent from the trickling filter contains dissolved oxygen, chlorides, carbonates and bicarbonates, nitrates, sulfates, and phosphates. The very small amount of organic matter which it contains is composed chiefly of bits of microbial film which have sloughed off from the rocks of the filter. This

A

B

FIGURE 52. A typical settling tank-trickling filter sewage treatment system.

A. Primary settling tanks. Solids settle out as the sewage flows slowly through these tanks. Note the layer of scum on the surface of the sewage in the foreground. The sludge which settles to the bottom of these tanks goes into the large cylindrical sludge digestion tanks in the background.

B. Trickling filter. The effluent from the settling tanks is sprayed intermittently onto the bed of rocks where aerobic microorganisms completely oxidize the organic matter in the liquid.

effluent is run into a final settling tank or clarifier, through which it flows slowly. In the clarifier, the organic matter in the effluent settles out of suspension. The settled organic matter is then run into a sludge digester, which is a large tank in which slow, anaerobic decomposition occurs. The liquid effluent from the clarifier contains little organic matter, usually less than 100,000 bacteria per ml., small amounts of nitrates, sulfates, phosphates, chlorides, and dissolved oxygen. It may be added to coarse, well-drained soil or to a river, lake, or ocean because it is relatively free from organic matter. If it is to be run into a river, lake, or ocean, it may be chlorinated (from two to five parts per million of chlorine added) in order to destroy pathogens which might be present, and to oxidize organic matter remaining in the effluent.

c. Trickling filter system. The disposal of sewage containing only organic matter which is readily hydrolyzed and oxidized may be accomplished by means of a trickling filter which is operated intermittently, or a "high-rate" filter. Wastes from malt houses, breweries, milk plants, condenseries, creameries, cheese factories, and many canning factories may be treated in this manner. If the sewage to be treated is acid in reaction, it must be neutralized with lye or lime before it is sprayed onto the filter. Most kinds of microorganisms in the filter, particularly those responsible for nitrification, require a near neutral reaction. After suitable clarification, the effluent from the trickling filter may be run onto a well-drained soil, or into a river or lake. The regular trickling filter is operated intermittently with a dosage rate of from 2,000,000 to 5,000,000 gallons of sewage per acre of filter surface per day. High-rate filters, which employ recirculation of part of the treated sewage, are operated at a rate 10 to 20 times higher.

d. Activated sludge system. The activated sludge system is the newest, and produces the highest degree of purification of the various biological systems of sewage treatment. Figure 53 is a schematic flow diagram of an activated sludge system.

The influent raw sewage flows first through a series of coarse screens and then through a tank in order to remove the large solids and grit it contains. Next, it flows through a tank which allows the grease to rise to the surface, from which it can be removed mechanically. The raw sewage from which grit, large solids, and grease have been removed is then caused to flow slowly through deep, long, narrow primary settling tanks. In these tanks from 50 to 70 per cent of the suspended organic matter settles to the bottom; upon settling it is pumped into the sludge digestion tank.

The liquid effluent from the primary settling tanks flows into an inoculation chamber: a small tank in which "activated" sludge (sludge from the final settling tank) is added to the primary settling tank effluent to form a

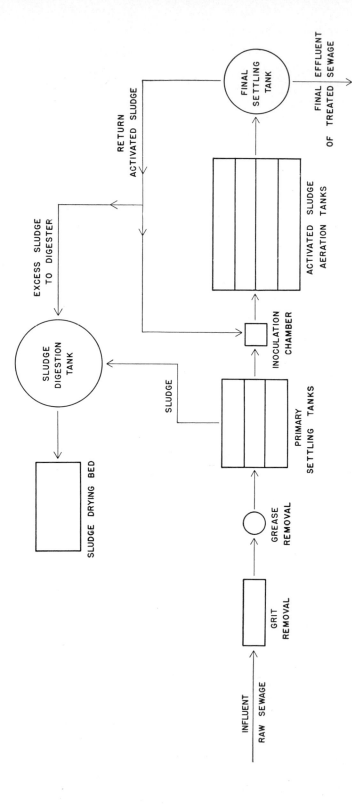

FIGURE 53. Schematic flow diagram of an activated sludge system.

mixture containing about 80 per cent by volume of effluent and 20 per cent of activated sludge. This sludge-sewage mixture is then pumped or caused to flow into the activated sludge aeration tanks. These may be long, narrow, deep tanks into which air is introduced through porous "filtrose" plates or carborundum cylinders located along one side of the bottom of each tank. Another type of aeration tank often used in smaller activated sludge disposal systems is either rectangular or circular, and is fitted with a stirring device which keeps the sludge-sewage mixture suspended and in constant motion. With mechanical agitation, maintenance of aerobic conditions in the sludge-sewage mixture is accomplished by means of oxygen absorbed from the atmosphere. In both types of aeration tanks the activities of microorganisms and the physical and chemical changes which occur are believed to be similar.

The activated sludge consists of flocculent masses of microbial cells on which particles of sewage become adsorbed during agitation and aeration of the mixture. Many kinds of heterotrophic and autotrophic, aerobic and facultative bacteria make up the gelatinous mass of these sludge particles; many kinds of protozoa, particularly *Ciliata* and some *Mastigophora* and *Sarcodina,* are also present. Although the microbial flora and fauna of activated sludge needs to be studied further, it may be assumed that it is made up of microorganisms similar in many respects to those comprising the film of microbial growth that covers the rocks of a trickling filter.

Under the aerobic conditions which exist due to aeration, and at the temperatures of from 55° to 70° F. usually found in aeration tanks, growth and aerobic respiration of the microorganisms in the flocs proceed rapidly. In the five to eight hours that the sewage-activated sludge mixture usually is aerated, practically all colloidal material is removed from the sewage, and its content of readily oxidizable organic matter is oxidized by the microorganisms of the activated sludge. Figure 54 shows an aeration tank in operation and an empty tank.

From the aeration tanks, the liquid which now contains settleable particles of activated sludge flows into a final settling tank. As it flows slowly through this tank or clarifier, the flocs of activated sludge settle to the bottom of the tank, and the water flows over baffles into pipes that drain into a creek, river, lake, or ocean. This liquid effluent is practically free from organic matter, contains a relatively low concentration of chlorides, carbonates and bicarbonates, nitrates, sulfates, and phosphates, and usually contains less than 100,000 bacteria per ml. It contains large amounts of dissolved oxygen. It may be chlorinated before being run into a body of water in order to prevent contamination of the water with pathogens which might be present.

Part of the sludge which settles out in the final settling tank is returned to the inoculating chamber to be mixed with raw sewage. The remainder of

A

B

FIGURE 54.   Aeration tanks in the activated sludge system.

    A. Aeration tank in operation. Air is pumped rapidly into the sewage that has been inoculated with activated sludge. The aerobic microorganisms in the activated sludge then cause rapid oxidation of the organic matter.

    B. An empty aeration tank. Many small bubbles are formed by forcing the air through the long porous plates visible in the shadow to the left at the bottom of the tank.

the sludge is caused to flow into the sludge digestion tank. In this tank the sludge is allowed to undergo a slow, anaerobic decomposition similar to that which occurs in the bottom of a septic tank or Imhoff tank. After the sludge remains in the digester tank for 30 to 90 days, and becomes stabilized, it is pumped onto the sludge drying beds, allowed to dry, and sold as fertilizer.

In the sewage treatment plant in Madison, Wisconsin, gas that is produced by the anaerobic fermentation and putrefaction of sludge in the sludge digestion tank is collected, stored, and used for several different purposes. Gas storage tanks are visible in the background of Figure 52. The gas contains approximately 70 per cent of CH_4, 28 per cent of CO_2 and 2 per cent of a mixture of H_2, H_2S, and N_2. It has a high heat value and is used for heating purposes and gas burners in the laboratory. It also is used as fuel for large internal combustion gas motors which provide power for the blowers; air from these blowers is used in the aeration tanks.

In the Milwaukee, Wisconsin, and in the Chicago, Illinois, Southwest sewage treatment plants, the excess sludge from the settling tanks is removed by filtration, dried with heat, and sold as fertilizer. These treatment plants do not employ a sludge digestion unit.

The microbiological, chemical, and engineering problems involved in the treatment and disposal of sewage are far from being solved. None of the methods described is perfect. A great deal of work remains to be done in order to obtain a full understanding of the microbiology and chemistry of the various sewage treatment processes, and to apply such knowledge in the improvement of the methods now available and in the development of new procedures. The best methods now available for the treatment and disposal of sewage produce an effluent that is relatively free from organic matter and microorganisms, and contains an abundance of dissolved oxygen. It will not support growth of heterotrophic microorganisms. It does, however, contain nitrates, phosphates, and sulfates which serve as nutrients for algae and aquatic plants.

REFERENCES

American Public Health Association, *Standard methods for the examination of water and sewage* (9th ed.). N. Y., American Public Health Association, 1946.

Babbitt, H. E., *Sewerage and sewage treatment* (6th ed.). N. Y., Wiley, 1947.

Ehlers, V. M., and Steel, E. W., *Municipal and rural sanitation* (4th ed.). N. Y., McGraw-Hill, 1950.

Hardenbergh, W. A., *Sewerage and sewage treatment* (3rd ed.). Scranton, Pa., International Textbook Co., 1950.

Imhoff, K., and Fair, G., *Sewage treatment*. N. Y., Wiley, 1940.

Rockey, J. W., and Simons, J. W., "Sewage and garbage disposal on the farm." *U. S. Dept. Agric. Farmers Bulletin No. 1950* (1946).

23. MICROBIOLOGY OF WATER AND AIR

MICROBIOLOGY OF WATER

Sources of Microorganisms in Water

In nature, water is seldom sterile. Water vapor in clouds that exist at high altitudes probably is sterile, but when it condenses to form rain, hail, sleet, or snow it becomes contaminated with microorganisms from the air. Upon reaching the earth it is further contaminated with microorganisms from the soil. Surface waters of rivers, lakes, and oceans therefore contain microorganisms from both air and soil; they may also contain microorganisms of sewage origin.

As surface waters seep through the soil, most of the microorganisms which they contain are removed by the filtering action of the soil, but the removal by filtration is seldom, if ever, complete. For this reason, water in shallow wells and springs, and even in deep wells, usually contains a small number of microorganisms. Supplies of subsurface water may also become contaminated with microorganisms of sewage origin.

Existence and Growth of Microorganisms in Water

Surface waters as a rule provide a better environment for the growth of microorganisms than do deep waters. Surface waters usually contain more organic matter, which serves as the main food for most kinds of microorganisms, and their temperature is generally more favorable for growth than that of subsurface waters. Many of the bacteria, algae, and protozoa, and a very few species of molds, which gain entrance to surface water are able to grow

272

and reproduce in it, and hence make up its normal population of microorganisms. Those microorganisms which grow in water cause decomposition
of organic matter and changes in inorganic compounds that are present, in
much the same manner as do microorganisms in the soil. Many species of
cocci, nonspore-forming bacilli, spirilla, actinomycetes, spirochetes, sheathed
or stalked bacteria, and other alga-like bacteria may be found growing in
surface waters. Protozoa, which consume bacteria as their main food, and
algae, which are capable of photosynthesis, are nearly always present in
surface waters.

Even in relatively cold subsurface waters that are practically free from
organic matter, small numbers of bacteria may grow slowly. The normal
microbial population of subsurface waters is usually smaller, and is made up
of fewer kinds of microorganisms than the normal population of surface
water.

Most of the microorganisms which gain entrance to water are unable to
grow in it. They may exist for only a short time if they are nonspore-formers,
but the spores of spore-forming species may live for months or years. Disease-producing microorganisms which get into water from sewage are unable to grow, and usually die in a comparatively short time. In general,
pathogens survive for a longer time in cold, clean water than in water which
is relatively warm and contains an abundance of organic matter.

Growth of the microorganisms which make up the normal microbial population of water may make it less fit for human consumption. If sheathed,
or slime-forming bacteria grow in water, they are apt to produce unsightly,
flocculent masses which are difficult to remove. The growth of these organisms, and of certain algae and protozoa may produce undesirable flavors and
odors in the water. Water stored in open reservoirs often becomes unsatisfactory for drinking purposes due to the growth of algae and protozoa which
contain chlorophyll. When these organisms die, they are decomposed by
bacteria, with the result that the water smells and tastes bad. These organisms are not known to produce disease in human beings, but their growth
in water used for drinking purposes is undesirable.

Contamination of Water with Pathogenic Microorganisms

Water used for drinking purposes may, as a rule, become contaminated
with pathogenic microorganisms from only one source, i.e., sewage. Water
in swimming pools and near bathing beaches may be contaminated directly
by infected persons, but practically the only way in which pathogens may
gain entrance to supplies of drinking water is by means of sewage pollution.
Sewage from normal persons is free from pathogenic microorganisms, but

as pointed out in Chapter 22, sewage from cases or carriers of typhoid fever, paratyphoid fever, enteritis, bacillary dysentery, amebic dysentery, or Asiatic cholera contains the causative microorganism of the specific infection. Transmission of disease-producing microorganisms by water is discussed in Chapters 30 and 31.

The use by persons or communities of rivers or lakes for the disposal of **untreated** human sewage renders such water unfit for human consumption. A sewage treatment and disposal system that allows seepage of sewage into a well or spring makes water from these sources unsafe for human consumption.

Purification of Water

If a supply of water which is free from sewage pollution cannot be obtained, one or more of several procedures may be employed to purify polluted water, and thereby make it safe for human consumption.

1. *Protection of the Water Supply against Sewage Pollution.* Proper treatment and disposal of sewage removes the most dangerous source of pollution. Cities may be required by law to install sewage treatment plants which will yield effluents that are free from pathogenic microorganisms. Unfortunately there are no means other than persuasion by public health authorities to induce individuals, families, or small communities to dispose of their sewage in such a manner that their own or their neighbor's water supply will not become polluted. Proper installation and operation of septic tank-dry well systems of sewage treatment and disposal, or proper construction and location of privies would aid in the prevention of pollution of the supplies of drinking water for rural homes and communities.

If deep wells are protected by a watertight casing, it is difficult for sewage to seep into the deep layers of soil from which the water is pumped. Watertight concrete covers on wells prevent the entrance of microorganisms of sewage origin that may be present in surface washings. The watershed, i.e., the area from which water to be used for human consumption drains into a stream, lake, or reservoir, may be inspected, and all sources of sewage pollution removed.

Removal of sources of pollution, and protection against sewage pollution, are the first steps to be taken in the purification of a supply of water.

2. *Sedimentation.* Most kinds of microorganisms in water tend to settle out of suspension when the water is allowed to stand undisturbed for a short period of time. The settling of microorganisms is hastened by the presence of flocculent material which adsorbs microbial cells on its surfaces and carries them more rapidly to the bottom. Sedimentation occurs under natural

conditions when the rate of flow of a river is reduced, or when it empties into a lake. It may be induced artificially by the storage of water in reservoirs or settling basins. The addition of alum or iron salts to water as it flows into a settling tank results in the formation of a flocculent precipitate which settles rapidly and carries with it the majority of the microorganisms and other suspended solids that are present.

Sedimentation alone will not completely purify polluted water, but will reduce the "load" of microorganisms it contains. It is often employed as the first stage of a purification system.

3. *Filtration.* As water seeps through soil many of the microorganisms it contains are removed by filtration. Modifications of this natural process are widely used in purification systems. In general, two main types of filters are employed in filtration of water. Slow sand filters are the older of the two types; rapid sand filters are a comparatively recent development.

Slow sand filters cover a comparatively large area. They are constructed of successive layers of rock, gravel, coarse sand, and fine sand. The water seeps through the filter slowly. Bacteria, protozoa, and algae in the water, along with other suspended solids, are caught in the deep surface layers of fine sand. As operation of the filter continues, a gelatinous mass of microbial cells and organic matter covers its surface and fills in the pore spaces of the fine sand. This mass increases the efficiency of the filter in so far as removal of microorganisms is concerned, but soon slows down the rate of flow; when this occurs the surface of the filter must be cleaned. For a short time after removal of this gelatinous mass, water flows through the filter with comparative rapidity, but not as many microorganisms are removed by filtration as when the filter was partly clogged. As a rule, slow sand filters are operated at a rate of flow of approximately 3,000,000 gallons of water per acre of filter surface per 24 hours.

Because slow sand filters occupy a large area and vary in efficiency, they are being replaced with rapid sand filters, which normally are operated at a rate of flow of 125,000,000 gallons of water per acre of filter surface per 24 hours. These rapid filters are constructed in batteries so that some of them can be kept in operation while others are being cleaned. A coagulant such as alum (which forms $Al(OH)_3$ in alkaline water) or $FeSO_4$ (which forms $Fe(OH)_3$ in alkaline water) is added to the water to be filtered. After thorough mixing, the water containing the coagulant is allowed to flow slowly through a settling tank in which most of the flocculent precipitate settles out of suspension, carrying with it many microorganisms. The effluent from the settling tank is then allowed to flow by gravity, or in some cases is forced under pressure, through a layer of fine sand underlaid with coarse gravel. As the water flows through the filter, the flocculent precipitate it contains is retained by the surface layers of sand. This creates a gelatinous mass through which the water must flow. When the filter becomes clogged, the flow of water through it is reversed in order to wash away the precipitated coagulant and bacteria. While some units of the battery of filters are being washed, the others remain in operation. Figure 55 is a diagrammatic drawing of a rapid sand filter.

Properly operated sand filters remove from 90 to 99 per cent of the microorganisms in water. While filters have been used for years to purify large supplies of water, their use for the purification of the small volume of water

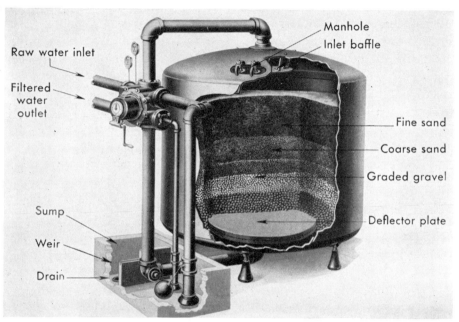

FIGURE 55. A vertical rapid sand filter. Water is forced under pressure through successive layers of fine sand, coarse sand, and graded gravel. Pressure filters are smaller than gravity filters because less area is needed for the same volume of water. (Courtesy of The Permutit Company, New York.)

consumed by one or a few families is not common. Filters must be operated with care by trained men; they cannot be put into operation and expected to function indefinitely without further care.

Filtration is seldom relied upon as the only means or the final step in purification because it does not remove all of the microorganisms from water. It does, however, remove most of the microorganisms and suspended organic matter from water, and therefore facilitates its final purification.

4. *Chlorination.* The most widely used final treatment in the purification of large supplies of drinking water is chlorination. This usually is accomplished by the addition of chlorine gas to water which has been purified

naturally or artificially by sedimentation or filtration, or by a combination of these processes. Ammonia is often added along with chlorine in order to cause the formation of monochloramine, which decomposes slowly and prevents rapid loss of the chlorine. The mode of action of chlorine, monochloramine, hypochlorites, and chloramine compounds, all of which may be used in water purification, is described in Chapter 10. Purification of water with chlorine or chlorine compounds is dependent upon many factors, the most important of which are: (a) concentration of "available chlorine" and time of action; (b) numbers and kinds of microorganisms present; (c) amount of organic matter; (d) hydrogen-ion concentration (pH); (e) temperature.

Water which contains few microorganisms, and is free from organic matter can be purified by the addition of a very small amount of chlorine. For example, enough chlorine to provide 0.2 parts per million of available chlorine is all that is needed to purify the artesian well water of the City of Madison, Wisconsin. If larger numbers of microorganisms or larger quantities of organic matter are present, more chlorine must be added. The practice in most water purification plants is to add sufficient chlorine to the water to provide a residual of available chlorine of approximately 0.1 p.p.m. The residual chlorine is defined as the concentration of available chlorine remaining in the water 20 minutes after its addition to the water. Maintenance of a suitable quantity of residual chlorine provides assurance that sufficient chlorine has been added to kill susceptible microorganisms, and also provides a measure of protection against possible secondary contamination.

Chlorine does not kill all the microorganisms present in water; Gram-positive bacteria, the spores of spore-forming bacteria, and encysted protozoa are resistant to the concentrations of chlorine usually employed. But the pathogenic bacteria most frequently encountered in water are nonspore-forming, Gram-negative species which are relatively susceptible to chlorine. In the concentrations used (seldom more than 2 parts per million of "available chlorine") chlorine is not harmful to human beings or to animals.

5. *Ultraviolet Radiations.* Water which is free from suspended organic matter, and which contains relatively few microorganisms, may be purified by exposure to ultraviolet radiations. This treatment is often used on bottled waters because it imparts no flavor to the water. It is subject to the limitations pointed out in Chapter 10.

6. *Boiling.* Since the pathogenic microorganisms most likely to be present in water are nonspore-formers, water may be purified by boiling for ten minutes. This does not sterilize the water, but serves only to kill pathogens and vegetative cells of other microorganisms which are present.

7. *Ozonation.* Ozone (O_3) is used to some extent in the purification of water supplies. Ozone has been used extensively in some European coun-

tries, but has not, until recently, been employed on a large scale in the United States. It is probable that ozone is effective because it decomposes to form nascent oxygen (O) and O_2. The nascent oxygen is a powerful oxidizing agent. Ozonation is comparatively expensive and provides no residual of disinfectant in the water following treatment. It has, however, the advantage of freedom from objectionable flavors or odors.

Determination of the Suitability of Water for Human Consumption

Water to be used for drinking purposes, and for washing utensils and equipment which come in contact with foods, should be free from suspended matter, undesirable tastes or odors, harmful chemicals, and pathogenic microorganisms. Such water is often designated as "pure" water to distinguish it from that which is "impure" because of its content of harmful substances or microorganisms. Organoleptic tests alone are insufficient for the determination of the purity of water. A sample of water may be clear and sparkling, free from objectionable tastes and odors, but if it contains even a small number of pathogenic microorganisms, it is impure.

Various chemical tests may be used to detect the presence of chlorides, ammonium salts, nitrites, and nitrates in water. These substances may get into water from sewage, but since they may also come from soil or from treated sewage that is free from pathogens, their value as indicators of dangerous sewage pollution is not great. Chemical tests are employed mainly to detect the presence of lead, copper, iron, manganese, or other salts that may occasionally be present in sufficient quantities to be harmful.

Bacteriological tests are relied upon to provide most information of value in the determination of the purity of water. Such tests usually are made by a state, county, or municipal public health laboratory; procedures prescribed by the American Public Health Association in *Standard Methods for the Analysis of Water and Sewage* are employed in these tests.

Water to be tested must be representative of the supply. The sample must be taken in a sterile container under conditions that exclude contamination from external sources. The water must be analyzed as soon as possible after the sample is taken; the time between filling the sample bottle and the beginning of the analysis should not be longer than 10 or 12 hours. The sample must be kept at a temperature of from 6° to 10° C. during storage or transportation in order to prevent changes in its microbial population.

In the routine bacteriological analysis of water no attempt is made to detect specific pathogenic microorganisms. Pathogens gain entrance to water through sewage pollution, and because they make up only a minority of the total microbial population of polluted water it is difficult to isolate them in pure culture and identify them positively. In addition, the pathogens possess few outstanding characteristics by which they may be distinguished from nonpathogenic microorganisms which will always be present in larger numbers in polluted water. But if the water is polluted with sewage it will always contain **coliform bacteria** (aerobic, nonspore-forming, Gram-negative bacilli which ferment lactose with the production of gas and acids; classified in the genera *Escherichia* and *Aerobacter*). In addition, water polluted with sewage usually contains lactose-fermenting bacteria of the genera *Clostridium* and *Streptococcus*.

Because coliform bacteria are always present in relatively large numbers in sewage, because they may be detected with comparative ease, and because purification procedures which cause their elimination or destruction usually are equally effective against pathogens, the routine bacteriological analysis of water is concerned mainly with testing for the coliform group of bacteria. The test to determine the presence of coliform bacteria is known as the **presumptive test.** It is performed by inoculating Durham fermentation tubes of lactose broth (0.3 per cent beef extract, 0.5 per cent peptone, 1 per cent lactose; pH 6.7–7.0) with measured quantities of water. The inoculated tubes are then incubated at 37° C. and examined to determine whether or not gas is formed in the lactose broth after 24 hours' and again after 48 hours' incubation. If gas is formed it collects in the inverted inner tube of the Durham fermentation tube. Production of gas in 24 hours is a **positive** test for coliform bacteria, and is accepted as evidence that the water is polluted with sewage. If no gas is formed in 24 hours, but is present after 48 hours' incubation the test is **doubtful;** if no gas is formed in 48 hours, the test is **negative,** and it is assumed that the water is free from coliform bacteria, and hence from sewage.

A doubtful test may be confirmed by streaking eosin-methylene blue agar plates with a loopful of broth from the tube of lactose broth inoculated with the least amount of water in which gas was formed in 48 hours but not 24 hours. The formation of colonies typical of coliform bacteria (either discrete, circular, slightly raised, dark-colored colonies of the *E. coli* type or large, circular, convex, watery, pink or lavender colonies of the *A. aerogenes* type) on the eosin-methylene blue agar after 18 to 24 hours' incubation at 37° C. confirms a doubtful presumptive test, and indicates sewage pollution of the water. To complete the test, cells in typical coliform colonies on the eosin-methylene blue agar plates are transferred to Durham fermentation tubes of lactose broth and to nutrient agar slants. Production of gas in the lactose broth and the growth of Gram-negative, nonspore-forming bacilli on the agar slants provides final evidence that the gas formed in the original Durham tubes of lactose broth was produced by coliform bacteria in the water that was added to the tubes.

The total number of bacteria in water is also estimated in the routine bacteriological analysis performed in many laboratories. Water from deep wells or water that has been purified should contain a small number of bacteria, usually under 100 per ml. If a relatively large number of bacteria is found in water from deep wells or in purified water, it is an indication that the well is polluted, or that the purification procedure is inadequate.

Although the bacteriological methods employed in the routine analysis of water to determine its suitability for human consumption are not very exact, the results which they yield are of practical public health significance. Water which is condemned because it gives a positive presumptive test may not contain pathogenic microorganisms, but the fact that it contains bacteria which produce gas from lactose is evidence that the possibility exists for pathogens to be present. Condemnation of water on such evidence errs on the safe side. The margin of safety thus established is one reason why so few epidemics of infectious diseases may be traced to water supplies that are tested frequently and graded as satisfactory only when they are free from bacteria that might come from sewage.

Water to be used for certain industrial purposes must be free from microorganisms or dissolved chemicals which might cause undesirable changes in the process or product. In addition, water for many industrial purposes must be safe for human consumption.

Microbiology of Air

The presence of microorganisms in air is almost entirely accidental. Air is relatively dry and contains little or no food for microorganisms. The cells of microorganisms are heavier than air and tend to settle out in the absence of currents which keep them in suspension. The ultraviolet rays of direct sunlight are germicidal. Rain, hail, snow, and sleet wash microorganisms from the air. Yet in spite of these adverse conditions, air as a rule contains at least a small number of microorganisms. They may exist as free, dry cells or spores, but more commonly they are found in and on dust. Microorganisms may also exist in the air for relatively short periods of time in droplets ejected by coughing or sneezing.

Of the different kinds of microorganisms that exist in air, bacteria as a rule are the most numerous, and there are more mold spores than yeasts. But the numbers and kinds of organisms in the air are determined largely by the sources of contamination and the opportunities which exist for cells and spores to be carried into the air.

Destruction or Removal of Air-Borne Microorganisms

Microorganisms in the air may be removed or killed through the use of one or more of the agencies which operate under natural conditions: settling; washing; and effect of ultraviolet light. In addition, filtration or various chemical treatments may be employed to remove or destroy air-borne microorganisms.

In the laboratory, tubes and flasks that are plugged with cotton before sterilization remain sterile because air which is drawn into them after sterilization is filtered through the sterile cotton. This principle of filtration is also used in some air-conditioning installations; for example those used for operating rooms. The wearing of a gauze mask over the nose and mouth is another application of the principle of filtration; in this case it is designed to prevent microorganisms in droplets from leaving or entering the respiratory system.

In air-conditioning and ventilating units air is often passed through sprays of water in order to wash it free of dust and microorganisms. Solutions of disinfectants are used in some air-washing installations.

Mercury vapor lamps which produce ultraviolet rays are often placed in refrigerators or operating rooms in an attempt to kill microorganisms that exist in the air.

It is also possible to kill many kinds of air-borne microorganisms with aerosols (clouds of finely divided particles) of disinfectant materials. Triethylene glycol and propylene glycol have been used for this purpose because they are relatively noninjurious to human beings and yet have comparatively high disinfectant activity.

Development of new procedures to remove or kill air-borne microorganisms, and work toward the perfection of the methods now in use have been stimulated by the increased use of air-circulating and conditioning equipment. The importance of air-borne microorganisms in relation to food preservation, food spoilage, certain industrial processes, and infectious diseases will be pointed out in the chapters to follow.

REFERENCES

WATER

American Public Health Association, *Standard methods for the analysis of water and sewage* (9th ed.). N. Y., American Public Health Association, 1946.

Ehlers, V. M., and Steel, E. W., *Municipal and rural sanitation* (2nd ed.). N. Y.,
  McGraw-Hill, 1937.
Prescott, S. C., Winslow, C. E. A., and McCrady, Mac H. *Water bacteriology* (6th
  ed.). N. Y., Wiley, 1946.
Turneaure, F. E., and Russell, H. L., *Public water supplies* (4th ed.). N. Y.,
  Wiley, 1940.
ZoBell, C. E., *Marine microbiology.* Waltham, Mass. Chronica Botanica, 1946.

AIR

American Association for the Advancement of Science. *Aerobiology.* Lancaster,
  Pa., Science Press Printing Company, 1942.
Rosebury, T., *Experimental air-borne infection.* Baltimore, Md., Williams &
  Wilkins, 1947.

PART VII

Microbiology of Foods

It has been noted in previous chapters that both numbers and kinds of microorganisms in anything decomposable are important in determining the course of decomposition. The **kinds** are important in that certain organisms may be able to use the particular substance or one or more of its constituents for food; and under proper environmental conditions these microorganisms may multiply and bring about decomposition or changes in composition. Sometimes these changes are desired and the growth and action of the organisms are encouraged; usually changes in composition are undesirable and precautions are taken to prevent them. The **numbers** of contaminating microorganisms may be of importance because the more numerous these organisms are the more likely they are to multiply and cause changes in the substrate, and the more difficult will be the hindrance of growth and the destruction of the microorganisms. Obviously kinds and numbers of pathogenic (disease-producing) organisms contaminating foods also are of great importance to the consumer.

The food bacteriologist is concerned with the questions of contamination and of growth of microorganisms. He tries to prevent contamination by spoilage microorganisms (or by pathogenic ones), growth of these organisms, and the consequent changes in the food. In some cases he encourages the growth and action of specific desirable types of microorganisms. The present-day civilization with its concentrated populations in thickly populated countries and large cities is dependent upon the methods of food preservation and transportation which have been worked out in comparatively recent times. Improved sanitary methods have made foods safe to consume and have added to the health and long life of the consumers.

24. FOOD PRESERVATION

Most of the food consumed by man falls into one of eight main divisions: cereals and cereal products, sugar and sugar products, vegetables, fruits, milk and dairy products, meats and poultry, eggs, and sea foods. All but the first two of these classes of foods are readily decomposed by microorganisms, and most of them must be stored so as to be available during seasons of shortage and must, at times, be shipped over considerable distances. All of this would be impossible without present methods of preservation.

The chief methods of food preservation may be listed as follows:

1. Asepsis (microorganisms are kept out)
2. Use of low temperatures: cellar storage, chilling, freezing
3. Use of high temperatures: pasteurization, cooking, sterilization by heat (canning)
4. Drying: this includes use of high concentrations of dissolved substances like salt or sugar
5. Use of chemical preservatives, either developed by microorganisms (fermentation) or added
6. Treatment by light waves (ultraviolet, for example), sound waves, high pressures, etc.

To these six main methods might be added: (7) Removal of microorganisms by filtration, sedimentation, centrifugation, washing, etc.; and (8) Maintenance of anaerobic conditions, as by use of an evacuated sealed container or of a film of oil over the surface.

In the preservation of most foods more than one of the above methods of preservation are used.

It will be noted that these methods of food preservation all involve one or more of the following general principles:

1. Prevention of the entrance of microorganisms
2. Inhibition of growth and activity of microorganisms
3. Killing or removal of microorganisms

Spoilage of food may be due to the action of microorganisms, to the action of the enzymes of the plant or animal cells of the food, or to both. Most of our preservative methods are pointed toward control of the microorganisms, while autodecomposition of the food is disregarded. Fortunately most methods of control of microorganisms are also effective against the action of enzymes of plant or animal cells; but in the preservation of some foods special procedures must be used to insure inactivation of these enzymes. For example, in the preservation of vegetables by freezing they are "blanched," or exposed to hot water or steam for a short time before the freezing process, in order to inactivate the plant enzymes which would continue to act, although slowly, at low temperatures.

It is important to remember that it is easier to prevent the start of growth by microorganisms than it is to stop growth, once it has started.

Asepsis

Numerous examples of the method of asepsis (keeping out microorganisms) are found in nature. Few or no living microorganisms are present in the interior of healthy plant or animal tissue, and in most cases this tissue is protected by a more or less impermeable skin, husk, or cover of some kind which prevents the entrance of microorganisms. Thus the orange is protected by its skin and the interior of most healthy oranges is sterile. The egg shell keeps microorganisms from the interior of the egg, and functions well as a protection as long as it is dry. Nut meats, inside intact shells, are sterile; muscle tissues are in most cases free from microorganisms. It is only when the protective covering has been damaged or decomposition has spread from the outer surface that these inner tissues are subject to decomposition by microorganisms.

The food technologist tries to use aseptic methods in the handling of many kinds of foods with the object of entirely preventing the entrance of spoilage organisms, or of reducing their numbers, or of cutting down the "load." Experience has shown that the fewer the microorganisms or the lighter the "load," the less readily the food will spoil and the better the methods of food preservation will function. Australian meat packers who ship meat to Great Britain find it absolutely essential to reduce to a minimum the contamination of meat during slaughtering, dressing, and chilling in order to ship the meat the long distance to England without spoilage; and they find that the less this initial contamination the longer is the keeping time of the meat. Canners find that the greater the contamination of foods with spoilage organisms before canning, the greater is the heat process necessary to preserve the product. Examples of this kind are numerous and are found in all parts of the food industry.

The packaging, bottling, or canning of foods serves to keep out microorganisms and should be considered a method of asepsis.

Low Temperatures

It is maintained that the use of low temperatures is the ideal method of food preservation, for if the temperatures are not below the freezing point the foods can be kept for a limited time in a condition very like that of the sh foods. It will be noted that most of the commonly used perishable ds are preserved at one stage or another by the use of low temperatures; me are so preserved all along the way from producer to consumer. As ated in Chapters 9 and 10, temperature is one of the controlling factors in ie growth and activity of microorganisms and in the action of the inherent nzymes in plant or animal tissues. This is the basis of preservation by low temperatures, for the action of microorganisms and enzymes is slowed down by a drop in temperature and may practically cease if the temperature is low enough. Then, too, low temperatures may be combined with other preservative factors and be effective at temperatures high enough to support microbial growth under other conditions.

Many of the terms used in connection with low temperature storage are applied very loosely. The term cold storage, as commonly used, might mean the use of temperatures above or below freezing and usually indicates the use of mechanical refrigeration. The English make more exact use of their terms, and their terminology is used in the following division of low temperature storage into three types:

1. *Common or Cellar Storage.* Temperatures usually are not much below that of the outside air and are not low enough to prevent the action of many spoilage organisms or of the plant enzymes. Decomposition is slowed up considerably, however. Root crops, potatoes, apples, and similar foods are stored for limited periods. Too low a humidity in the storage cellar may cause excessive losses of moisture from the stored product, while too high a humidity favors spoilage by microorganisms.

2. *Chilling.* By the term **chilling** is meant storage at temperatures not far above the freezing point These low temperatures are obtained and maintained by means of ice or mechanical refrigeration. Eggs, dairy products, fruits, sea foods, meats, and vegetables are stored in this way. Environmental factors important in preservation by chilling are:

a. Storage temperature: The best temperature for storage of many foods, eggs for example, is slightly above the freezing point of the food. Other foods, like potatoes and apples, have an optimum temperature of storage somewhat above the freezing point. The optimum temperature of storage, then, varies with the product and is fairly specific for a given food.

b. Relative humidity: The optimum relative humidity will vary with the kind of food stored and the temperature of the storage chamber. A low humidity and active circulation of air may serve to dry the surface of foods like meat and eggs and aid in their preservation, but may at the same time cause an excessive loss in moisture and hence in weight. A high humidity, on the other hand, permits little loss of moisture from the food, but is likely to favor the growth of microorganisms on the surface. A rise in the temperature of the storage room or removal of the food to higher outside temperatures us- ally causes condensation of moisture on the food and hence favors microb decomposition. This may happen to chilled meats or eggs.

c. Ventilation: The circulation of air during storage keeps both temper ture and relative humidity uniform throughout the storage room. In this wa "cold storage flavor" may be reduced.

d. Composition of the atmosphere: The amounts and proportions of oxygen and carbon dioxide are important in their influence on preservation by chilling and will be discussed later in the chapter.

3. *Cold Storage or Freezing.* **Cold storage** involves the freezing of the food product and storage in the frozen condition. This method has been used for centuries with the freezing accomplished by outdoor temperatures. The use of frozen foods has increased greatly during recent years, due chiefly to the introduction of mechanical refrigeration and especially of the new quick freezing processes, in which low temperatures and special methods are used so that the products are frozen very rapidly. Less change in the physical and chemical properties of most foods takes place with quick freezing than with ordinary slow freezing methods, and foods can be preserved for long periods. Fruits, vegetables, meats, and sea foods have been frozen successfully and can be bought at retail markets. Temperatures of $0°$ to $-25°$ F. (-17.8 to $-31.7°$ C.) are used in the freezers. Frozen foods are stored at temperatures of $0°$ to $30°$ F. (-17.8 to $-1.1°$ C.).

It will be recalled from Chapter 10 that low temperatures, even those far below $0°$ C., do not exert a marked killing effect on microorganisms. The numbers may be reduced more or less, depending upon the kinds of organisms present; and the relative proportions may be changed; but sterilization will not result. Thawed frozen foods will spoil as rapidly as fresh foods and sometimes more rapidly. Pathogenic bacteria may survive low temperature exposure, although usually in reduced numbers. The chief bacteriological problems are those connected with the handling of foods prior to freezing. Contamination with microorganisms, increase in numbers, and even incipient spoilage may take place and affect the quality of the product; for the frozen product can be no better in quality than the food frozen. Recommendations are being made for a bacterial standard for frozen foods as an indication of sanitary methods of production.

Low temperature as a means of food preservation often is combined with some other method of preservation. It has been noted above that drying the surface of chilled foods aids in their preservation. In storage of meats and fruits at chilling temperatures, the atmosphere about the food is sometimes controlled so that definite amounts of oxygen and carbon dioxide are present, or gases like carbon dioxide or ozone may be introduced. This will be discussed below under the heading "Preservatives." Irradiation, smoking, and pickling are often combined with low temperature storage.

High Temperatures

Increase in temperature within the growth range of an organism increases the rate of growth and of metabolic activity. A temperature approaching the maximum of growth usually causes the catabolic activity to exceed the anabolic and in time causes death of the microorganisms. This factor may play a part in the treatment of foods by high temperatures, but the main purpose of the elevated temperature is to kill directly the cells present. Since microorganisms vary considerably in their resistance to heat, a definite heat treatment may kill most but not all of the cells, or the vegetative cells and not the spores, or may kill only some kinds of organisms and spare the others. The factors which influence the heat treatment necessary to kill microorganisms and their spores have been discussed in Chapter 10. The extent of the heat treatment given a food for its preservation will depend upon the heat resistance of the microorganisms to be destroyed and the effect of heat upon the quality of the product. Some foods, like milk or peas, can be heated to only a limited extent without loss in appearance and palatability and for this reason the canner is tempted to underheat or underprocess them. A food like pumpkin, on the other hand, is not damaged by a fairly long heat treatment.

1. *Pasteurization.* Pasteurization is the term applied to a heat treatment

that kills part but not all of the microorganisms present, and usually is applied to the use of temperatures below the boiling point of water (100° C.). Pasteurization often is applied to food products the quality of which would be harmed by higher temperatures. Usually additional methods of preservation are used, such as storage at low temperatures, sealing, etc. The organisms which survive pasteurization either are unable to grow well in the products or have their growth inhibited by other preservative methods following heat treatment. Then, too, reduced numbers of microorganisms make the other preservative methods more effective. Pasteurization is used widely in the treatment of market milk and other dairy products. This phase of the subject will be treated in more detail in Chapter 26. Dried fruits, honey, fresh or fermented fruit juices, and other food products may be pasteurized. Pasteurization of dried fruits, for example, is carried out under conditions which vary with the kind of fruit. The time of heating may vary from 30 to 70 minutes, the temperature from 150° to 185° F. (66 to 85° C.), and the relative humidity during heating from 70 to 100 per cent. Heating may be done with live steam or some other source of heat. The process may be carried out on packaged or bulk products.

2. *Boiling.* Boiling or treatment with flowing steam is used in the heat treatment of foods in which spoilage by spore-forming bacteria is not likely to be a problem, or of foods which because of their composition would not be spoiled by any bacteria able to withstand treatment of 100° C. It was pointed out in Chapter 10 that less heat treatment is necessary in killing microorganisms in an acid medium than in a neutral or slightly alkaline one. Food as acid as sauerkraut may be heated to a temperature below 100° C., yet keep well if hermetically sealed in a container. Sour cherries, rhubarb, cranberries, and acid fruits do not require temperatures above boiling; tomatoes and tomato products are heated in flowing steam during commercial processing.

Ordinary methods of cooking foods in the home involve the use of temperatures not much above 100° C. Even in baking with the oven at a high temperature, the food will not attain a temperature above 100° C. until all of the water has been boiled off, hence bread or cake does not reach a temperature high enough to kill most bacterial spores. Therefore cooking or baking of nonacid foods does not sterilize them, but may kill most of the vegetative cells. Since microorganisms may survive the cooking processes, they may spoil the foods unless storage is at low (refrigerator) temperatures.

3. *Canning (Autoclaving).* Temperatures above 100° C. are obtained usually by use of autoclaves or steam pressure sterilizers. Such temperatures are necessary for the heat treatment of most types of low acid and medium acid canned foods; the time and temperature of heating necessary for sterilization

will vary with the type of food. Most vegetables, meats, poultry, and fish are nearly neutral in reaction and are subject to spoilage by spore-forming bacteria; hence they should be heated, during the processing of the canned material, at the high temperatures obtained with steam pressure. Canned foods usually are sealed under a vacuum produced by a vacuum pump or by heating of the "head space" above the food just before the sealing.

It has been pointed out that in general the heat treatment necessary to sterilize a product decreases with increase in acidity. The canner finds that foods for canning fall into four groups on the basis of their acidity expressed as *pH*: (a) **low acid** (*p*H 5.3–7.0), such as peas, corn, and meats; (b) **medium acid** (*p*H 4.5–5.3), such as spinach, asparagus, beets, and pumpkin; (c) **acid** (*p*H 3.7–4.5), such as tomatoes, pears, and pineapple; and (d) **high acid** (*p*H 3.7 and below), such as sauerkraut, berries, cherries, and rhubarb. These groups of foods differ not only in the average process necessary for their sterilization but also in the type of spoilage most commonly encountered. The canner attempts to give the canned food enough of a heat treatment to make it "commercially sterile"—that is, enough to kill all organisms which would be able to grow under ordinary storage conditions for the cans of food. This does not always involve the killing of all the microorganisms present; and as a matter of fact many cans of food contain live spores of microorganisms, or even live vegetative cells in some instances. Conditions are such, however, that these microorganisms cannot grow or produce changes in the food. For example, spores of aerobic bacteria often are present in the can, but because of a lack of oxygen in the evacuated can they are unable to germinate and grow. Spores of obligate thermophiles may survive the heat treatment, but be unable to grow as long as the cans are stored at ordinary room temperatures. Organisms may survive the heating of acid foods, but be unable to grow in such an acid medium.

The heat treatment necessary to commercially sterilize a food varies not only with the acidity of the product but also with the kind and number of microorganisms present and their condition, as well as with any factor that affects the penetration of heat to the center of the can, such as the consistency of the food, its composition, and the size and shape of the container. Typical heat processes recommended by the Research Laboratory of the National Canners Association for No. 2 (pint) cans of some low acid foods are as follows: corn, cream style, 90 minutes at 240° F. (115.5° C.) or 80 minutes at 245° F. (118.3° C.); peas 35 minutes at 240° F.; string beans 20 minutes at 240° F. With higher processing temperatures, shorter times of heating would be used. The above treatments may be contrasted with heating of an acid food like sauerkraut at 212° F. (100° C.) or lower for only a few minutes.

The canner has two main objectives in the heat treatment of canned foods: (a) to prevent spoilage of the food, and (b) to make it safe to eat. At the same time, of course, he tries to avoid harm to the quality of the product due to heat. Of the toxin-forming and the pathogenic bacteria, the spore-forming anaerobes *Clostridium botulinum* and *C. parabotulinum* are the most heat resistant; and most of the heat processes for canned foods are made sufficient to guarantee the killing of these dangerous organisms. Botulism will be discussed further in a later chapter.

In home canning the filled jar or can of food usually is heat processed by one of three methods: (a) in boiling water or flowing steam; (b) in the oven; or (c) in the steam pressure cooker or sterilizer. Comparatively few foods, and these very acid ones like rhubarb, can be preserved by means of a heat treatment at temperatures below the boiling point of water. Acid foods like tomatoes and pears can be processed successfully at 100° C. Most medium acid and low acid foods should be processed at temperatures well above 100° C.; these temperatures are most conveniently obtained by use of the steam pressure sterilizer. Treatment with boiling water or flowing steam is processing at 100° C. or slightly below; heating in the oven brings the contents of the jar or can only to (or just below) the boiling point of the food, i.e., not much above 100° C. It is true that part of the low acid or medium acid canned food processed at the lower temperatures may not spoil on storage; on the other hand, part or all of the batch may spoil and be lost. It is an unnecessary gamble, then, to use 100° C. for heat processing, when proper use of the steam pressure cooker will guarantee the keeping of the food. Moreover, only a process at temperatures considerably higher than 100° C. will guarantee death of the toxin-forming *Clostridium parabotulinum* and *C. botulinum* in low acid or medium acid foods.

DRYING

Many foods are preserved naturally by drying or by lack of moisture; this method of preservation undoubtedly was used by primitive man. It has remained a commonly used method, although in recent years other methods have partly replaced it. Ordinarily drying is thought of as the removal of water; but the combination of the water in a food with some other substance in such a way that it is not available to microorganisms is another form of drying. Materials in true solution, for example, tie up water, and increasing the concentration of dissolved substances is a method of drying. Incidentally, the removal of water from a food increases the concentration of soluble substances in the remaining water. Similarly, colloids, such as agar or gelatin, may tie up water so that it is unavailable to microorganisms.

Not only do solutes bind moisture, but they also increase the osmotic pressure. Hence, solutes tend to dry the microbial cells themselves, by removal of water—and may even injure or kill them.

The minimum amount of available moisture necessary for growth varies with the microorganism. It will be recalled that for active growth, in general, molds require the least moisture; yeasts, the next most; and bacteria, the most. This means that a food dry enough to prevent the growth of bacteria and yeasts might still allow the growth of molds.

Drying has the advantages that it allows the preservation of foods for fairly long periods and saves on space and weight during handling and transportation. It has the disadvantage that there is likely to be a change in some of the properties of the food, such as flavor and texture, during the drying process, and possibly a loss in vitamins. Among the foods which may be preserved by drying are: milk and milk products, fruits, vegetables, and eggs. Drying may be done by removal of the water by the sun or by artificial heat, with or without mechanical circulation of air; by running the material over a hot roller and scraping off the dry material; or by spraying a liquid material into a hot, evacuated chamber or into one in which hot, dry air is kept in constant motion.

Many foods, as they occur naturally or as they are manufactured, contain so little moisture that their preservation is relatively easy. Thus, flours and cereals need only be stored under dry conditions to prevent spoilage by microorganisms.

When high concentrations of dissolved substances are used, they usually include sugar or salt. High sugar concentrations are present in sweetened condensed milk, honey, molasses, and candy, and help preserve these foods against spoilage by certain types of microorganisms. Fish and meat often are preserved by salt, usually in combination with some other preservative factor. In addition to its drying effect, salt also may have some action as a chemical preservative.

PRESERVATIVES

Preservatives may be added to foods or may be developed in them as a result of fermentation. Sodium benzoate and sulfur dioxide are the only so-called chemical preservatives which may be added legally to foods in the United States, and laws in many of the states prohibit their use. Sodium benzoate is most effective in acid foods like fruit juices or catsup. Sulfur dioxide is permitted in fruit juices and often is added when the juices are to be fermented to wines. It also is used in the drying of some fruits, although it is added for the production of a desirable color in the dried fruit rather than for its preservative action. Most of the sulfurous acid is removed during the soaking of dried fruits. Organic acids such as lactic, acetic, and citric acids, the first two of which are often produced during fermentation for preservation, may be added to foods as preservatives. Examples of their use are: Vinegar in sweet-sour pickles, pickled beets and pickled meats, lactic acid in similar products in smaller proportions, and citric acid in soft drinks.

Among the chemical substances which have been used as preservatives for food, but which are not now permitted in the United States, are boric acid and borates, salicylic acid and salicylates, and formaldehyde. These compounds are believed to be harmful to the health of the consumer if taken in appreciable amounts, but their use still is permitted in some countries.

Smoking by means of wood smoke is a method of food preservation which has been in use for centuries, although by itself it is not very effective. Usually the drying effect of the smoking process, especially on the outer surface of the food being smoked, is responsible for part of the preservative effect. Salt, sugar, or spices also may be added and may play a part in preservation. The effect of the smoke supposedly is due to the formaldehyde and pyroligneous acid (chiefly a mixture of creosote compounds) sent into the foods. Meats and fish are the foods most commonly preserved by smoking.

The **curing** of meats involves the use of salt as a preservative and, usually, sodium nitrate or nitrite, smoking, and low temperatures. The curing of ham will serve as an example. The hams are placed in a curing or "pickling" solution, which is a salt brine containing sodium nitrate or nitrite, or both, and in some cases a small amount of sugar. During the cure the hams and brine are kept at a low temperature, usually not far above freezing. Large hams are "pumped," that is the curing solution is injected into the interior tissues by means of a syringe. The salt and low temperature are probably the chief preservative factors during the time of curing, for nitrites and nitrates are not considered effective preservatives, but are used to produce a desired red color in the product. The curing solution effectively inhibits the growth of many kinds of microorganisms, but permits the growth of some kinds of bacteria which may cause changes in the meat during the cure. The smoking of the hams after the curing process also is an important preservative factor.

Spices have little antiseptic effect in the concentrations used in most foods and hence are of little use as preservatives. The antiseptic effect varies with the kind of spice, the kind of organism subjected to its action, and even with the lot of spice used. It is unsafe, then, to rely upon spices to preserve a food, but their presence may aid to a slight extent the preservative action of some other factor. Some manufacturers process the spices with ethylene oxide to kill most of the microorganisms and their spores, so that the addition of spices to food products will not increase the microbial content. This has been found to be important in the preparation of foods like sausage, pickled products, etc.

The use of controlled amounts of certain gases in the atmosphere about stored foods might be considered preservation by means of chemicals. This method usually is used along with storage at low temperatures and has been mentioned in that connection. In recent years the so-called "gas storage" of foods has increased and it has been shown that the storage temperature and humidity need not be as low when gas storage is used as when storage is in the air. Although several kinds of gas have been tried, the only ones used successfully in practice at present are carbon dioxide and ozone.

It has been found that when the concentrations of carbon dioxide and of oxygen are controlled at percentages found to be optimum for the particular food being stored, the keeping time of the product can be greatly prolonged. In some instances the quality of a food may be maintained better than with ordinary storage, because a higher relative humidity can be used in the storage room with gas-controlled atmosphere. Fruits, meats, and eggs have been preserved on a commercial scale by this method. Shipments to England of meat from Australia and fruits from South Africa are made in ships especially equipped to carry out low temperature storage in a controlled atmosphere of carbon dioxide and oxygen. Molds apparently are inhibited to a greater extent than bacteria.

Living cells, especially those from plant sources, continue to respire during the storage of foods and consequently take up oxygen and give off carbon dioxide. Thus there is a tendency in the storage of fruits, for example, for the percentage of carbon dioxide in the atmosphere to increase and the percentage of oxygen to decrease. The optimum concentration of carbon dioxide and of oxygen varies with the product, and with apples even varies with the variety. Therefore, in the gas storage of fruits, it is necessary to remove carbon dioxide from the atmosphere about some fruits and to add it to the atmosphere of other fruits. For the storage of eggs, about 2.5 per cent of carbon dioxide in the air is recommended; for beef, about 10 to 20 per cent; and for apples the optimum percentage of carbon dioxide and oxygen varies with the variety—about 3 per cent of oxygen and 5 per cent of carbon dioxide are best for a number of varieties.

Ozone in a concentration of 3 to 5 parts per million has been used in the preservation of eggs and has been recommended for other foods stored at chilling temperatures. Ozone is an active oxidizing agent and cannot be used with foods, such as butter, that are harmed by oxidation. It has a further disadvantage in that it is irritating to the mucous membranes of workers.

Other gases have been tried experimentally. Nitrogen and hydrogen have been shown to be effective in a few cases, but their use has not replaced that of carbon dioxide.

Preservation of foods by the **development** of preservative substances in the food by the action of microorganisms is legal and is widely used. The lactic acid fermentation is the most important and involves the fermentation of sugar, chiefly to lactic acid, by special lactic acid bacteria, usually by a succession of species. Sauerkraut, cucumber pickles, green olives, and fermented milk are prepared by means of such a fermentation, as is silage for animals.

Sauerkraut. Cabbage is shredded and 2.5 per cent by weight of salt is added. The salt draws the juice from the cabbage tissue. This juice contains fermentable sugar which, under anaerobic conditions produced chiefly by respiration of the plant cells, is acted upon first by lactic acid-forming cocci (usually of the species *Leuconostoc mesenteroides*), then by nongas-forming lactobacilli (like *Lactobacillus plantarum*), and then by gas-forming lactobacilli of the *Lactobacillus brevis* type. The cocci bring the acidity up to about 0.7 to 1.0 per cent calculated as lactic acid; then the nongas-forming rods increase the acidity up to 1.5 to 2.0 per cent. The gas-forming rods may raise the acidity to as high as 2.4 per cent, although in most lots of sauerkraut this third group does not play an important part. In addition to lactic acid, acetic acid, carbon dioxide, and small amounts of other by-products are formed. The salt in the kraut helps eliminate the competition from bacteria other than the lactics early in the fermentation and, together with the anaerobic conditions and the acidity, is a preservative factor in the finished kraut. The kraut usually is kept pressed down by means of a weight to keep liquid on the surface, and sometimes mineral oil is poured onto the exposed surface of the expressed liquid in order to prevent aerobic growth. The sauerkraut often is canned to avoid further changes after the fermentation is complete. The desired lactic acid fermentation of the cabbage juice may not always take place, especially if conditions do not favor the lactic acid bacteria. Other microorganisms may greatly outnumber and outgrow the lactics; or temperature, oxygen supply or salt concentration may favor organisms other than the lactics—in which event the resulting fermentation will be termed abnormal and the product inferior. Such "off" fermentation will be discussed in the next chapter in connection with the spoilage of sauerkraut.

Cucumber Pickles. In the preparation of cucumber pickles a lactic acid fermentation takes place: one that in most ways resembles that of sauerkraut, although the same succession of organisms does not seem to be concerned. Most of the organisms responsible for the pickle fermentation have not been positively identified, although *Lactobacillus plantarum* is considered important. The difference in flora in the two fermentations is due, in part, to the higher concentrations of salt used for pickles. The two chief types of pickles ordinarily prepared are dills and salt pickles or salt stock. A high salt concentration is used in the preparation of salt pickles, 10 to 15 per cent, and the lactic acid fermentation should take six weeks or two months. The acidity attained varies with a number of factors (such as the sugar content of the original cucumber, temperature, salt content, etc.), but usually does not exceed 0.9 to 1.0 per cent, expressed as lactic acid. Salt pickles are used in the preparation of sweet-sour pickles, mixed pickles, and other pickle products. The fermentation is more rapid in the making of dill pickles because a salt content of only about 5 or 6 per cent is used. The lower salt content, however, increases the likelihood of abnormal fermentations or spoilage. Dill pickles are so named because they are flavored with the extract of the dill herb.

Green Olives. A lactic acid fermentation also is involved in the preparation of green olives, with lactobacilli chiefly concerned. The olives, after a lye treatment, are placed in an 8 to 10 per cent salt brine where the lactic fermentation takes place. Often the olives do not contain enough sugar to permit the development of the desired amount of acidity (0.7 to 0.9 per cent as lactic) and some sugar must be added.

Silage. Feeds for animals may be preserved by fermentation; the outstanding example of such a feed is silage. Corn is the plant usually ensiled, but numerous other forage crops like grasses, leguminous plants, sunflowers, and beet tops are used. In Europe, grass silage is commonly prepared; in the United States, corn silage.

In the manufacture of corn silage the corn plant is cut into small pieces and packed into the silo. This corn contains sufficient moisture for bacterial growth, a large percentage of carbohydrates like cellulose and hemicellulose, with a small percentage of sugar, and a small amount of protein. A variety of bacteria, together with some yeasts and molds, are on the surface of the pieces of corn and in the expressed juice. These bacteria start to grow, but soon the small amount of oxygen present is used up by the plant cells in their process of respiration, and the aerobic microorganisms are unable to continue growth. The fermentable carbohydrates are converted to acid by bacteria, first by lactic cocci and then by bacteria of the *Lactobacillus brevis* type, and other kinds of bacteria are inhibited. The few million bacteria per gram of freshly cut corn increase to several billion per gram within a few days, but the variety of bacteria decreases until the lactic acid-formers are predominant. The chief products of the fermentation are lactic acid and carbon dioxide, with smaller amounts of acetic, propionic, and other acids and a little alcohol. Molds are the chief cause of spoilage of silage, and since they are strictly aerobic they can grow only on the upper surface and cause this part to become unusable. The deeper layers of silage will keep indefinitely if the proper lactic acid fermentation has taken place and the air is excluded. Faulty fermentations sometimes take place (the butyric acid fermentation by anaerobes), but if the lactic acid fermentation is proceeding at the desired rate such undesirable fermentations are inhibited.

The ensiling of leguminous plants requires the use of special methods because of the comparatively high protein and low sugar content and the consequent tendency toward protein decomposition with little acid production. If the high protein content is balanced by the addition of a fermentable carbohydrate in sufficient amounts, a normal lactic acid fermentation will take place, and a silage of good quality will be produced. This may be accomplished by the addition of 50 to 100 pounds of molasses to each ton of chopped leguminous plants or by admixture of ground shelled corn, corn-and-cob meal, or sweet sorghum in appropriate amounts. The molasses or other added material must be thoroughly mixed with the plant material. The fermentation then is practically the same as in corn silage.

Recently, the so-called AIV [1] method of silage manufacture has come into use and has been applied to the ensiling of leguminous plants. At the time of filling the silo, the chopped leguminous plants are treated with a mixture of four parts of hydrochloric acid to one part of sulfuric acid in the proportion of 100 liters of twice normal acid to each ton of plants. This patented mixture of inorganic acids brings the reaction of the silage down to about pH 4.0, which is low enough to prevent protein decomposition by bacteria but not low enough to prevent lactic acid fermentation by bacteria to carry the pH still lower. Similarly, phosphoric acid has been used to acidify the green forage, with 20 to 30 pounds of 75 per cent acid added per ton of chopped leguminous plants.

Fermented Milks. Fermented milks are another example of preservation of foods by means of an acid fermentation, chiefly lactic. They will be discussed in Chapter 27.

LIGHT WAVES, SOUND WAVES, AND HIGH PRESSURES

The effect of these various physical factors on microorganisms has been discussed in Chapter 10. Lethal rays and waves of various sorts have been suggested for food preservation. Ultraviolet rays have been used successfully in the treatment of transparent liquids or thin films of translucent materials, as well as the outer surfaces of foods like meat, cake, and bread.

---

[1] Named **AIV** from the initials of the inventor of the method, Dr. A. I. Virtanen, of Finland.

Water for soft drinks or for other purposes has been treated with ultra-violet rays and the bacterial counts thereby greatly reduced. The process has been tried on milk, but not with entire success because it changes the flavor, and because the opacity of milk requires that a very thin layer of milk be exposed to the rays. It is claimed that the growth of molds on chilled meats is inhibited when the storage room is equipped with ultraviolet lamps and that meat can be "ripened" or aged in a shorter time and at a higher temperature than ordinarily used. The irradiation of cakes and of the knife used in slicing bread in bakeries has been reported to reduce spoilage by molds. Some ultraviolet lamps give off ozone in amounts which may have an added preservative effect.

The use of sound waves, audible and inaudible, is still in the experimental stage and has not been put on a commercial basis. It has been tried in the reduction of numbers of bacteria in milk and other liquid products.

As has been mentioned in Chapter 10, high pressures are lethal to bacteria, but their use has been limited because of the high costs and technical difficulties involved. A high pressure of carbon dioxide plus a cool temperature have been used successfully in the preservation of grape juice previous to sterilization by filtration and bottling. High pressures of oxygen (8 to 10 atmospheres) have been combined with low temperatures in the "Hofius Process" for the preservation of milk. The method has been recommended by European workers, but is not in use in this country.

Removal of Microorganisms

Removal of all or part of the microorganisms from a food may be considered a method of preservation, for the fewer the organisms and the less the number of kinds the greater is the likelihood of a good keeping quality. The washing of a food may remove appreciable numbers of organisms. A good example is the washing of cabbage heads to be shredded for the manufacture of sauerkraut; not only is the total number of bacteria decreased, but the proportion of desirable lactic acid bacteria is increased, all of which is favorable to the lactic fermentation and hence to the preservation of the food. Washing some food products may have the reverse effect and favor spoilage instead of preservation. This may be due to the added moisture or to contamination with spoilage organisms.

Removal of microorganisms by filtration is a commonly used method of preservation, but is limited to those liquid food products without much suspended matter. Filters vary from those like diatomaceous earth filters which remove all microorganisms to those like sand or gravel beds which remove numbers of bacteria but do not sterilize the liquid. The filtration of water has been discussed in Chapter 23. Fruit juices or other liquids may be sterilized by filtration.

Sedimentation and centrifugation may be used to remove microorganisms from liquids, but they do not effect sterilization. As noted in Chapter 23, drinking water is often subjected to sedimentation during the process of purification.

REFERENCES

Annual Reports and Special Bulletins of the Food Investigation Board (Great Britain). London, H. M. Stationery Office.

Bohstedt, G. Peterson, W. H., and Duffee, F. W., "Grass silage." *Wisconsin Agricultural Experimental Station, Circular 299* (1940).

Cronshaw, H. B., "The training of the food technologist." *Food Manufacture* (1935), *10:*169–172.

Cruess, W. V., *Commercial fruit and vegetable products* (3rd ed.). N. Y., McGraw-Hill, 1948.

Prescott, S. C., and Dunn, C. G., *Industrial microbiology* (2nd ed.). N. Y., McGraw-Hill, 1949.

Prescott, S. C., and Proctor, B. E., *Food technology.* N. Y., McGraw-Hill, 1937.

Shrader, J. H., *Food control. Its public health aspects.* N. Y., Wiley, 1939.

Tanner, F. W., *The microbiology of foods* (2nd ed.). Champaign, Ill., Garrard Press, 1944.

Thom, C., and Hunter, A. C., *Hygienic fundamentals of food handling.* Baltimore, Md., Williams & Wilkins, 1924.

25. FOOD SPOILAGE

It is not always easy to judge when a food is spoiled and when it is fit to eat; what one person thinks fit to eat may not be so considered by another. Many people like a certain amount of aging or "ripeness" in the beef they consume, whereas others think that meat so aged is spoiled. It is considered that a lactic acid fermentation spoils some foods; yet in others, such as sauerkraut or pickles, this type of bacterial action is encouraged. Putrefaction is a type of decomposition that is considered very undesirable, yet that type of change has taken place in the ripening of the best quality of Limburger cheese. Most of us are able, however, to detect spoilage of raw foods without the use of any complicated tests and can decide whether or not we consider them fit to eat.

As mentioned in Chapter 24, spoilage may be due to the enzymes of the plant or animal material, to the action of microorganisms, or to both. Only spoilage due to microorganisms will be considered here; raw foods will be discussed first, then heated foods.

On the basis of ease of spoilage, foods may be classed as stable or nonperishable, semiperishable, and perishable. Sugar would be comparatively stable, potatoes semiperishable, and meats perishable.

Bacteria, yeasts, and molds are present in most raw food products and are concerned in the spoilage of foods as in the decomposition of all kinds of organic matter. The kind of decomposition and the type of microorganism involved will depend upon the physical and chemical make-up of the food and the other environmental conditions. The principles discussed in Chapters 8, 9, and 10 in regard to the nutrition of microorganisms and the influence of chemical and physical factors upon them may be applied to the spoilage of foods, and thus enable the investigator to predict the type of spoilage and the probable kind of spoilage organism. In competition between bacteria, yeasts, and molds, if conditions are equally favorable to all three, the relative rate of growth or increase in numbers will determine which type will predominate and cause the spoilage—in any event the bacteria will outgrow the others. If yeasts and molds are competing, the yeasts will be the more likely to predominate. If, however, because of a lack of available moisture (due to desiccation or to concentration of dissolved substances), too great an acidity, too low an incubation temperature, or similar adverse conditions, the bacteria are unable to grow well, yeasts or molds may predominate in the decomposition of the food.

The previous treatment of the food will influence the numbers, kinds, and proportions of microorganisms, as well as their condition or state of health, and therefore will influence the rate and kind of spoilage. Exposure to any of the preservative treatments discussed in the previous chapter (Chapter 24) might change the kind of spoilage and the microorganisms involved from what would be expected with the original, untreated food. Thus, a heat treatment would cause a reduction in numbers and kinds of microorganisms—the harsher the heat treatment the greater would be the reduction. Pasteurization of milk, for example, would kill most of the vegetative cells of bacteria, the yeasts, and the molds; but would not destroy the more heat resistant vegetative bacterial cells or the bacterial spores. Boiling (100° C.) would kill all but the bacterial spores; a temperature of 115° C. would permit the survival of only the most resistant bacterial spores. As a consequence, the type of spoilage of milk heated at the different temperatures would be different. In the discussion to follow, raw, pasteurized, and canned foods will be discussed separately.

Raw Foods

As has been stated, the kind of spoilage will depend upon the kind and number of microorganisms and the environment surrounding them. It is obvious that most raw foods will contain a large variety of microorganisms and that a complex combination of environmental conditions will be present. Therefore, at the start of growth of organisms in the food, a number of different types will start to grow and produce different changes in the food. Usually, however, one kind of microorganism will outgrow the rest and initiate the spoilage. Other organisms may, however, be helpful or antagonistic and thus influence the course of the spoilage. The spoilage of raw foods usually is accomplished by action of a succession of organisms, one preparing the way for the next. A good example is the normal series of changes in raw milk described in Chapter 26.

In the spoilage of food, the food and its surroundings constitute the environment in which the microorganisms must grow. The following characteristics of the food are most important: the chemical composition, the amount of available moisture, the amount of free oxygen, and the hydrogen-ion concentration (pH). The temperature of the food and of the surroundings is important, as are other characteristics of the surroundings such as humidity and gas content of the atmosphere, light or other rays, etc.

Composition of Food. In the discussion of the nutrition of microorganisms (Chapter 8) it has been noted that they require food for energy and for growth, and that carbohydrates and similar carbon compounds are good sources of energy for most organisms, whereas proteins and their decomposition products are good nitrogen sources. It also was pointed out that organisms vary considerably in their nutritional requirements; what one organism can use, another may be unable to assimilate. It is obvious, then, that the decomposition or spoilage of most foods will depend largely upon their composition and the availability of their constituents to the microorganisms present.

The action of microorganisms on the carbohydrates and related carbon compounds of a food will depend on their availability; the amount present; and the presence of proteins, fats, and other compounds. There is considerable difference in the availability to microorganisms of carbohydrates. Starch, for example, is attacked by most molds, few yeasts, and by only part of the species of bacteria. Pectins are broken down by a limited number of species of microorganisms; hence softening of pickles is limited to these organisms. The number of kinds of microorganisms able to decompose cellulose is still less; and this compound may remain undecomposed unless the special organisms and special conditions for their growth are present. Examples of this kind could be multiplied.

The amount of soluble carbohydrate present will influence the kind of microorganism that grows. If there is no available carbohydrate or similar carbon compound present, proteoyltic or at least nonacid-forming bacteria are most likely to grow. If moderate amounts of sugar are present, an acid fermentation is most likely, as in raw milk or wet cereal. If a considerable amount of sugar is present, an alcoholic fermentation by yeasts is likely to take place, especially if the food is acid enough in character to inhibit bacteria; fruit juices, honey, and dilute sirup are examples. Most of the true yeasts need a fermentable carbohydrate for good growth. If the sugar concentration is very high, molds are the most likely to grow, as they do in concentrated sirups, sweetened condensed milk, and similar foods. The presence of fat, since it is not as readily available to most microorganisms, does not ordinarily affect the decomposition of the carbohydrate part of the food; but it may have a physical effect in sealing to keep out air or a protective effect against adverse conditions. The presence of proteins or their decomposition products may stimulate the decomposition of carbohydrates in that they provide the nitrogenous food for the causative microorganisms.

Most yeasts and many bacteria are not able to decompose pure proteins; hence proteolysis is carried on for the most part by a limited number of species of bacteria, although under certain conditions molds may be concerned. This decomposition of proteinaceous material in a food is most likely to go on in the absence of a fermentable carbohydrate and the consequent absence of an acid fermentation. If conditions are anaerobic, putrefactive changes may take place with the evolution of obnoxious odors due to hydrogen sulphide, mercaptans, ammonia, etc. The rotting of eggs is a good example of this type of spoilage. Under aerobic conditions the proteolysis may be carried out by bacteria without the production of unpleasant odors. Such changes may go on in meat or fish and are termed "souring" in commercial language; under anaerobic conditions these same products may undergo putrefaction.

Fats (lipids) are decomposed by a limited variety of microorganisms and usually only under aerobic conditions. The changes, usually oxidative, in the fat of foods are more likely to begin as a result of the action of light or of chemical catalysts (e.g., copper) than as a result of microbial action. Rancidity of fats in foods may be due to microorganisms; or, on the other hand, may be due to fat-splitting enzymes from the plant or animal from which the food came. Such fatty foods as butter, olive oil, and salad dressings are spoiled occasionally by lipolytic bacteria or molds.

The presence in food of specific inhibitory substances will influence the kind and amount of spoilage. These substances may be natural to the fresh food, may be developed by fermentation, or may be added. Organic acids in berries and fruits may be effective in controlling the type and extent of spoilage not only by the low pH produced but also in some cases by specific inhibitory action of the acid. The benzoic acid in cranberries would be an example. Acetic and propionic acids, either developed in foods or added to them, are inhibitory to most molds. Salts, such as chlorides, nitrates or nitrites, and other chemical substances present would influence spoilage.

Moisture Content of Food. The amount of **available** moisture in a food will determine the number of kinds of spoilage organisms which can grow and the type of decomposition likely to ensue. As has been emphasized previously, the availability of the water depends upon the percentage tied up

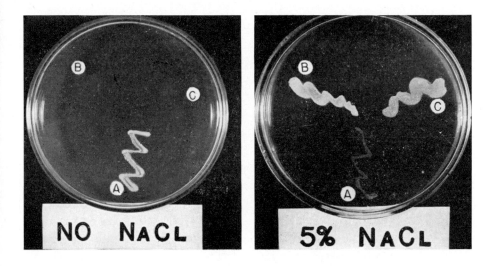

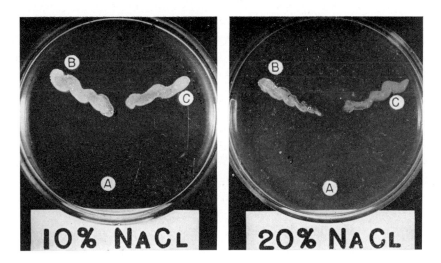

FIGURE 56.　A demonstration of the effect of sodium chloride on the growth of *Escherichia coli* (streak **A**) and the two halophilic bacteria (streaks **B** and **C**). *Escherichia coli* grows very poorly with 5% salt in the medium, while the halophiles grow well on 5 to 20% salt but will not grow without salt.

by solutes, colloids, etc. In general, molds are more tolerant of low moisture content or high concentration of solutes than are yeasts; yeasts, in turn, are more tolerant than bacteria, although there are some rather notable exceptions. Consequently, molds grow on fairly dry foods like bread, moist flour, and egg shells, and on foods with high concentrations of dissolved substances such as sweetened condensed milk and sirups. Many yeasts can grow in a fairly high concentration of sugar and some yeasts, like those involved in the spoilage of honey, seem to prefer a high concentration of sugar. Because of the favorable sugar content, trouble with yeasts is encountered in sirups, candies, honey, figs, and dates. Bacteria differ in the concentrations of dissolved substances which permit growth, and in the minimum amount of moisture necessary; most bacteria, however, are unable to grow well in the presence of much salt, sugar, or other dissolved compounds. Exceptions to the rule are a few kinds of bacteria able to grow in fairly high percentages of sugar, as in sirups or candy. Other exceptional bacteria are **salt tolerant,** that is they grow in the presence of considerable amounts of sodium chloride; others are **halophilic** and grow better with a high salt concentration than without, and may grow even in saturated solutions of salt. Halophilic and salt tolerant bacteria are important in the spoilage of brines in cheese factories and pickle plants, and of brines used in the preservation and curing of meats and fish. These bacteria are known to cause the reddening of hides and the discoloration of salt fish. Figure 56 shows petri dish cultures in which halophilic bacteria are growing.

Oxygen. The amount of available oxygen is important in its influence on the types of microorganisms which can grow, and hence on the kind of spoilage most likely to take place. It will be recalled that molds are strictly aerobic; that yeasts grow better in aerobic conditions, but will grow to some extent in an anaerobic environment; and that different kinds of bacteria may be aerobic, facultative, or anaerobic. The decomposition of foods under aerobic conditions and under anaerobic conditions may be very different; as has been mentioned in the case of spoilage of meats or fish, where putrefaction occurs under anaerobic conditions, and simple proteolysis or "souring" takes place under aerobic conditions. Ordinarily bread will mold, but if it is immersed in water, the lack of oxygen will prevent mold growth; this condition, together with the increased moisture, will favor bacterial growth.

Acidity. Since molds can, in general, grow in a more acid medium than yeasts, and yeasts in a more acid food than most bacteria (although species of bacteria vary considerably in their tolerance of acid), the acidity of a food influences both the kind of spoilage and the kind of organism causing it. Neutral or nearly neutral foods with enough moisture are most likely to undergo spoilage by bacteria; thus milk, meats, and seafood (pH 6.0–7.0) usually undergo spoilage by bacteria; more acid foods with a fermentable carbohydrate, like fruit juices (pH 3.5–4.5), will probably be spoiled by yeasts. Very acid foods, especially those low in fermentable carbohydrate, like rhubarb (pH 3.2) and cranberries (pH 2.6) may be spoiled by molds. Acid-forming bacteria have their growth stopped by the acidity they produce; this acid material, if conditions are aerobic, is then subject to the growth of molds. Thus the products of acid fermentations like sauerkraut, sour milk, pickles, cheese, and silage all are likely to have mold growth on their surfaces. Film-forming yeasts develop under similar conditions; like molds, the film yeasts grow best under aerobic conditions and are able to destroy organic acids. When the acidity of an acid food has been reduced by the action of molds or film yeasts, bacteria again find conditions favorable for growth; and, depending on the composition of the material and the environmental conditions, acid production, proteolysis, or some other kind of decomposition may take place due to their activities. Pickles or olives may be spoiled by the destruction of acid by film yeasts and the subsequent action of pectin-fermenting bacteria which cause softening of the product. Growth of *Oospora lactis* (*Geotrichum candidum*) or other molds on the surface of milk curd and the consequent reduction of acidity may first lead to the production of more lactic acid by bacteria, and then to putrefaction by proteolytic bacteria.

Temperature. Very important in the determination of the kind of growth and of spoilage is temperature. The minimum, optimum, and maximum growth temperatures for bacteria, yeasts, and molds have been discussed in Chapter 9. It will be recalled that ordinary room temperatures or slightly higher are best for most yeasts and molds, while the optimum for bacteria may vary considerably with the species. Very high temperatures permit only the growth of thermophilic microorganisms. Few molds or yeasts are thermophilic; consequently, growth at temperatures of 55°–60° C. or above is limited to a comparatively small number of species of bacteria. Thus we have spoilage, by thermophilic bacteria, of milk held at high temperatures and of canned vegetables cooled too slowly after the heat processing.

Variation in temperature, although comparatively slight, may favor one group of organisms at the expense of others and thus influence the type of spoilage. For example, raw milk held at temperatures near freezing will be spoiled eventually by cold-tolerant microorganisms, probably proteolytic bacteria; the same milk held at room temperature (20°–23° C.) will probably be soured by *Streptococcus lactis;* at 37° C. coliform bacteria find conditions favorable, although other acid-forming bacteria may be active; at

45° C. *Streptococcus thermophilus* or one of the thermoduric lactobacilli may carry on a lactic acid fermentation; while at 55°–60° C. the thermophilic *Lactobacillus thermophilus* or related bacteria will be most likely to grow. Grape juice held at low temperatures undergoes bacterial spoilage, at room temperatures is subject to alcoholic fermentation by yeasts, and at 37° C. (a temperature too high for most desirable yeasts) undergoes an abnormal fermentation due to lactic acid bacteria or to undesirable yeasts. Most molds, too, grow better at temperatures below 37° C. (except species of the genus *Aspergillus*); mold growth on foods usually is slow or lacking if the foods are held at 37° C. or above.

At low temperatures, 0° C. and slightly above, a limited variety of microorganisms is able to grow. Many species of molds grow fairly well at refrigerator temperatures and will outgrow other microorganisms. Such molds are often found on chilled meats, eggs, cheese, vegetables, and fruits. Bacteria tolerant to low temperatures may grow slowly if there is sufficient moisture; and may cause slime on stored meats, rotting of eggs, and spoilage of poultry, fish, and milk. Some yeasts can tolerate low temperatures and grow slowly in products the composition of which is more favorable to their growth than to the multiplication of bacteria.

Other environmental conditions than those discussed above may influence the type of decomposition of a food. It has been mentioned that preservative methods may eliminate spoilage by the microorganisms commonly concerned, but may permit growth and activity of others. An atmosphere of carbon dioxide or an inert gas may prevent the growth of aerobes but favor anaerobes; a certain amount of drying may stop bacteria and yeasts but permit mold growth; irradiation may inhibit film-forming yeasts and molds but allow bacteria to flourish; high salt concentrations may hold back other microorganisms but favor halophiles, and so on.

In summary, it should be emphasized that it is usually not one factor in the environment, but a combination of factors that determines what microorganisms are most likely to be concerned in the spoilage of a food. This combination may be such that one group of microorganisms is favored much more than other organisms present, and a spoilage typical of that group of organisms results. It should be remembered, too, that in the spoilage of raw foods with a large variety of microorganisms present, the first organisms to grow eventually make conditions unfavorable to their own increase but favorable to the organisms which grow next, and that a series of organisms may be concerned in the changes in the food. A brief discussion of the spoilage of the main groups of human foods (listed at the beginning of Chapter 24) will aid in the summary of the principles involved in the spoilage of raw foods.

Cereals and Cereal Products

Cereals and most cereal products, if properly prepared and handled, are too dry for growth of any microorganism. A little added moisture, as in the case of bread, permits spoilage by molds, provided that aerobic conditions are present. A considerable amount of added water would permit bacterial or yeast growth. Wet flour or corn mash is likely to undergo an acid fermentation due to lactic acid bacteria and possibly a yeast fermentation. This is to be expected because of the presence of fermentable carbohydrates, which, although consisting mostly of starch, contain some sugar for the bacteria and yeasts. The storage of the dry products tends to reduce the predominating organisms to those most resistant to drying. Spores of bacteria and of molds are, therefore, apt to be present in large proportions in cereals and cereal products.

Sugar and Sugar Products

Sugar is a nonperishable product. It is only when it has taken up water that sugar will undergo microbial decomposition. Sirups, because of their high concentration of sugar, are likely to support the growth of yeasts or molds. Candies of the soft center type may be spoiled by yeasts or by bacteria able to grow in fairly high sugar concentrations. The so-called bursting or "explosion" of chocolates may be caused by the production of gas by microorganisms, usually anaerobic bacteria, and the expulsion of part of the fondant through some weak spot in the chocolate coating. The spoilage of honey is usually due to yeasts which are termed **osmophilic** because they grow best in high concentrations of sugar.

Vegetables

In a consideration of the spoilage of vegetables and fruits it is especially important to remember that deterioration may be due to action of the plant enzymes as well as to activity of microorganisms. In some cases self-decomposition of the plant products is the main cause of spoilage; microbial growth is only incidental. Damage to fruits and vegetables may begin before harvesting as the result of growth of plant pathogens (organisms causing diseases of plants). These organisms usually are fungi, such as molds, but may be viruses or bacteria. The "rots," so begun, may expand during handling of the products. Other rots may begin after the fruit or vegetable has been harvested.

The leafy vegetables, such as lettuce, spinach, and broccoli, undergo decomposition due to their own enzymes, even when the growth of micro-organisms is prevented. If these products are moistened and piled, however, they heat due to their own enzymes and to bacteria, and the further growth of bacteria is favored. Enormous numbers of bacteria may accumulate on piled lettuce or spinach under these conditions, and sliminess and off odors may result. This does not mean that the vegetable is necessarily unsafe to eat; it is, however, unattractive. The leafy vegetables usually are stored at temperatures low enough to favor growth of slime-forming bacteria, but at higher temperatures may undergo an acid fermentation of the carbohydrates present. Similarly string beans, shelled peas, and ears of sweet corn heat and have large increases in bacterial content in a similar manner. Because of the considerable amounts of available carbohydrate they contain and because storage is customarily at room temperature an acid fermentation is favored, and it is said that the product "sours."

In contrast to the perishable leafy vegetables, most root and tuber vege-tables, such as carrots, beets, and potatoes, are considered semiperishable products. Since the inner tissues of such vegetables ordinarily are sterile, spoilage by microorganisms must start from the outside, usually at some damaged spot or wound in the outer covering. There, conditions are dry and aerobic, and molds are most likely to grow and cause rotting. As a matter of fact, microbial spoilage of these foods is less common than self-decomposi-tion.

The spoilage of finished sauerkraut and pickles has been discussed briefly earlier in this chapter in the paragraph on the influence of acidity of a prod-uct on the type of spoilage. It will be recalled that molds and film yeasts are likely to grow upon the upper surface of such acid products, reduce the acidity, and prepare the way for the growth and action of bacteria. Sauer-kraut and pickles also are subject to spoilage during the course of their fermentations. A darkening at the surface of sauerkraut is due to growth of aerobic organisms. Uneven salting of the cabbage sometimes causes dark spots within the regions of high salt content. The salt inhibits the action of the desired lactic acid bacteria and permits the growth of proteolytic or other undesirable bacteria able to withstand 5 to 7 per cent of salt. High con-centrations of salt also may favor the growth of yeasts, and a pink nonspore-forming yeast has been found to cause pink kraut. Soft kraut results from a faulty fermentation, and has been blamed on too high temperatures, aera-tion, and the use of old vats. Slimy kraut is due to the growth of certain capsule-forming strains of *Lactobacillus plantarum*.

In addition to spoilage caused by film yeasts and molds, pickle makers have trouble with several other defects among which are: (1) Slippery pickles, due to the growth of capsulated bacteria on the surface of the cucumber; this takes place when the cucumbers or pickles are not properly "keyed down" or weighted down, and consequently are exposed to the air. (2) Soft pickles, the result of the action of pectin-fermenting bacteria, which in their decomposition of this binding substance cause a softening of the pickle. This defect usually is attributed to too low a salt content of the brine, and too high a temperature; exposure to air also induces the trouble. (3) Black pickles, the darkening of which sometimes is blamed onto iron and gypsum in the water, has been shown to be due to the growth of *Bacillus nigrificans* in some instances.

Fruits

Fruits have sterile inner tissues and dry protective skins or coverings; and, like vegetables, are usually attacked by molds through a damaged spot or wound which allows a little of the juice to escape. In addition, most fruits are acid and thus favor the growth of molds. If much of the juice exudes, however, yeasts are apt to grow and cause an alcoholic fermentation within the fruit. While the rotting of most fruits is caused by molds, the so-called rotting of the banana is merely over-ripeness due to action of its own enzymes. Most fruits have a stage of ripeness or maturity considered most desirable and are unfit to eat when over-ripe. Such spoilage should not be confused with microbial spoilage.

Fermented fruit juices, such as wines or ciders, because of their content of alcohol are most likely to undergo an acetic acid fermentation if conditions are aerobic. If conditions are anaerobic, bacteria may cause acid formation, cloudiness, and bitterness.

Milk and Dairy Products

The decomposition of milk and milk products will be discussed in Chapters 26 and 27. Milk is a good culture medium for many bacteria, for it contains the necessary food substances and plenty of moisture, and is nearly neutral in reaction. Since lactose or milk sugar is available to many bacteria, an acid fermentation is the one most likely to occur, unless environmental conditions are such as to prevent it. For instance, milk may undergo proteolysis if the storage temperature is too low for the acid-formers or if the acid-formers have been killed and only proteolytic bacteria survive, as is the case in boiled milk.

The acidity of dairy products like cheese or fermented milks favors spoilage by molds; in addition, cheese may be fairly dry on the surface. Butter, because of its high fat, low moisture, and salt content is likely to mold if air is available.

Meats

Meats, like milk, contain the nutrients needed by most bacteria, and are high in moisture and neutral in reaction. At room temperatures bacteria grow rapidly in meats and may reach enormous numbers. Most of the growth will ordinarily be on the surface in an uncut piece of meat, but when the amount of surface is increased and the bacteria are distributed, as in ground meat, growth is very rapid and takes place throughout the meat. Since there is much protein and little carbohydrate present, nonacid-forming bacteria will predominate, and proteolysis will be the chief type of decomposition. Anaerobic conditions favor putrefaction and aerobic conditions favor simple proteolysis or "souring." Meat held at room temperatures usually shows putrefaction because anaerobic conditions exist throughout most of it; at the surface, sliminess or simple proteolysis would be expected. Refrigerator temperatures, however, are too low for most putrefactive bacteria and sliminess and "souring" are likely. When dressed meat is hung at chilling temperatures, the growth of most kinds of bacteria is prevented. If the meats are moist on the surface, a slimy growth of bacteria may result, but the meats are usually too dry on the surface for anything but mold growth. Change from refrigerator to room temperature may cause condensation of moisture on the surface and may encourage the growth of bacteria. This often happens with wieners, and as a result they become slimy on the surface.

In addition to changes caused by microorganisms, stored raw meats undergo changes caused by their own enzymes. Some consumers prefer beef which has been "hung" for a period at chilling temperatures to permit this "ripening" due to enzymes to take place.

Undrawn poultry undergoes changes due to growth of bacteria on the skin and on the mucous membranes of the intestinal tract. When the chicken is drawn there is a distribution of bacteria throughout the body cavity and a probability of hastened deterioration.

Eggs

The contents of most fresh eggs are free from microorganisms and will remain so unless contamination enters through the shell. As long as the shell remains dry, penetration by microorganisms is difficult, but high humidity in the surrounding air will allow molds to enter, and condensed moisture on the shell surface will permit bacterial invasion. Eggs are stored commercially at temperatures slightly above freezing; hence during storage, conditions are more favorable to molds than to bacteria.

Fresh eggs are high in moisture, neutral in reaction, high in protein and low in carbohydrate, and contain other nutrients favorable to microbial growth. Such a composition favors proteolysis, and the spoilage of eggs may be putrefactive or proteolytic without objectionable odors, depending upon the type of proteolytic organism involved.

Over long storage periods, even at chilling temperatures, the contents of the egg gradually become more alkaline and changes take place in the physical properties. These changes should not be confused with microbial spoilage. Special preservative methods, such as treatment of the shells with hot mineral oil under a vacuum, or storage of the eggs in an atmosphere with a definite percentage of carbon dioxide, slow down these physical changes.

Sea Foods

The general principles discussed under the heading of spoilage of meats, hold for spoilage of fish and other sea foods. Breakdown due to autolysis and to bacteria is very rapid unless special preventive methods are used. The chief sources of bacteria are the gills, the intestinal tract, and the slime on the outside surface of the fish. Bacteria are believed to spread to the flesh of the fish from the gills by means of the blood. There are many chances for heavy contamination with bacteria during the handling and dressing of fish, starting with the boat in which they are landed.

Unopened fish at ordinary temperatures usually spoil with bad odors, but cleaned fish held at icebox temperatures usually undergo autolysis together with "souring" or proteolysis by bacteria without such bad odors. Oysters may sour at room temperatures or undergo proteolysis at ice box temperature.

The foregoing examples of the spoilage of different classes of food illustrate the fact that the composition of a raw food and the environmental conditions govern the type of spoilage that will take place, and select the microorganisms which will cause this decomposition.

HEATED FOODS

Thus far the discussion has been concerned chiefly with the spoilage of raw foods. Pasteurized and canned foods, which have been heated, are subject to special types of decomposition due to the selective action of the high temperature on the microorganisms present in the raw food. Naturally the greater the heat treatment the fewer will be the kinds and numbers of surviving microorganisms. It will be recalled from Chapter 10 that vegetative cells of microorganisms are more easily killed by heat than are spores of these organisms; that vegetative cells of different species vary considerably in their resistance to heat, as do the spores of the spore-formers; and that bacterial spores are, in general, considerably more resistant to heat than are mold or yeast spores. It would be expected, then, that a moderate heat treatment would kill only part of the vegetative cells of bacteria and most of those of yeasts and molds. A harsher heat treatment (e.g., exposure to 100° C. for 5 minutes) would be expected to kill all microbial vegetative cells, spores of yeasts and molds, and some of the less resistant bacterial spores. As the temperature of heating is increased, fewer and fewer kinds of bacterial spores could survive, until finally a high enough temperature would destroy all. Therefore the time and temperature at which foods have been heated are very important in the determination of the organisms to survive and hence the type of decomposition likely to take place. The treatment of the food following the heat process is important, of course; unless the food is protected from contamination after heating, spoilage like that of raw food may take place. The canning of food and other methods of packaging prevent such recontamination.

Pasteurized Foods

Since the usual methods of pasteurization kill only the yeasts, molds, and some but not all of the vegetative cells of bacteria, a variety of bacteria may be left, and the type of spoilage will depend upon the conditions under which the food is kept. Enough acid formers usually survive the pasteurization of milk to cause souring, but they may be eliminated to such an extent that proteolysis may take place. Often pasteurized foods spoil as a result of recontamination or under-pasteurization, and the spoilage is then similar to that of the raw foods.

Canned Foods

The heat treatments given foods in glass containers or tin cans vary with the product, and may range from pasteurizing temperatures to those obtained with high pressures of steam. Since these heat processes have been proved efficient by practical test, spoilage of the product should result only when the food is underprocessed, or when it is contaminated subsequent to heating. A heat process that is effective for preservation of an average sample of raw food may be insufficient if the food has been more heavily loaded with spoilage organisms than usual, or if the heat penetration is slower than usual because of increased thickness or difference in composition. Recontamination may result through a leak in the container or may occur after the container has been opened. Acid foods such as tomatoes and sauerkraut, processed at 100° C. or below, may even be spoiled by nonspore-formers, chiefly lactobacilli. Spore-formers of the "flat sour" type, to be discussed in following paragraphs, are a common cause of spoilage of tomatoes and tomato juice. Tomato catsup often is underprocessed and goes acid and "off" in flavor. As acid a fruit as pineapple, with a pH ordinarily below 4.5, may be spoiled by a spore-forming anaerobe unless properly heat processed.

Spoilage of **commercially canned foods** processed with steam under pressure is limited almost entirely to the action of very heat-resistant, spore-forming bacteria. In low acid or medium acid foods four types of spoilage by spore-forming bacteria are important; three by thermophilic bacteria, and one by a mesophilic organism.

1. **"Flat sour"** spoilage, occurring chiefly in low acid vegetables, is caused by spore-forming bacilli which are facultative anaerobes and may be faculative or obligate thermophiles. The spores of some strains of these flat sour bacteria are very resistant to heat, and may survive the heat process ordinarily given to canned peas, corn, or similar products. If the can of food is cooled too slowly after the process, growth may take place at temperatures favorable to thermophiles, and if facultative thermophiles are present they will be able to continue growth at ordinary storage temperatures. The term "flat sour" is used because the cans remain flat, i.e., not swollen, and a sour or acid flavor develops in the food as the result of the formation of lactic acid. A flat sour spoilage also may occur in canned tomato juice with production of an off flavor which has been described as "phenolic."

2. **"T.A."** spoilage is spoilage by the anaerobic, spore-forming, obligate thermophile *Clostridium thermosaccharolyticum*. It is characterized by the production of large amounts of carbon dioxide and hydrogen which cause swelling of and even bursting of the can. As the gas is evolved and the gas pressure gradually increases, the can, as it goes through stages of swelling, is termed: a **flipper** when both ends of the can may be pushed in, but one end bulges when the side of the can is tapped; a **springer** when one end of the can is bulged and the other flat, and pressure on the bulged end flattens it and bulges the opposite end, or when both ends are bulged, but one end can be flattened readily; a **soft swell** when the gas pressure has increased, but the swelling leaves the can soft enough for the ends to be pushed in slightly; and a **hard swell** when the gas pressure is so great that no part of the can can be pressed in. Ultimately the pressure may cause bursting of the can. The flavor of the product usually is harmed by the bacterial action, and

the texture may be damaged. Figure 57 shows different degrees of gas production in cans of food.

3. **Sulfide** or "stinker" spoilage is due to the survival and growth of *Clostridium nigrificans*, a spore-forming, anaerobic, obligate thermophile which produces hydrogen sulfide. Since this gas is very soluble in water, the can does not swell and shows no outward evidence of spoilage of the contents. The hydrogen sulfide may react with any iron present to form the black sulfide of iron. The spoilage is characterized, then, by the odor of hydrogen sulfide and the darkening of the food. Canned corn or peas are most often affected, although the trouble is not encountered as often as the two previously mentioned types of spoilage caused by thermophiles. The

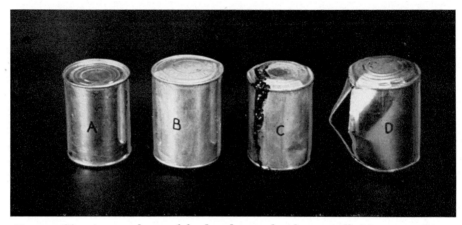

FIGURE 57. A normal can of food and cans that have swelled because of gas produced by anaerobic spore forming bacteria. **A.** The normal can has concave ends because of the partial vacuum inside. **B.** A swelled can with ends bulged out. **C.** A swelled can with leaks where the seams are breaking. **D.** A burst can.

spores of *Clostridium nigrificans* are not as resistant to heat as are those of *Clostridium thermosaccharolyticum*, and these spores in turn usually are less resistant than those of the bacteria causing flat sour spoilage.

4. **Putrefaction** by mesophilic, putrefactive, spore-forming anaerobes may cause the spoilage of canned meats and other canned proteinaceous foods. The resistance to heat of spores of these anaerobes differs with the species or strain. In general, this resistance is not as great as that possessed by the spores of the thermophiles, but a few strains have been shown to form very heat-resistant spores. The type of spoilage is characterized by gas production with obnoxious odors and flavors; hydrogen sulfide, mercaptans, butyric acid, ammonia, hydrogen, and carbon dioxide are among the volatile products of bacterial action; swelling of the can usually is produced, with all of the degrees of gas pressure described above. Among the putrefactive, ana-

erobic spore-formers is *Clostridium parabotulinum,* a food poisoning organism which will be discussed further in Chapter 31. Commercial canners give canned foods heat processes more than sufficient to kill the spores of this organism, but home canners sometimes use processes that are insufficient.

The four types of spoilage which have been described are the ones usually encountered in commercially canned foods, but when cans of food have leaks or have been grossly underprocessed, vegetative cells or spores which are not especially heat resistant may survive, grow, and cause spoilage similar to that encountered in pasteurized or raw foods.

The kinds of spoilage of canned foods discussed above are those caused by microorganisms, and therefore are termed biological spoilage as contrasted with chemical spoilage in which no microorganisms are involved and the spoilage is the result of the chemical action alone. The most common type of chemical spoilage results in the so-called "hydrogen swells," which are caused by the action of acid in the foods on the iron of the tinned iron container or can, and the resultant evolution of hydrogen. All of the different degrees of gas pressure described under "T.A." spoilage may accumulate and here, too, bursting may result eventually. Hydrogen swells are the commonest type of spoilage of very acid canned foods like sour cherries, sauerkraut, and rhubarb. The higher the temperature of storage, the faster is the evolution of the hydrogen and hence the more rapid the swelling; the presence of oxygen in the can due to poor evacuation likewise hastens the action.

It is the accepted practice to discard all swollen cans of food, even if only a small amount of pressure is present in the can.

The type of spoilage encountered in **home canned foods** will vary with the food involved and the heat treatment used. When temperatures no higher than 100° C. (212° F.) are employed in heat processing, bacterial spores with comparatively low heat resistance may survive and cause the spoilage. For this reason spoilage by sugar-splitting anaerobes or putrefactive anaerobes sometimes occurs. Fortunately the housewife usually cans food that is fairly fresh and carries a light "load" of microorganisms. Because she does things on a small scale, she is not likely to encounter trouble with the highly resistant spores of the flat sour or "T.A." bacteria, which enter the commercial product chiefly from apparatus and equipment of the canning plant. Therefore she may have what she calls good luck, despite a mild heat treatment; but may have trouble when resistant spores get into the food. Leakage of the closure of the container is a common difficulty in home canning, with the resulting growth of molds or other aerobic microorganisms over the surface of the food. Flat sour spoilage of tomatoes is fairly common. When the pressure sterilizer is used properly, little spoilage should be encountered.

REFERENCES

Annual Reports and Special Bulletins of the Food Investigation Board (Great Britain). London, H. M. Stationery Office.

Jensen, L. B., *Microbiology of meats* (2nd ed.). Champaign, Ill., Garrard Press, 1945.

Tanner, F. W., *The microbiology of foods* (2nd ed.). Champaign, Ill., Garrard Press, 1944.

Thom, C., and Hunter, A. C., *Hygienic fundamentals of food handling*. Baltimore, Md., Williams & Wilkins, 1924.

26. MICROBIOLOGY OF MILK

In Chapter 24 it was pointed out that methods based on one or more of the following principles may be used in the preservation of foods: (1) asepsis, or keeping out microorganisms, by reduction or prevention of contamination; (2) inhibition or prevention of growth and activity; and (3) killing or removal of microorganisms. Methods which are used in the preservation of milk and milk products employ these same principles.

Milk is a good culture medium for many microorganisms, for it has a nearly neutral reaction and is well buffered. It contains plenty of water; a sugar, lactose, which is fermentable by many microorganisms; a variety of nitrogenous foods, including several proteins and small amounts of simpler nitrogenous compounds; and an assortment of minerals. Since a main criterion of the quality of milk is the number of bacteria present, the prevention of contamination and of growth, and the killing of microorganisms, are important in the production of milk of high quality.

Contamination of Milk and Its Prevention (Asepsis)

In the course of production of milk or the manufacture of dairy products there is opportunity for entrance of molds, yeasts, and bacteria, and under many conditions there is a chance for growth of these microorganisms. But because of the composition and the conditions of handling of dairy products, certain types of microorganisms and of bacteria in particular are most apt to increase in numbers. The bacteria most likely to be of importance are the "lactics," the coliform bacteria (species of the genera *Escherichia* and *Aerobacter*) and species of the genus *Clostridium*. Usually of lesser importance

319

are the proteolytic bacteria, lipolytic bacteria, acid-forming micrococci, and others.

The "lactics" are bacteria which have been grouped together because they produce mostly lactic acid and but small amounts of other products in their fermentation of sugars. In a medium such as milk, acid-forming bacteria are apt to grow rapidly and predominate under ordinary conditions. *Streptococcus lactis,* the most commonly encountered member of the group of milk "lactics," is usually responsible for the souring of raw milk and is used in the manufacture of many dairy products. It grows well at temperatures of from 20° to 30° C., and will increase in numbers at temperatures as low as 10° to 15° C. or as high as 40° C. Lactic bacteria of the genus *Lactobacillus* are important in the manufacture of certain dairy products and are responsible for the very high acidity developed in milk on standing, especially if the milk has been held at 37° to 50° C.

Bacteria of the **coliform** group form acids (chiefly lactic and acetic) and gases (carbon dioxide and hydrogen), and are considered undesirable in all dairy products. *Escherichia coli* and *Aerobacter aerogenes* are the commonly found representatives of the group.

Spore-forming, anaerobic bacteria of the genus *Clostridium* may cause gas and off-flavors in some dairy products. In milk these organisms usually are crowded out by acid-forming bacteria; but may grow and cause a "stormy" fermentation, so-called because the curd is torn to shreds by gas.

The proteolytic and lipolytic bacteria, micrococci, etc., usually are outgrown and suppressed by the acid-formers, but may be active under special conditions. For example, proteolysis may take place in milk held at 5° C., a temperature too low for most acid formers, or in boiled milk in which all vegetative cells have been killed and only spores of proteolytic bacteria have survived.

Of the pathogenic bacteria which may enter milk only a few kinds are able to grow there: *Salmonella typhosa,* the cause of typhoid fever; other species of the genus *Salmonella,* some of which cause intestinal disorders; hemolytic (red blood cell-dissolving) species of the genus *Streptococcus;* and *Brucella abortus,* the cause of undulant fever. These bacteria are able to grow rapidly only at temperatures of from 30° to 40° C. If the number of pathogens already present in milk were to increase due to growth, the likelihood of consumer infection would also increase.

Contamination from the Udder. Although milk usually is sterile when secreted by the cow, it becomes contaminated with bacteria before it leaves the udder. The milk cisterns and ducts of a normal, healthy udder contain a characteristic flora of bacteria which grow there between milkings and contaminate the milk before it is drawn. Since the first streams of milk contain more bacteria than milk drawn subsequently, this foremilk is sometimes discarded when milk with especially low bacterial content is desired. Milk samples from different cows and even from different quarters of the udder of the same cow may vary considerably in numbers of bacteria present. Aspetically drawn milk from a healthy udder may contain numbers of bacteria ranging from a few per milliliter to several thousand. The most commonly found bacteria are cocci, mostly micrococci, with occasional streptococci. Many of the micrococci are chromogenic and form yellow or orange colored colonies when grown on an agar medium. The udder cocci do not grow rapidly in milk under ordinary conditions and cannot compete successfully with some of the bacteria which enter the milk later from other sources. Many of the udder cocci are acid-proteolytic; that is, they form some acid and have enzymes which aid in curdling the milk and partially decompose the proteins of milk.

Diseased udders may introduce into the milk organisms pathogenic to animals or to man, and may cause a considerable increase in the numbers of bacteria in aseptically drawn milk. Bacteria which cause tuberculosis, undulant fever, or mastitis may be introduced in this way. This subject will be discussed in more detail in Chapters 30, 31 and 32.

Contamination from the udder, then, introduces comparatively few bacteria into milk, and these are kinds that ordinarily are not involved in the spoilage of milk or in the manufacture of dairy products. Consequently, this contamination is not of great commercial importance.

Contamination of milk from the udder may be reduced by selection of animals giving milk with low counts of bacteria. This usually is not practicable, except when the extra cost of such a procedure is balanced by a high price for the milk.

Contamination from the Air. Under ordinary conditions neither numbers nor kinds of microorganisms in the air of the stable or elsewhere are important in the contamination of milk, but this contamination may be significant when dust has been raised previous to or during milking. Sweeping, feeding dry fodder, or bedding down or brushing the cows may bring enough dust into the air to introduce appreciable numbers of microorganisms into the milk, although only a few thousand per milliliter are added under the worst conditions. Ordinary precautions will reduce contamination from the air to negligible amounts. Use of milking machines will reduce contamination from the air.

The kinds of bacteria introduced from air are those found in fodder, soil, and manure. Most of these organisms cannot compete with the more actively growing acid-forming bacteria in milk, and consequently are not concerned ordinarily in the spoilage of milk. If, however, acid-formers are absent, bacteria from the air may grow and change the milk. "Sweet curdling" by rennin-forming bacteria may take place under such conditions. These bacteria contain an enzyme which is similar to the casein-coagulating enzyme, rennin, found in the rennet extract from calves' stomachs and used in coagulating milk for cheese manufacture.

Contamination from the Coat of the Cow. Among the foreign materials which may drop into the milk during milking are manure, bedding, soil, and hair. The amount of this contamination is decreased by keeping the cows under conditions that will reduce the mud and manure on the animal's coat, by clipping the flanks, by wiping the flanks and udder with a damp cloth before milking, and by use of a small-topped milk pail or a properly treated milking machine. The numbers of microorganisms introduced will depend, of course, upon the kind and amount of foreign matter dropping into the milk, and will vary from a few per milliliter up to thousands; many of these grow well in milk and may increase in numbers rapidly if given the opportunity. Bacteria of the coliform group or gas-forming species of *Clostridium* which get into milk from this source may cause undesirable fermentations in the milk, or may ruin the quality of cheese or other products made from the milk. There is also a slight possibility of the entrance of animal or human pathogens into the milk by contamination from the animal's coat.

Contamination from the Milker. Comparatively small numbers of microorganisms are introduced into the milk by the milker directly, but his methods may influence the extent of contamination from other sources. The milker may, however, contaminate the milk with bacteria which cause human diseases.

Contamination from Flies. The number of microorganisms introduced into milk by flies is not large, but may include undesirable kinds of bacteria such as those of the coliform group, clostridia, lactics, etc., and sometimes pathogenic bacteria.

Contamination from Utensils. Of all sources of contamination of milk with microorganisms, the utensils are most likely to cause a large increase in numbers of microorganisms. These contaminants are likely to be able to grow rapidly in milk or dairy products, and can cause undesirable changes or spoilage. Classed as utensils are the equipment and containers with which the milk comes in contact, such as: milk pails, milking machines, strainers, cans, coolers, stirrers, separators, clarifiers, pipes, pumps, homogenizers, vats or kettles, bottle fillers, and bottles. Usually milk or some residue of organic matter derived from milk constituents, is left in a utensil after it has been cleansed by ordinary methods, especially if there are cracks, open joints, corners difficult to brush, rust spots, or similar defects. With this food present, all that is needed for growth of bacteria to take place is sufficient moisture and a favorable temperature. Because of this increase in numbers, there will be an increased amount of contamination of milk when it comes into contact with the utensil, and hence there will be larger bacterial counts on the milk. Depending upon the condition of the utensils, this increase in count may range from comparatively few bacteria to several millions per milliliter of milk. And since the culture medium in the utensil has been very much like milk, the organisms which have grown will undoubtedly be bacteria favored by a milk medium, and therefore of importance in the spoilage of milk. The so-called "lactics," and especially *Streptococcus lactis*, often predominate. Some of the lactics multiply at fairly low temperatures and all can cause souring of milk. The gas-forming, acid-forming coliform bacteria usually are present in improperly treated utensils; they grow well in milk and are undesirable in milk to be used for the manufacture of dairy products. Spore-forming bacteria occasionally enter the milk in considerable numbers from utensils, and thermophiles have been traced back to this source.

The method of treatment to reduce and keep low the number of bacteria will vary with the kind of utensil. First the utensil is made as clean as possible by a rinse of cool water, scrubbing, and thorough cleansing with aid of a washing powder or other detergent solution. Pails and cans may be steamed or immersed in hot water (180°–200° F.) and inverted to drain and dry, or may be treated with a disinfectant solution of calcium or sodium hypochlorite, one of the "chloramines" (100 to 200 p.p.m. of available chlorine), or a quaternary ammonium compound. The pail or can should be not only clean but thoroughly dry to prevent growth of microorganisms. Separators, clarifiers, and similar equipment may be taken apart to be cleaned and dried. Milking machines, cream separators, and homogenizers present special problems and are often the source of heavy contamination of milk with bacteria. Equipment of this kind is hard to take apart and clean and dry effectively. A commonly used procedure is to clean and then steam or disinfect pipelines and similar parts which can be reached readily, and then place the remaining parts in an antiseptic solution of caustic soda (0.3 to 0.5 per cent aqueous solution of lye), trisodium phosphate, or a similar alkaline compound. This soaking is continued until time for use of the equipment; it is then emptied and rinsed with water. The teat cup assembly of the milking machine needs such special attention.

Utensils, then, unless properly treated and cared for may be the most important cause of increase in the numbers of bacteria in milk due to outside contamination and are a source of undesirable kinds of microorganisms.

PRESERVATION BY USE OF LOW TEMPERATURES (INHIBITION OF GROWTH
AND ACTIVITY)

It has been pointed out that the microorganism count in milk or other
dairy products at any stage of production will depend not only on the numbers which enter, but on their growth or increase in numbers. Freshly drawn
milk is at the body temperature of the cow, and unless cooling is prompt
and thorough, there will be opportunity for considerable increase in numbers of bacteria. It will be recalled from the discussion of growth phases of
bacteria in Chapter 9, that upon inoculation there is usually first a lag phase
during which there is little or no growth of bacteria; this phase precedes the
phase of rapid growth. The prolongation of the lag phase by any of the
means mentioned in Chapters 9 and 10 is of importance in the maintenance
of a low bacterial count in milk. Milk as it comes from the cow has antiseptic properties, but the growth of bacteria is inhibited only briefly, and
then only certain kinds are inhibited. The condition of the microbial cells
present, their number, and their adaptation to the milk and to the conditions under which it is being held will influence the length of time before
rapid multiplication of microorganisms will begin. A sudden drop in temperature, as in the cooling process, or a sudden rise, as in pasteurization, will
tend to lengthen the lag period.

The extent of multiplication of the bacteria present in the milk will depend not only upon the temperature at which the milk is held, but also
upon the time of holding. The lower the temperature is reduced toward
freezing, the slower will be the increase in numbers of bacteria; and the
longer the time of holding, the greater will be the increase in numbers.
Milk cooled to 60° F. (15.5° C.) will show only a slow growth of bacteria
—and growth of certain kinds only, such as the lactic acid bacteria. A temperature of 50° F. (10° C.) is still more effective in slowing down or stopping bacterial growth. Lactics, for example, would be greatly inhibited, and
ropy milk bacteria or some of those causing bitterness might predominate
after long storage. It should be recalled, however, that some bacteria can
grow at temperatures only slightly above the freezing point. Therefore, if
enough time is allowed, bacteria will grow and spoil milk even when it is
held at low temperatures. Properly produced milk cooled to 50° F. (10° C.)
and held there will keep long enough for practical purposes, especially if
other preservative methods, e.g., pasteurization, are used in addition to low
temperatures.

Milk that has been frozen slowly or held in the frozen condition for some
length of time does not regain its normal appearance or consistency on
thawing. Hence, market milk is not preserved in this way, although growth

of bacteria would be prevented by such low temperatures. Cream to be used for certain purposes may be stored in the frozen condition, and thus protected against bacterial action. But it will deteriorate, in time, due to enzymatic action and oxidation.

PRESERVATION BY HEAT

Pasteurization has been defined in Chapter 24 as the heat treatment, usually below the boiling point of water, that kills part but not all of the microorganisms present. Milk and some milk products are pasteurized by one of two methods: (1) the low-temperature, long-time or holding method; or (2) the high-temperature, short-time or flash method. In the holding method the milk is heated to 143° to 145° F. (61.7° to 62.8° C.) and held at that temperature for 30 minutes. In the high-temperature, short-time method heating usually is at 160° F. (71.1° C.) or higher for at least 15 seconds. The higher the temperature used, the shorter is the necessary time of exposure. After pasteurization by either method the milk or milk product is rapidly cooled to 50° F. (10° C.) or lower, and held at that temperature so that the heat treatment is terminated and the temperature is low enough to inhibit bacterial growth. In the holding method comparatively large volumes of milk are heated in special vats. In the flash method there is a continuous flow of milk through the apparatus, with the milk in thin layers at the time of heat exposure, due to the use of small-bore tubes, plates that are close together, or similar devices. One method uses electricity as the heating agent, and thus effects a rapid generation of heat throughout the milk.

In the pasteurization of milk an attempt is made to destroy a large percentage of the microorganisms present without harm to the appearance, flavor, creaming power, or nutritive value of the milk. These objectives are accomplished by the correct application of the methods of pasteurization mentioned. In addition, these methods guarantee the killing of pathogenic microorganisms which might be present in the raw milk. The times and temperatures used allow a margin of safety in that the heat treatment is more than is necessary to kill the more resistant pathogens like the tubercle bacillus, *Mycobacterium tuberculosis*. This organism is killed in 15 minutes at 140° F. (60° C.), in 10 minutes at 142° F. (61.1° C.), and in 6 minutes at 145° F. (62.8° C.); all other pathogens likely to be present in raw milk are more easily killed. Therefore a heat treatment of 30 minutes at 142° to 145° F. (61.1° to 62.8° C.) or 15 seconds at 160° F. (71.1° C.) is considerably more than enough to kill the common pathogens.

Care should be taken to prevent recontamination of the milk following pasteurization, for not only may spoilage organisms enter in this way, but there is a possibility of the entrance of pathogenic bacteria, such as *Salmonella typhosa* and other *Salmonella* organisms. Recontamination may come from the entrance of unpasteurized milk because of some defect in the apparatus, from improperly treated equipment, from the workers, or from flies. The remedies are obviously a careful checkup of apparatus and operations, periodic examination of employees by physicians, and proper screening and other methods for the elimination of flies.

The percentage reduction of numbers of bacteria by pasteurization will vary with the numbers and kinds originally present, but usually is between 90 and 99 per cent. The kinds of bacteria most likely to survive pasteurization, and therefore called "thermoduric" bacteria, are the spore-forming bacteria, some of the lactobacilli, certain micrococci, *Streptococcus thermophilus* and similar streptococci, and thermophiles. The number of thermophilic bacteria sometimes increases during forewarming previous to pasteurization; during the heating and holding, especially in parts of the milk like foam and splash which do not receive the full heat treatment; and after the heating if cooling is not prompt. The increase of bacteria due to growth of thermophiles does not affect the keeping quality of the milk, but will give increased counts when the milk is tested by control laboratories. Most of the bacteria which survive pasteurization are not significant in the spoilage of milk and will not grow well as long as the milk is kept cool. Pasteurized milk ordinarily will sour if exposed to room temperatures, but bacteria other than lactics often are concerned in the spoilage, particularly species which cause protein decomposition.

Sterilization of milk by steam under pressure (at 240° to 245° F. or 115.5° to 118.3° C. for 15 or more minutes) is used in the preservation of canned evaporated milk. Most cans of evaporated milk are really sterile and contain no living microorganisms; a few cans contain spores of bacteria, but are "commercially sterile" because conditions in the can will not permit the growth of the surviving bacteria.

Preservation by Drying

Drying is used in the preservation of milk and some milk products. Not enough water is removed in the manufacture of evaporated milk to inhibit the growth of most microorganisms. The same is true of sweetened condensed milk, but here the added sugar ties up water which would otherwise be available and increases the osmotic pressure to a level inhibitory to most bacteria. The high sugar content (53–60 per cent), together with the evacuation and hermetic sealing of the can, are the chief factors concerned in the preservation of sweetened condensed milk. Whole milk, skim milk, and whey may be dried sufficiently to preserve them. Exposure of a thin film or fine spray of milk or whey to high temperatures rapidly removes most of the water; the resulting dry milk (milk powder) or dry whey, with only about 4 per cent of water, contains insufficient available moisture to permit the growth of microorganisms. Buttermilk may be condensed for use as an animal feed and may even be dried to a powder.

Preservation by Fermentation (Chemical Preservation)

The preservation of milk by fermentation to buttermilks or fermented milks will be discussed in Chapter 27. Enough acid is produced by lactic acid bacteria to prevent the growth and activity of proteolytic or lipolytic bacteria. Lactic acid produced by fermentation also is partly responsible for the preservation of most kinds of cheese. As will be pointed out in Chapter 27, other factors such as salt, low temperatures, and drying play a part in the preservation of cheese.

Preservation by Rays, Sound Waves, and Pressure

Ultraviolet rays have been tried in the preservation of milk, but are not used to any extent at present. The flavor is affected by too much exposure to ultraviolet radiations, and the opacity of milk makes penetration of the rays difficult unless the milk is in such an extremely thin layer that the flow is slow. The use of sound waves for the treatment of milk is still in an experimental stage. The "Hofius Process" for the preservation of milk at low temperatures under high pressures of oxygen has been mentioned in Chapter 24.

Growth and Activity of Microorganisms in Milk

The rate and amount of growth of microorganisms in milk, as well as the kind and extent of the changes they produce, depend upon environmental conditions. The temperature of the milk and the length of time it is held influence the numbers and kinds of microorganisms to develop, and the type of spoilage which results. In general, the higher the temperature is raised from freezing toward the respective optimum temperatures of the bacteria in the milk, the more rapid will be their growth and the spoilage of the milk. Changes in storage temperature favor the growth of different types of bacteria and hence different types of spoilage. Acid-formers are not likely to grow at temperatures just above freezing; instead, proteolytic bacteria are apt to predominate and cause bitter or other off-flavors in the milk without much outward evidence of growth. At temperatures to which milk often is cooled, around 15° C., *Streptococcus lactis* and related bacteria may grow, produce acid, and finally curdle the milk. *Aerobacter* species likewise may be able to grow and may increase in numbers enough to make the milk undesirable for use in cheese making. Both of these types of bacteria can grow well when the temperature is raised to 20° C. and above. When the temperature is as high as 37° C., coliform bacteria can grow well, but most of the lactic acid-forming streptococci are inhibited. *Streptococcus thermophilus* and various species of *Lactobacillus* grow well at 37° C. and above. At 45° to 50° C. these lactic bacteria are most likely to predominate, produce acid, and curdle the milk. At 55° to 60° C. obligate thermophiles grow, and may or may not cause obvious changes in the milk.

The series of changes usually undergone by raw milk at room temperature has been mentioned in Chapter 25. It is to be expected that a good culture medium like milk, nearly neutral in reaction and containing moderate amounts of a fermentable sugar, would first be subject to fermentation with the production of acid. *Streptococcus lactis* or other lactics are most likely to grow, form acids (mostly lactic), curdle the milk, and cease growth when a limiting amount of acid has been developed. Members of the coliform group, micrococci, and other acid-formers may aid in this first formation of acid. Next to grow are the more acid-tolerant lactobacilli, which develop still more acidity, until in some cases the titrable acidity may be as high as 4 per cent (calculated as lactic acid) and often reaches 2.5 to 3 per cent. This high acidity effectively prevents the growth of other bacteria; but permits the growth of molds and film yeasts, which are not sensitive to high acidity and can, in fact, use lactic and similar organic acids as food. These aerobic organisms grow over the surface of the curd or on the whey, and destroy enough acid to permit further lactic acid fermentation of the remaining lactose. Finally the molds and film yeasts may destroy the acid with the result that the reaction becomes neutral or even slightly alkaline. This gives the protein-splitting bacteria, hitherto held back by the presence of acid, an opportunity to decompose the milk proteins. This proteolytic decomposition may be a simple hydrolysis or digestion without the production of bad odors, or it may be an anaerobic putrefaction which yields obnoxious odors.

While the average sample of raw milk held at room temperature or thereabouts undergoes changes similar to those just described, exceptional conditions may favor other changes. If there were no acid-forming bacteria present in the milk, due to aseptic precautions or to killing or removal of acid-formers, certain so-called abnormal fermentations might take place. If rennin-forming, proteolytic bacteria are given an opportunity to predominate, "sweet curdling" or coagulation due to bacterial rennin may take place without acid production. This usually is followed by proteolysis and the consequent production of a bitter flavor. Bitter flavors may be produced by action of other bacteria which are not actively proteolytic; for example, *Escherichia* and *Aerobacter* species produce formic acid, which is bitter.

Milk may contain slimy or stringy particles when drawn from the udder of a cow suffering with mastitis, or ropiness may develop later in the milk due to the growth of certain capsulated bacteria. Bacteria of the coliform group are often the cause of this condition; ropiness caused by these bacteria may decrease as the acidity increases. A water organism, *Alcaligenes viscosus*, has also been incriminated in the production of ropiness. This organism is aerobic, and the ropiness is chiefly in the cream layer; ropiness due to facultative bacteria is found throughout the milk. Figure 58 shows ropy milk caused by *A. viscosus*. The chief sources of the bacteria causing ropiness are manure and water, especially stagnant water in the pasture or barnyard, cooling tank water, or water from a shallow well. Once they have become contaminated, the milk utensils serve as a source of ropy milk bacteria. The rem-

FIGURE 58. A bottle of ropy milk. The growth of *Alcaligenes viscosus* has made the milk so viscous that it can be picked up with a forceps.

edy for such trouble is prevention of contamination from the original source and sterilization of all apparatus and utensils with which the milk comes in contact. Certain strains of lactic acid-forming bacteria may produce enough capsular material to cause ropiness. Usually such ropiness is considered undesirable, but in Norway a fermented milk drink is prepared with a culture of a slimy lactic acid bacterium.

Gassy milk may be caused by facultative bacteria of the coliform group or by anaerobes of the genus *Clostridium*. The *Aerobacter aerogenes* type of gas-former is very undesirable in milk to be used for cheese or other fermented products, and may cause blowing up or swelling of the cheese and reduction of the quality of the final product. This type of organism may come originally from vegetation, manure, or water, and may contaminate utensils, which when improperly treated may serve as a continuous source of the gas-formers. Bacteria of the *Escherichia coli* type, which usually come from manure, are not as dangerous to the success of the cheesemaker as are the *Aerobacter* organisms, but are considered undesirable in milk. The coliform bacteria produce: acid, partly lactic and partly acetic; volatile acids; and gas, consisting of a mixture of hydrogen and carbon dioxide. *Aerobacter* species in general produce more gas and less acid than the *Escherichia* spe-

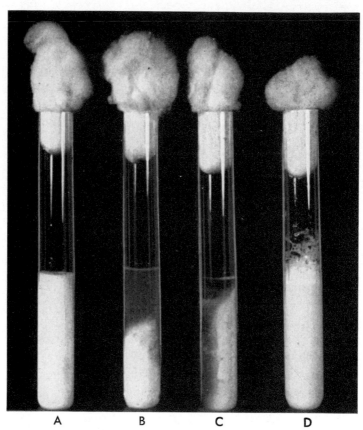

A   B   C   D

FIGURE 59.   Changes produced in milk by some common bacteria. **A.** *Streptococcus lactis* produces lactic acid to form a solid curd with no gas or proteolysis. **B.** An aerobic spore former, *Bacillus cereus,* produces a soft curd due to bacterial rennin followed by rapid proteolysis. **C.** *Streptococcus lique-faciens* produces acid and rennin enough to form a shrunken curd, and then rapidly digests the curd with a caseinase. **D.** *Aerobacter aerogenes* produces much gas from lactose and little or no curd.

cies and curdle the milk more slowly. Some *Aerobacter* organisms are able to grow at fairly low temperatures and increase in numbers in cooled milk. The *Escherichia* species have a higher optimum temperature and grow best at about 37° C.

Anaerobic, spore-forming bacteria of the genus *Clostridium* are able to form gas in milk if the conditions are anaerobic enough and the temperature is fairly high. Some clostridia ferment lactose to produce hydrogen and carbon dioxide as gaseous products; others can also ferment lactates with gas production. These anaerobes may be important in gas formation during the ripening of cheese, and may at times even cause "blowing" of cheese in the

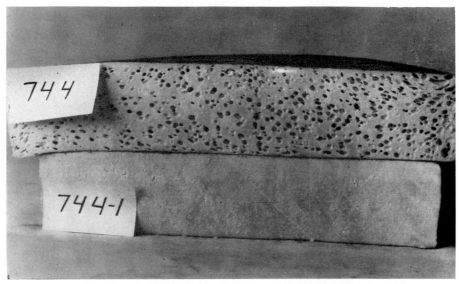

FIGURE 60. Twenty-four-hour old Swiss cheese produced from clean and from dirty milk. The bottom cheese (744–1) was made from clean milk; the top cheese (744) was made from dirty milk that probably contained *Aerobacter aerogenes* or *Clostridium* species. The top cheese has little or no market value.

press. In milk they usually cause a "stormy" fermentation, in which the curd is blown to shreds by the rapid production of gas. Figure 59 shows test tubes cultures of bacteria which cause acid production, protein decomposition, and gas production in milk. Figure 60 shows blown cheese.

Yeasts rarely cause gassiness in milk because they are unable to compete with the bacteria; they may, however, cause trouble in acid products like sour cream, whey, or cheese. Lactose-fermenting yeasts are not common, and most of the yeasts which enter milk are unable to grow because of lack of a fermentable carbohydrate.

Although unable to compete with the lactics or the gas-formers under ordinary conditions, certain bacteria grow well in the absence of these forms. The micrococci from the udder or elsewhere, water bacteria, soil bacteria, and miscellaneous chromogenic forms may be able to cause changes, not commonly encountered, in the milk. Thus, there are exceptional cases of yellow, blue, or red milk, as well as the sweet curdled and proteolyzed milk mentioned previously. Some of the pathogenic bacteria are able to increase in milk if the competition is not too great and the temperature is favorable (between 25° and 40° C.). *Salmonella typhosa* (typhoid fever), other *Salmonella* bacteria (enteric diseases), *Brucella abortus* (undulant fever), hemolytic streptococci (scarlet fever, septic sore throat), and others can grow.

Milk Quality and Control

Milk of high quality should have high nutritive value, satisfactory keeping quality, a desirable flavor and odor, and should be clean and safe to drink. Milk freshly drawn in an aseptic manner from clean, healthy cows is of the highest quality according to these criteria, and an attempt is made to bring this milk to the consumer as little changed as possible. Bacteria are present in the milk from the start, are added along the way from cow to consumer, and increase in numbers not only through contamination but through growth. Since decrease in quality during handling is due almost entirely to bacteria, the number of bacteria present in milk can be used as a measure of quality to indicate whether large numbers of bacteria have entered due to contamination or whether conditions favorable to growth have been present. Large numbers of bacteria, then, would be indicative of poor methods of production or handling of the product, with the possibility of less desirable tastes or odors, lowered keeping quality, or even contamination with disease-producing organisms.

The number of bacteria in milk may be estimated by means of the plate count, the direct microscopic count, the methylene blue reduction test, the rate of development of acidity, or some other method. At present the plate count method is the most extensively used. In the routine bacteriological analysis of milk, no attempt is made to detect the presence of pathogenic bacteria or estimate their numbers, because present methods either will not reliably give such information or involve too much effort to be useful in routine work.

The control of the quality of market milk is usually left in the hands of the various cities in the United States. Many of the cities have adopted the United States Public Health Service Milk Ordinance and Code. Some of the regulations of this model ordinance may serve as an example of a city code:

Grade A raw milk should have a bacterial plate count or direct microscopic clump count of not over 50,000 per milliliter, or a methylene blue reduction time of not less than 7 hours; also it must be produced in accordance with rules in regard to sanitation on the farms. **Grade A raw milk for pasteurization** need not meet such strict bacteriological requirements. Rules for sanitation on the farms and at the bottling plants include those on: health of personnel and cows, construction of barns and milk houses or rooms, disposal of manure, cleanliness of milkers and cows, condition of cow yard, toilet facilities for workers, purity of water supply, facilities for cooling of milk, and place and methods of bottling and capping.

Grade B raw milk conforms to all standards for Grade A raw milk except the bacterial ones; the bacterial plate count or the direct microscopic clump count must not exceed 200,000 per milliliter, or the methylene blue reduction time must be not less than 5½ hours. **Grade B raw milk for pasteurization** has less strict bacterial standards.

Grade C raw milk is raw milk which violates any of the requirements for **Grade B raw milk.**

Certified raw milk is raw milk which conforms with the requirements of the American Association of Medical Milk Commissions, Inc., and is produced under the supervision of a medical milk commission reporting monthly to a health officer of the state, county, or municipal health authority. Usually a plate count of not more than 10,000 bacteria per milliliter is permitted and a coliform colony count of not more than 10 per milliliter. Personnel and cows are examined periodically for disease and strict regulations are laid down concerning sanitation throughout production. This milk usually sells for more than ordinary milk, because of the added cost of production. **Certified milk-pasteurized** should have a plate count of less than 500 per milliliter and a coliform count no greater than one.

Grade A pasteurized milk is Grade A raw milk for pasteurization which has been pasteurized, cooled, and bottled in a milk plant conforming to specified rules of sanitation. The pasteurized milk must be phosphatase negative, indicating efficient pasteurization, and at no time up to delivery should give a plate count exceeding 30,000 per milliliter or a coliform count above 10 per milliliter.

Grade B pasteurized milk violates the bacterial standard or bottle cap requirements, or both, for Grade A, or is produced from Grade B milk for pasteurization. The bacterial plate count should not exceed 50,000 per milliliter of pasteurized milk.

Grade C pasteurized milk violates one or more of the requirements for Grade B.

It is obvious that each added expense in the production of milk will add to the cost of the milk to the consumer. The consumer should decide how much extra care in production he is willing to pay for, and whether a lower grade of milk will serve his purpose as well as a higher and more expensive grade.

The quality of milk (or cream) to be used in the manufacture of dairy products usually is judged by the kinds and numbers of microorganisms and the amount of their growth. In general, the fewer the number of kinds, the lower the total number; and the less the growth of the microorganisms, the better is the quality of the milk. Use of cream (or condensed or dry milk) with a high bacterial content as an ingredient of ice cream may raise the bacterial count of that product to such an extent that it will not meet the bacterial standards set by a city or state. The highest quality of cream for butter is that in which there is a low number of microorganisms and in which growth of organisms has been inhibited as far as possible. Growth of microorganisms in the cream may cause changes in its flavor and hence in the flavor of the butter; the enzymes of organisms carried over from the cream may continue to act in the butter and cause its deterioration, even when growth of the microorganisms has ceased. Milk of the best quality for cheese making (or for the preparation of other fermented dairy products) is that which is low in microbial content and little changed by action of microorganisms. Not only is an attempt made to obtain milk with as low a bacterial count as possible, but the milk to be used for many products is pasteurized to destroy most organisms present. A high bacterial count in milk indicates the probable presence of appreciable numbers of undesirable bacteria, such as the gas-formers, which may cause abnormal fermentations and reduce the quality of the product. High counts are likewise an indication that growth of organisms and hence changes in the composition of the milk may have taken place. Modern methods of manufacture of cheese and other fermented dairy products involve the use of starters or special cultures of microorganisms, rather than the use of methods to encourage the growth of organisms already in the milk. Starter cultures added to milk which contains comparatively few microorganisms will have little competition, and hence will be likely to cause the desired fermentation.

REFERENCES

American Public Health Association, *Standard methods for the examination of dairy products* (9th ed.). N. Y., American Public Health Association, 1948.

Associates of L. A. Rogers, *Fundamentals of dairy science* (2nd ed.). N. Y., Reinhold, 1935.

Elliker, P. R., *Practical dairy bacteriology.* N. Y., McGraw-Hill, 1949.

Hammer, B. W., *Dairy bacteriology* (3rd ed.). N. Y., Wiley, 1948.

Orla-Jensen, S. (transl. by P. S. Arup, 2nd English ed.), *Dairy bacteriology.* Philadelphia, Pa., P. Blakiston's Son and Co., Inc., 1931.

Russell, H. L., and Hastings, E. G., *Outlines of dairy bacteriology* (12th ed.). Madison, Wis., H. L. Russell, 1928.

Sommer, H. H., *Market milk and related products* (2nd ed.). Madison, Wis., H. H. Sommer, 1946.

U. S. Public Health Service, recommended "Milk ordinance and code." *Public Health Bull. No. 220* (1939) (tentative revised ed., 1949).

27. MICROBIOLOGY OF MILK PRODUCTS

Milk products are manufactured from milk or cream for the purpose of preservation, or for the production of special flavors or physical characteristics. These products may be divided into two or possibly three classes, depending upon whether or not microorganisms are essential to their manufacture. No microorganisms are needed for the preparation of evaporated, sweetened condensed, or dry milk, or ice cream. Butter may be made with or without the aid of bacteria; fermented milks, cheese, and similar products require the action of microorganisms in their preparation.

UNFERMENTED MILK PRODUCTS

Since no microorganisms are involved in the manufacture of these products, it may be considered desirable to have a low bacterial content and a minimum of growth in the milk to be used. The numbers and kinds of microorganisms in dry milk and in ice cream are of importance, as will be pointed out later.

Evaporated, Sweetened Condensed, and Dry Milk

Evaporated milk is made by concentration of whole milk under a vacuum at 54° to 60° C. to about half its original volume. Although the numbers of bacteria are reduced during this removal of water, evaporated milk will not keep indefinitely. It is therefore canned and sterilized by steam under pressure (at 240°–245° F. for 15 minutes or more). Most canned evaporated milk is free from living microorganisms; occasionally, however, bacterial spores will survive the heat treatment—but are usually unable to germinate and grow because of a lack of oxygen in the can or because of some other limiting factor like food or temperature. An opened can of evaporated milk will spoil readily. This is due usually to the growth of organisms which have entered from external sources, but can be caused by organisms which were originally present.

In the manufacture of sweetened condensed milk, about 60 per cent of the water is evaporated from whole milk to which about 40 per cent of sucrose has been added, after which the product is canned. The heating process during forewarming and evaporation kills yeasts and molds and reduces the numbers of bacteria, but the preservation of the canned product is due to the high concentration of sugar together with the evacuation and hermetic sealing of the can. The milk is not sterile, but these conditions will not permit the growth of organisms present.

So much water is removed in the manufacture of dry milk (milk powder), dry whey (whey powder), or dry buttermilk that the remaining water is insufficient for growth of microorganisms. There is no problem of spoilage due to microorganisms as long as the products are not allowed to become moist. These products do, however, contain numbers of microorganisms which have survived the drying process, and these become important when the product is to be used in a food in which number of microorganisms is considered a measure of quality. For example, many states have set standards for the bacterial content of ice cream, and use of dry milk containing large numbers of microorganisms would raise the bacterial count of the ice cream. The kinds of bacteria in the dry milk may also be important at times. For example, it may contain enough spores of the ropy bread organism, *Bacillus subtilis,* to cause ropiness in bread or other bakery products of which dry milk is an ingredient.

Ice Cream

It has been mentioned that many states and cities have established standards for the bacterial content of ice cream; some states and cities also have a limit on the numbers of coliform bacteria per gram or milliliter of the product. The microbial content of the ingredients used in making the ice cream "mix" are, of course, important in determining the bacterial count. The mix usually is pasteurized to reduce numbers of microorganisms and kill any pathogens that may be present. Unless proper precautions are taken, however, there is a possibility of recontamination afterwards during manufacture and handling. Because of the low temperature of freezing and storage, there are few problems of spoilage, but organisms present may survive for long periods. This is important if pathogenic bacteria are present.

FERMENTED MILK PRODUCTS

It was noted in Chapter 26 that lactic acid fermentation usually takes place in raw milk stored at ordinary temperatures of from 15° to 30° C., and also at temperatures between 40° and 50° C. This souring of raw milk by *Streptococcus lactis* and other lactics gives a clean-flavored sour milk, or fermented milk, relished by many. A similar fermentation is involved in the manufacture of most fermented dairy products. Sour cream, "culture buttermilk," and cottage and cream cheese usually are prepared by such a simple lactic fermentation, although the cultures used usually contain "aroma" bacteria in addition to *Streptococcus lactis*. These aroma bacteria, *Leuconostoc dextranicum* and *L. citrovorum*, growing with S. *lactis*, produce volatile substances, such as diacetyl, which improve the aroma and flavor of the product. Similar "aroma-formers" are included in butter cultures and are used to increase the flavor of butter. Examples of other special flavor-producing organisms used with the lactics are the propionic acid bacteria in Swiss cheese and the molds in Roquefort and Camembert cheese.

Butter

Formerly most butter was made from cream which had been soured naturally, by lactics and other bacteria already present; or artificially, by inoculation of the cream (usually after pasteurization) with a starter of lactic acid bacteria and incubation until the desired acidity was obtained. It was found that butter so made did not keep as well as butter made from sweet cream; consequently, much of the butter made now in this country is sweet cream butter. Often, however, to add flavor, milk cultures of bacteria are worked into the butter or mixed with sweet cream before the butter is made. The cream or butter absorbs the flavor and aroma of the culture, but the bacteria are not permitted to grow. Some makers buy a distillate of cultures of flavor-producing bacteria and work this flavoring material into the butter.

The lactic starters used in butter consist of a true "lactic," usually *Streptococcus lactis* or S. *cremoris* and one or more kinds of aroma-forming bacteria which are able to form acetyl-methyl-carbinol and diacetyl from the citrates in the milk. Diacetyl is the most important flavor and aroma-producing compound in butter.

Butter owes its keeping quality to low storage temperatures, its salt content, and its low moisture content. The defects of butter due to microorganisms are most likely to result from activity in the milk or cream from which the butter is made and subsequent action of the enzymes of these organisms and not to growth during storage of the finished product. Molds may grow on butter on any surface exposed to air, as may certain bacteria causing off-flavors known as "surface taints."

Fermented Milks

Raw milk normally undergoes a lactic acid fermentation due to the action of lactic acid-forming bacteria, and such acid milk will keep well if not exposed to the air. This fact has long been known by various peoples who have used this method for preserving milk and at the same time preparing a palatable beverage that is more easily digested than fresh, unfermented milk. These fermented milks, prepared in different parts of the world, have a general resemblance one to the other, but differ somewhat in the organisms concerned in their manufacture. Usually, when milk sours, the first lactic acid fermentation is due to *Streptococcus lactis* or closely related cocci. They may be followed by bacteria of the genus *Lactobacillus*, with further production of lactic acid. So-called "culture buttermilk" is usually prepared with *Streptococcus lactis* plus aroma formers, which are grown in pasteurized skim milk. Butter fat may be added in the form of cream or as small lumps of fat. These lactic cocci are active in the early stages of preparation of some other kinds of fermented milks, but in many kinds of fermented milks the lactobacilli are most important. The same kind of fermented milk may be made in different countries under different names.

Most of these buttermilks are not manufactured with pure cultures, but contain a variety of organisms, some of which may be necessary to the fermentation and others only incidental. Each type of fermented milk, however, is the result of the action and growth of certain lactic acid bacteria and perhaps other bacteria and yeasts. Bulgarian buttermilk is made with *Lactobacillus bulgaricus*, which may be added to pasteurized milk in pure culture or may be carried from one lot of milk to the next, in which case contaminating organisms of various kinds may be present. Acidophilus milk is made by the inoculation of sterilized milk with *Lactobacillus acidophilus* and incubation at 35° to 37° C. until a mildly acid curd has developed. It has been reported by some workers that this lactobacillus can establish itself in the human intestinal tract and by its action maintain an acid condition there. For this reason acidophilus milk has been recommended as a remedy for certain intestinal disorders. Kefir is a type of fermented milk in which not only the lactic acid bacteria are active, but also lactose-fermenting yeasts, which produce small amounts of alcohol and considerable amounts of carbon dioxide gas. The associated microorganisms grow together and form from the milk constituents the kefir grains, which have the appearance of small pieces of cauliflower. These grains are used to inoculate milk for the preparation of kefir; after the fermentation is complete, the grains may be strained out, washed, and used to inoculate the next lot of milk. Kumiss also is made by a combined lactic acid and yeast fermentation by a mixture of microorganisms similar to but not exactly like that in the kefir grain. The inoculum in this case comes from a previous lot of kumiss. It is commonly made with mares' milk in eastern Europe and western Asia; cows' milk has been used elsewhere. Among other fermented milks resembling or identical with the ones discussed are: yogurt, mazun, leben, etc.

Cheese

Cheese is made by the coagulation of the casein of milk and the draining off of whey; this may or may not be followed by a period of ripening for changes in flavor, texture, and body. The coagulation may be brought about by acid alone (produced by acid-forming bacteria), by rennet alone, or by a combination of the two. On the basis of methods of coagulation, cheeses are divided into **acid curd** cheeses, which are made from milk coagulated by acid produced by acid-forming bacteria, and **rennet curd** cheeses from milk coagulated by rennet. The ingredients necessary in making all kinds of cheese are milk and microorganisms; rennet and salt are also needed for most cheeses.

It has been pointed out that the numbers and kinds of microorganisms in the milk are very important in cheese making. For some kinds of cheese a limited amount of action of certain bacteria on the milk is desirable to produce what the cheese maker calls "ripeness" of the milk. Milk for most kinds of cheese, however, should have a low bacterial count, so that cultures of the desired kind may be added as "starters" and not have too much competition from others. Milk for many kinds of cheese is pasteurized to assure predominance of the added starter bacteria. Poor milk may contain appreciable numbers of undesirable bacteria, such as the gas-formers, which will cause defective cheese unless suppressed. The production of milk satisfactory for cheese making is one of the most important problems of the industry, but is one that can be solved by application of the principles of asepsis and preservation discussed in Chapter 26.

Microorganisms have two functions in the making of most varieties of cured cheese: (1) to make acid, and (2) to aid in the ripening process. The chief function of the "starter" bacteria is to form lactic acid, which coagulates the milk or hastens coagulation by rennet, favors expulsion of whey and fusion of curd particles, protects against gas and putrefaction, and favors the action of the pepsin of the rennet during ripening. The enzymes of starter bacteria may also play a part in the ripening of the cheese, even after the bacterial cells have autolyzed. Other microorganisms, usually not added as "starter" but present in the milk and in brine baths or on shelves, aid in the ripening of the cheese and especially in the development of flavor.

Using practically the same ingredients, the cheese maker, by varying his methods of manufacture, may produce any of several hundred different kinds of cheese. These methods attempt to favor the growth of the desired kinds of microorganisms in the proper order; if the wrong kinds or sequences of organisms are active, abnormal cheese will result. The amount of acid formed, the amount of rennet, the temperature at which it is used, the temperature to which the curd is heated, the amount of drainage of curd permitted, the amount of salt used, and the time and method of salting, the size and shape of the cheese and its treatment during ripening, all influence the kind of cheese that will result. Ripening is the term applied to the changes which take place in flavor, body, and appearance when the cheese is held under specified conditions of temperature, humidity, and handling; it will be discussed for separate kinds of cheese. It is usually characterized by a softening or mellowing of the cheese with an increase in soluble nitrogenous compounds and a decrease in acidity. Bacteria of the lactobacillus type are commonly concerned in the ripening of the interior of most types of cheese, although propionic acid-forming bacteria, proteolytic and lipolytic cocci, and molds may play a part in the changes in some kinds of cheese. Some cheeses are surface ripened, that is, certain bacteria, yeasts, and molds are encouraged to grow on the outer surface and produce enzymes which diffuse into the cheeses and aid in their ripening. In rennet curd cheeses in which the curd has not been subjected to high temperatures, the proteolytic action of the enzyme pepsin (normally present in rennet) is important in the "breakdown" of cheese proteins, with the accompanying increase in softness or mellowness of the cheese.

Most of the acid curd cheeses must be used soon after manufacture, for they are readily decomposed by yeasts and molds. They have a high moisture content, favorable to the growth of microorganisms, and usually little or no added salt. Cottage cheese is a good example of this type. It is made by the spontaneous souring of milk, or souring by means of an added culture of lactic acid and aroma-forming bacteria like that used in butter making. A moderate amount of acid is allowed to develop; the curd is cut and the whey drained off. Small amounts of rennet are sometimes used in commercial manufacture of cottage cheese. Special types of acid curd cheese may be ripened; some of these in which the curd is cooked may have molds concerned in their ripening.

The rennet curd cheeses may be divided into soft cheeses, which have a comparatively high moisture content and hard cheeses, which are drier. In general the soft cheeses have a short ripening period and poor keeping quality. They may be separated into two classes on the basis of whether they are ripened by bacteria alone or by bacteria and molds. The ripening is mostly from the outside inward; a surface flora produces enzymes which diffuse into the cheese and cause decompositions incidental to ripening. In cheeses ripened by bacteria, Limburger and Liederkranz, for example, such lactic acid bacteria as *Streptococcus lactis* carry on the acid fermentation during the early hours of making; but a mixture of aerobic and facultative bacteria and yeasts on the surface of the cheese makes up a "smear" during ripening, breaks down proteins at the surface, and produces enzymes which diffuse into the cheese to decompose protein compounds there. The cheese maker uses methods which transfer bacteria from the "smear" to the surface of newly made cheese.

Camembert and Brie cheese are examples of mold-ripened soft cheeses. In the ripening of Camembert cheese, conditions are made favorable to the growth on the surface of the cheese of *Penicillium camemberti,* an organism important in the ripening process. Bacteria and yeasts also grow in a "smear" on the surface at certain stages of the ripening.

Most of the more important cheeses on the market are hard, rennet curd cheeses which have been ripened by bacteria. Cheddar (American), brick, and Swiss (Emmenthal) cheese belong in this group, as do the less common Edam, Gouda, and Parmesan (Grana). A few kinds of hard, rennet curd cheese, like Roquefort and Gorgonzola, have molds also concerned in the ripening.

A lactic starter is used in the manufacture of Cheddar cheese, usually a culture similar to the one used for butter. This culture contains *Streptococcus lactis* and aroma-forming bacteria, and causes the development of acid in the curd until it will mat together. The curd is salted in the vat and then pressed in hoops. The cheese is cured or ripened at a low temperature, usually below 10° C., for a number of months. The amount of ripeness desired determines the length of the ripening period. The pepsin added with the rennet plays an important part in the hydrolysis of proteins and mellowing of the cheese, while micrococci and lactobacilli are concerned in the development of flavor. Figure 61 illustrates the cutting of the curd and the matting of the cut curd following removal of whey in the manufacture of cheddar cheese.

A

B

FIGURE 61.   **A.** Cutting the curd, a step in the manufacture of Cheddar cheese. After the milk has been coagulated by the combined action of the rennet and "starter" bacteria, the curd is cut into small cubes.
   B. Draining the whey off the curd. After the curd has reached the desired moisture content it will be salted and placed in hoops or molds. During all of these operations the "starter" bacteria are producing lactic acid from the lactose of the milk. (Courtesy The Borden Company, New York.)

In the manufacture of Swiss cheese, the curd in the kettle is cooked to a fairly high temperature, about 53° C., and allowed to cool slowly. *Streptococcus thermophilus* and *Lactobacillus helveticus, L. bulgaricus,* or *L. lactis,* which are able to grow at high temperatures, are used as starters to produce the desired amount of lactic acid in the cheese. This kind of cheese is salted by immersion in brine and rubbing salt upon the surface. After the cheese has been cooled for a week or two it is placed in the warm or "fermentation" cellar. Here, special bacteria cause the formation of holes or "eyes,"— by the production of carbon dioxide from salts of lactic acid in the cheese— and form propionic acid to contribute to the flavor. When these eyes are sufficiently large, the cheese is moved to the cold cellar where eye formation is stopped and hydroylsis of the protein and development of flavor continues. A Swiss cheese should be at least four months old to exhibit a desirable stage of ripeness.

Brick cheese is intermediate between Swiss and Limburger. The curd is cooked, but at a lower temperature than the Swiss. Salting is done from the outside, usually in brine; and the development of a "smear" of yeasts and bacteria on the surface to aid in ripening, and more especially in flavor production, is encouraged. Some types of brick cheese develop a distinct Limburger flavor; others are more like Swiss cheese.

The mold ripened, rennet curd cheeses include Roquefort, Gorgonzola, and Stilton cheese. Lactic acid bacteria of the *Streptococcus lactis* type develop the acid necessary in the early part of the manufacture of Roquefort cheese. The curd is inoculated with spores of *Penicillium roqueforti* grown on bread crumbs. The cheese is salted heavily by means of salt rubbed onto the surface. It is then pierced in 30 or 40 places with long slender needles so that air can reach the interior and favor the growth of the mold. The green, mottled appearance of ripened Roquefort cheese is due to the growth and sporulation of *Penicillium roqueforti* throughout the cheese, and the sharp, biting, characteristic flavor is due to the methylamylketone and fatty acids from the decomposition of butter fat by the mold.

Cheese, because of its acidity and its low moisture content, usually is subject to spoilage by molds growing on the surface or in cracks or openings in the cheese. Cheeses with moist surfaces may support the surface growth of yeasts and bacteria. It will be recalled that growth of a surface smear of bacteria and yeasts is encouraged as part of the ripening of certain types of soft cheese. Growth of the wrong organisms or action of such a smear on the wrong kind of cheese would be called spoilage. Likewise, abnormal fermentations during the making of cheese or its ripening are forms of spoilage and will lead to inferior or even spoiled products.

REFERENCES

American Public Health Association, *Standard methods for the examination of dairy products* (9th ed.). N. Y., American Public Health Association, 1948.

Associates of L. A. Rogers, *Fundamentals of dairy science* (2nd ed.). N. Y., Reinhold, 1935.

Elliker, P. R., *Practical dairy bacteriology.* N. Y., McGraw-Hill, 1949.

Hammer, B. W., *Dairy bacteriology* (3rd ed.). N. Y., Wiley, 1948.

Orla-Jensen, S. (Transl. by P. S. Arup, 2nd English ed.), *Dairy bacteriology.* Philadelphia, Pa., P. Blakiston's Son and Co., Inc., 1931.

Russell, H. L., and Hastings, E. G., *Outlines of dairy bacteriology* (12th ed.). Madison, Wis., H. L. Russell, 1928.

PART VIII

Infectious Diseases of Animals and Plants

The demonstration that microorganisms could produce diseases among higher animals and plants was a major contribution of the first bacteriologists. The causative or etiological agents of many diseases have since been shown to be bacteria or other forms of life or the toxins developed by them. The diseases of animals and plants as well as of man often seriously affect the economic and physical security of society.

It should be reemphasized that this is a textbook of general microbiology and that the infectious diseases of animals and plants are only a part of that subject. It is the purpose of the following chapters to describe in general terms how microorganisms cause disease, to discuss a few representative infectious diseases, and to point out ways to prevent infectious diseases.

28. THE NATURE OF DISEASE AND DISEASE-PRODUCING AGENTS

Disease and Causative Agents of Disease

Disease is defined as a deviation from the normal either in structure or function of the body. Alteration of function is often expressed by symptoms which the patient himself recognizes, or by the signs the clinician observes. Symptoms are the manifestations of disease, not the disease itself. The cause of disease may be intrinsic or extrinsic. Intrinsic or internal causes of disease include metabolic and endocrine disturbances, constitutional or hereditary abnormalities, aging, and tumors. It is possible that certain of those disorders now believed to be due to intrinsic causes may be initiated by external, as yet unrecognized causes.

The extrinsic causes of disease are those originating outside of the body and may be living bacteria, viruses, rickettsiae, yeasts, molds, algae, protozoa, or metazoa; or they may be nonliving agents, such as heat, cold, radiations, mechanical forces, chemical toxins or poisons, and nutritional deficiencies. Only those diseases caused by the growth or activity of biological agents in the body of the host are classed as infectious diseases. Production of an **infectious disease** or **infection** therefore involves three main steps: (1) the entrance of the infectious agent into the tissues of the host; (2) its growth in the tissues; and (3) injury to the host. The causative agents of infectious diseases are termed **pathogenic agents, or pathogens.**

Microorganisms as Causative Agents of Infectious Disease

Proof of the "germ theory" of disease was not forthcoming until late in the nineteenth century when Villemin showed that tuberculosis could be transmitted from an infected person to rabbits. Many of the leading scientists of that period, however, were loath to concede that disease could be transferred from one individual to another. Because of such statements as "the phthisical soldier is to his mess-mate what the glandered horse is to his yoke-fellow," Villemin was barred, for a time, from membership in the French Academy of Medicine. Robert Koch soon thereafter established beyond question that tuberculosis is caused by a bacterium. The following procedures for ascertaining the etiological (causative) relationship of microorganisms to disease worked out by Koch still satisfy the requirements for demonstrating that a given disease is caused by a microorganism.

1. Koch stained and demonstrated bacteria in tuberculous tissues from various animals.
2. He induced tuberculosis in experimental animals by inoculating them with tuberculous tissues.
3. He isolated and propagated tubercle bacilli from tuberculous tissues in pure culture on artificial media.
4. He demonstrated that these pure cultures could produce tuberculosis when injected into experimental animals.

These procedures now formulated as **Koch's postulates,** have been revised as follows: (1) finding the organism in all cases of the disease, isolating it in pure culture, and describing it in detail; (2) inoculating the pure culture into an experimental animal and producing the same disease; (3) reisolating the organism from the diseased animal and proving it to be identical with the original pure culture.

ESTABLISHING THE SPECIFIC CAUSE (ETIOLOGY) OF AN INFECTIOUS DISEASE

The specific causative (etiological) agents of many infectious diseases have been determined by means of Koch's postulates. Certain other diseases, however, can be ascribed to specific infectious agents without fulfilling all of these postulates. An example of such a disease is leprosy, the ubiquitously and intimately associated bacterium of which has not been cultivated successfully in conventional culture media; furthermore, the human type of leprosy has not been produced in experimental animals. Likewise, there are diseases caused by viruses which fail to grow on lifeless media; in fact, some of these viruses have not been described despite the greatly improved facilities now available for microscopic examination of infected tissues. In some cases it may be necessary to utilize specific immunological and serological tests to establish or verify the specific relationship of a certain parasite to an infectious disease.

While many infectious diseases are caused by a single agent, others may be of multiple etiology, e.g., influenza in man, which may be caused by any of several distinct types of influenza virus acting alone or in association with the bacterium, *Hemophilus influenzae.* Some infections, such as boils or abscesses, may be induced by a variety of bacteria, e.g., micrococci or streptococci. Pneumonia may be produced by any one of more than 30 types of *Diplococcus pneumoniae,* several species and varieties of streptococci, certain nonspore-forming, Gram-negative bacilli, and various viral, rickettsial, and fungal agents.

At times, infections may become established only following prior action of devitalizing intrinsic or extrinsic causes, e.g., fever blisters, or herpes virus infection occurring after febrile disturbances or indigestion. Pathogenic streptococci may be found in some apparently normal guinea pigs. If these animals are injected with the tubercle organism, the devitalizing effects of the tuberculosis results in invasion and death of the guinea pigs by the pathogenic streptococci.

These facts emphasize that proof of the specific role of a microorganism in a given disease is not easy to establish. Certainly the mere presence of an organism (e.g., the presence of coliform bacteria, which are always found in the intestinal tract, in the blood stream just prior to death or after death) is not sufficient evidence of an etiological relationship to the disease.

INFECTION AND CONTAGION

A contagious disease is one which spreads readily from one individual to another by direct or indirect contact and without the active participation of insect vectors. All contagious diseases are infectious, since their spread depends upon transmission of the parasite from an infected to a noninfected individual. However, all infectious diseases are not contagious. Tetanus, for example, is caused by the toxins engendered in the tissues by the tetanus bacillus, *Clostridium tetani,* which has entered a deep wound. The tetanus organisms are not transmitted readily from one animal to another. Contagiousness, or the degree of transmissibility, depends on the way and extent to which the infectious agent is eliminated from the host as well as upon the opportunity for reaching other susceptible hosts. Diseases of the respiratory system frequently meet the requirements of ready elimination and direct transfer to other hosts, and hence are highly contagious.

VIRULENCE OF PATHOGENIC ORGANISMS

Any microorganism which can produce disease in any host is, by definition, pathogenic. This is a qualitative term, and in order to quantitate it another term is introduced—**virulence.** A pathogenic agent may be of high, low, or intermediate virulence according to its ability to produce disease. Since virulence is measured in terms of production of disease, the host as well as the pathogenic organism must be considered. The bovine type of tubercle organism, for example, is highly virulent for guinea pigs and human beings, but is of only slight virulence for the chicken.

ALTERATION OF VIRULENCE

Changes in virulence of a given infectious agent may be observed in nature, and the pathogenic power or virulence of many organisms may be altered easily in the laboratory; other infectious agents are resistant to such modification. The change wherein virulence is reduced is called **attenuation.**

Attenuated organisms, particularly the true bacteria and viruses, are often put to practical use in the form of vaccines which may be employed to immunize individuals. An effective means of attentuation of some pathogens is successive transfer of cultures in artificial culture media. Attenuation may be accomplished by cultivation at temperatures near the maximum temperature for growth of the organism or cultivation on media of unfavorable pH or deficient in essential nutrients. Attenuation also may be accomplished by cultivation in media containing small amounts of injurious substances such as metallic salts, certain dyes, various disinfectants, or specific antisera. Inoculation into animals, and one or more passages of the pathogen (in this case usually viruses) through animals of a species **moderately resistant** to it, may also attenuate the pathogen.

These methods serve as means of selecting less virulent strains of the organism. The entire culture does not change but a few less virulent individual cells in the culture survive and they give rise to the "attenuated" strain.

Microbic dissociation (see Chapter 14) generally modifies virulence profoundly. The change from the typical smooth or S colony form to the atypical rough or R form, or vice versa (if the R form is the typical, virulent form), induces alteration in physiological as well as cultural and morphological properties, and may bring about a complete loss of virulence. Loss of capsules or flagella, and of resistance to phagocytosis (engulfment by certain tissue cells) during the S to R transformation virtually insures decreased virulence. During dissociation from the S to R form, or vice versa if the R form is the virulent form, changes occur in the organisms which alter their usefulness as vaccines or diagnostic test agents. Means of minimizing the dissociation which sometimes occurs during artificial cultivation, and occasionally during infection, include frequent plating of cultures to allow selection of smooth colony forms, and the occasional passage of the culture through **susceptible** animals. Thus, animal passage is used to select typical, virulent organisms from those of less virulence.

Attempts to increase the virulence of infectious agents often fail regardless of the method utilized. This may happen especially if the agent has been highly attenuated. The procedure usually employed is to inoculate large numbers of the pathogen into susceptible animals with the hope of producing overwhelming infection. If inoculation is successful other animals are inoculated heavily with the passage material (infected tissues or cultures from such tissues), and the procedure is continued serially. In some cases, the virulence of a pathogen may be greatly augmented by such procedures.

Changes in virulence of pathogens play an important role in the history and nature of infectious disease. Many infectious maladies are today much less destructive than they were in the past, while others have become more destructive. Changes in host susceptibility and resistance may be of major consequence in that they affect the ability of parasites to produce disease. Mass immunization and natural selection or survival of susceptible individuals obviously are influencing factors in an evaluation of the virulence of a pathogen. Studies of epidemics indicate that the rise and fall of infection rate in certain diseases may depend largely on the proportion of susceptible hosts rather than on variations in virulence of the infectious agent. Adequate hygiene and nutrition have a salutary effect on the resistance of the host in many cases.

Mechanism of Infection by Microorganisms

Infection means invasion by living pathogenic microorganisms of a part of the body in which the conditions are favorable for their growth and where they may act injuriously upon the tissues of their host. The qualities which make biological agents capable of producing disease are complex, and it is apparent that disease production depends not only upon the microorganisms but also upon the response of the host.

The older belief that microorganisms might produce disease by mechanical action alone is no longer acceptable. The capacity of tissues to rid themselves of large quantities of solid, inert materials emphasizes the importance of toxic substances elicited by pathogenic organisms in the production of infectious disease. In certain cases, however, where bacteria are growing in the membrane lining the heart, clumps of these organisms may get into the blood stream and may lodge in capillaries of the kidneys causing reduction of kidney function. In certain diseases—for example, filariasis, caused by a worm; and malaria, caused by a protozoan—the mechanical blockage of the lymphatics and capillaries respectively causes damage to the host.

Toxins

The ability to produce poisonous substances called **toxins** is characteristic of a number of bacteria. Those toxins that diffuse readily from the bacterial cell into the surrounding medium are termed **exotoxins** and those toxins that form part of the bacterial protoplasm are termed **endotoxins.**

Certain plants, animals, and bacteria produce soluble exotoxins which are highly poisonous to animals. Bacterial exotoxins may be produced *in vitro* and are easily separated from the bacteria by filtration. While possessing certain common properties, most bacterial exotoxins manifest highly specific features. One exotoxin usually can be distinguished from another by its pharmacological action. Tetanus toxin, for example, affects the motor nerve cells with resultant muscle spasms; botulinum toxin induces early ocular and pharyngeal paralysis; diphtheria toxin injected into rabbits causes hemorrhage in the adrenals, and in rabbits that survive, late paralysis.

Some bacteria produce several exotoxins which may exhibit different tissue affinities. Micrococci may produce a hemotoxin which lyses red blood cells, a leucocytic toxin which kills white blood cells, an enteric or enterotoxin which affects the gastrointestinal tract, a lethal toxin which kills rabbits, and a skin-destroying or dermonecrotic toxin. It is possible that some of these toxins may be similar, and that they function in different ways under different conditions.

All of the exotoxins are highly antigenic; when they are injected into animals, the animals produce specific antibodies called antitoxins. Additional properties of exotoxins are as follows:

1. They are relatively large molecules or groups of molecules. Diphtheria toxin has been purified as a protein and, recently, both tetanus and botulinum toxin have been crystallized and the physical properties of their respective protein molecules have been studied.

2. They are relatively thermolabile. Most exotoxins are destroyed by heating at 58° to 80° C. for ten minutes. A notable exception to this, which is unfortunate for human beings, is the enterotoxin of micrococci; this toxin will withstand 100° C. for 1 hour.

3. They deteriorate with age; this change is hastened by warmth, moisture, light, and microbial contamination. Dried toxins stored in sealed containers keep for long periods. Usually the toxic fraction or activity deteriorates first, leaving an antigenic, relatively nontoxic toxoid. Toxoids also may be prepared by chemical treatment of the toxin.

Chemical substances mildly poisonous to animal tissues are present in the protoplasm of many organisms, both saprophytes and pathogens. These substances, called **endotoxins,** consist of lipoid-carbohydrate complexes as well as proteins and protein degradation products, which are produced by the organisms and retained within their cells until the cells disintegrate. As a rule, endotoxins are relatively thermostable, e.g., the endotoxin of *Vibrio comma* requires one hour of heating at 80° to 100° C. for inactivation. The substances commonly termed endotoxins possess little if any appreciable antigenicity, i.e., capacity to stimulate the animal body to produce substances called antibodies.

Spreading Factor

Certain bacteria, e.g., highly invasive streptococci, excrete a **spreading factor** which favors their penetration into the deeper tissues of the host. Enzymic dissolution of intercellular substances may so facilitate dissemination of the infectious agent that the formation of a **lesion** (morbid change in tissue) at or near the point of infection may fail to occur prior to a generalized, systemic infection. The spreading factor produced by some pathogens has been found to consist largely of **hyaluronidase,** which is an enzyme that catalyzes hydrolysis of hyaluronic acids; these acids make up part of the intercellular substances that hold tissue cells together.

Other Active Bacterial Products

Several products and reactions of pathogenic bacteria other than toxins and toxic responses have been identified as playing a role in disease processes. A plurality of substances known to be capsular material, bacterial protein, and enzymes, apparently function individually and collectively to permit invasion and multiplication of the parasite in the host's tissues. These substances may be the so-called **"aggressins"** first described by Bail and others. Such a substance or mixture of substances present in cultures of certain bacteria, as well as in the infected tissues, may be an effective antigen or immunizing agent in some cases.

Some of the streptococci produce a material that dissolves fibrin in a blood clot. This material is known as **fibrinolysin.** In a study of scarlet fever it was found that all of the streptococci cultures from the cases with complications produced fibrinolysis, while only a few cultures from the noncomplicated cases produced fibrinolysis.

A substance that coagulates blood is produced by certain micrococci and is known as **coagulase.** While it is difficult to associate coagulase and virulence, nevertheless it has been found that pathogenic micrococci possess co-agulase and nonpathogenic forms do not possess this material.

During the course of an infection the host may develop a state of increased susceptibility or reactivity to the pathogen. This state is called hypersensitivity. Some evidence indicates that the varying degrees of hyper-sensitivity or allergy sometimes demonstrable, especially in chronic infec-tion, may play a major role in the outcome of the disease process. Koch early showed that infection with the tuberculosis organism engendered a considerable resistance or immunity to superimposed infection. Yet, upon injection of small quantities of tuberculin (an extract of killed cultures of *Mycobacterium tuberculosis*) into the naturally sensitized tuberculous ani-mal, a fatal shock often ensued. This result showed that the animal had be-come allergic or hypersensitive to substances present in the extract of the tubercle bacillus.

It has been found that similar hypersensitivity may be produced by injec-tion into the animal body of extracts of other organisms or even by injection of pure proteins. A second injection of similar or closely related substances produces a reaction indicative of hypersensitivity. It would appear that the hypersensitivity developed in an infected animal may be found to have a greater influence on the course of infectious disease than is now recognized. Hypersensitivity may be helpful in localizing a small focus of infection by producing an intense tissue reaction around it.

RESISTANCE OF BACTERIA TO THE DEFENSE MECHANISM OF THE HOST

In order to produce infection, microorganisms must not only invade the host but they must also be able to survive and grow. To do this they must be protected from the defense mechanism of the host. Certain of the ways that bacteria may be protected from these defense mechanisms are known and may be used as a measure of virulence of the pathogen.

One way that the animal body removes bacteria is by phagocytosis, i.e., the ingestion of microorganisms by certain body cells. Bacteria that possess a capsule are resistant to phagocytosis; thus the capsule protects the patho-gen. Virulent strains of the anthrax bacillus possess a well defined capsule; avirulent strains do not.

Another protective measure is the elaboration by certain pathogens (such as micrococci) of **leucocidin,** a toxin that destroys leucocytes. Certain leucocytes are active phagocytic cells, and destruction of these leucocytes serves to protect the invading pathogen.

Invasiveness

Some highly pathogenic bacteria have little invasiveness; tetanus and diphtheria infections, for example, require only localized invasion. Such limited residence established, the organisms produce powerful soluble exotoxins which may be disseminated throughout the body by the circulating lymph and blood. Those infectious agents which lack soluble toxins must be highly invasive if they are to produce disease as a result of their generalized distribution in the body. Examples of such infectious agents are those that cause tularemia, plague, and syphilis. Many infectious diseases of the skin and mucous membrane surfaces, as well as most wound infections, may remain localized for a time, at least. **Metastasis** or spread of infections to the local lymph glands, and thence through the lymph and blood, may follow escape of the organisms from the primary disease site. Invasiveness, therefore, does not imply a physical capacity for propulsion into or progress through the host's tissues. Like an inert particle introduced into the tissues, the parasite may be carried by the fluids or be taken up by phagocytes and transported to other parts and tissues. Upon engulfing a foreign particle or bacterium the phagocyte may succeed in digesting or destroying it. Sufficiently resistance or virulent organisms, uninjured by phagocytosis, may be carried by the phagocyte to a lymph gland or other point with resulting localized infection, and metastasis may occur from this new site.

Some pathogens, particularly the higher fungi, may colonize, and through the simple process of extension by growth invade the deeper tissues. If these pathogens possess adequate virulence, metastasis follows, and the infection may become generalized throughout the body, or systemic.

Seldom does growth of the parasite occur in the circulating fluids of the body. **Bacteremia,** or infection characterized by the presence of bacteria in the blood stream, is usually the result of outpouring of the organisms into the blood from one or more sites of massive infection in fixed tissues. The term "septicemia" implies the presence of "septic" products in the blood and indicates the presence throughout the body of bacteria or other organisms as well as the by-products of the related disease process. **Toxemia,** as usually defined, indicates the presence of toxin throughout the body, either derived from the parasite or the host or both.

Where death of the host occurs as a result of infection, survival of the parasite is imperiled. With destruction of the cadaver or carcass the entire resident population of parasites may perish. Theobald Smith has called this "bungling parasitism." Chronic prolonged infection often provides greater opportunity for perpetuation of the parasite and its transmission to susceptible individuals. The ideal host-parasite relationship predicates minimal conflict between the two. According to Burnet, this ideal relationship is exemplified by *Herpes simplex* infection in man, wherein 90 per cent of the individuals carry the virus through 90 per cent of the life span.

A number of ways in which virulent agents may cause infection and a pathological condition have been elucidated, but we know that these ways do not represent all that exist. No pathogenic agent possesses all of the properties or activities considered under mechanism of infection. Indeed, some highly virulent agents apparently possess none of the properties or activities which have been described, and cause disease by means not yet understood.

REFERENCES

Boyd, W., *A textbook of pathology* (4th ed.). Philadelphia, Pa., Lea & Febiger, 1943.

Boyd, W., *Fundamentals of immunology* (2nd ed.). N. Y., Interscience Publishers, 1947.

Burnet, F. M., *Biological aspects of infectious diseases.* London, Cambridge University Press, 1940.

Burrows, W., Gordon, F. B., Porter, R. J., and Moulder, J. W., *Jordan-Burrows textbook of bacteriology* (15th ed.). Philadelphia, Pa., Saunders, 1949.

Dubos, R. J., *The bacterial cell.* Cambridge, Mass., Harvard University Press, 1945.

Hagan, W. A., *The infectious diseases of domestic animals.* Ithaca, N. Y., Comstock, 1945.

Harvard School of Public Health Symposium, *Virus and rickettsial diseases.* Cambridge, Mass., Harvard University Press, 1943.

Kabat, E. A., and Mayer, M., *Experimental immunochemistry.* Springfield, Ill., C. C. Thomas, 1948.

Kelser, R. A., and Schoening, H. W., *Manual of veterinary bacteriology* (5th ed.). Baltimore, Md., Williams & Wilkins, 1948.

Raffel, S., "Mechanisms of pathogenicity and virulence," *Standford Med. Bull.* (1948), 6:207–214.

Smith, D. T., and Martin, D. S., *Zinsser's textbook of bacteriology* (9th ed.). N. Y., Appleton-Century-Crofts, 1948.

Treffers, H. P., "Immunochemistry." *Annual Review of Microbiology,* Vol. I. Stanford, Calif., Annual Reviews, Inc., 1947.

Wilson, G. S., and Miles, A. A., *Topley and Wilson's Principles of Bacteriology and Immunity,* Vol. II. Baltimore, Md., Williams & Wilkins, 1946.

29. DEFENSES OF THE BODY AGAINST DISEASE

The requisites of infection are: (1) the entrance of the infectious agent into the tissues of the host; (2) its growth in the tissue; and (3) injury to the host. As was noted in the previous chapter, some pathogens possess mechanisms that enable them to carry out the infectious process. Normal animals, however, have reasonably effective barriers and mechanisms through which they can protect themselves against the entrance of pathogenic agents, prevent the growth of the pathogenic agents if they do gain access to the tissues, and guard against injury if entrance and growth have occurred. Most pathogens reaching the body surfaces are removed or destroyed and the resistance so afforded constitutes the line of **primary defenses** of the body against infections. If the pathogen evades or penetrates these initial barriers, the fate of the host depends upon the effectiveness of the **secondary defenses,** chiefly represented by humoral and cellular mechanisms.

Resistance of the host to infection is properly termed **immunity.** In present usage, immunity implies a variation in degree of resistance against infection ranging from barely perceptible resistance to that which is absolute, or nearly so.

Primary Defenses of the Body Against Infection

Intact Skin and Mucous Membranes

Experience with most ordinary injuries emphasizes the value of the intact skin and mucous membranes as barriers against the introduction of pathogenic microorganisms into the body. The deeper tissues of the body have

357

little ability to prevent the invasion of pathogens. The intact skin and mucous membranes act effectively in a mechanical way, augmented by complex biochemical mechanisms.

Most exposed areas of the normal skin and mucous membranes support a normal microbial flora adapted to the environmental conditions peculiar to that part or area. The microbes constituting this population colonize and thrive as "residents" in contrast to the adventitious and sometimes pathogenic "transients" which, fortunately, through inability to establish a residence, are not likely to invade and infect the surface or deeper tissues of the host. However, certain normal microbial inhabitants of the skin and mucous membranes are pathogenic, and may initiate infection if through injury to or defect of the skin or membranes they are enabled to pass into or beyond these barriers. Such normal microbial inhabitants, e.g., the micrococci of the skin, are usually so well established in their normal habitats that no amount of washing or use of alleged skin disinfectants may eliminate them entirely. A few pathogens, of which the tularemia organism is an example, may pass through the intact skin.

Secretions

Sweat, mucus, and tears mechanically carry or flush away foreign substances. The acid reaction of sweat is unfavorable to many bacteria; in addition, known bactericidal agents such as lysozyme, and unknown or as yet undefined substances, may be present in varying concentrations in secretions of the body. The mucus tends to trap and clump bacteria and thus aid in expelling them. Suction currents carry the bacteria in the saliva and nasal secretions to the base of the tongue, from which area they are swallowed. Most of the microbes which pass the glottis (the opening of the windpipe) are coughed up or swept upward to the pharynx (the upper part of the throat) by the action of the cilia on the lining cells of the trachea (the windpipe).

When bacteria are swallowed they enter the highly acid environment of the stomach. Unless protected by food against the inimical stomach acidity, many pathogens are harmed or destroyed. In the intestine, the microbial population increases progressively until, in the colon and rectum, enormous numbers are present. The bile, lysozyme, and additional unknown inhibitory factors influence adversely many transient organisms which reach the various parts of the intestine. Certain highly virulent enteric infectious agents, e.g., *Salmonella typhosa,* may withstand these defenses, in which case penetration of the mucous membranes of the intestine may occur.

The efficacy of the surface barriers and secretions of the intestine may be demonstrated by the fact that 1000 to 100,000 times more cells of certain *Salmonella* organisms are needed to cause infection when introduced by way of the mouth than when injected into the peritoneal cavity.

Pathogenic microorganisms on the skin or on the surfaces of the mucous membranes which line the alimentary, respiratory, and genitourinary tracts are outside the physiological interior of the body. They cannot produce infection unless they break through these primary barriers.

The specific effectiveness of the primary defenses of the body against infections is difficult to estimate, although it is obviously considerable. If these primary barriers are penetrated or evaded the result of the struggle between the pathogen and host depends largely on the secondary defenses: (1) phagocytic action; (2) antibodies, the humoral defenses; (3) connective tissue.

SECONDARY DEFENSES OF THE BODY AGAINST INFECTION

Should the infectious agent break through the primary barriers or defenses of the body it promptly encounters the secondary or parenteral mechanisms. These defensive agencies and functions may be versatile and even spectacular in their action. They frequently function in a more specific manner than the essentially mechanical primary barriers.

Phagocytic Action

Introduction of finely divided inert materials such as carbon into the blood stream results in the early disappearance of the particles from the circulation. Within a few hours the greater portion of the particles may be found in certain tissues, especially those of the spleen, liver, lymph nodes, and bone marrow. They are fixed there by removal from the circulating fluids by phagocytic cells of the type called **macrophages.** Some of the macrophage cells are not fixed, but migrate in the blood and fluids of the body. These wandering or circulating macrophages are called **large monuclear leucocytes,** or **endothelial leucocytes.** In addition to these macrophage cells there are circulating white blood cells, called **polymorphonuclear** or **neutrophilic leucocytes,** which are active against many infectious agents. Figure 62 shows normal leucocytes and some that have engulfed bacteria.

Inert particles, as well as bacteria, which gain entrance into the tissues may be clumped or agglutinated into groups or masses. With agglutination, the particles or bacterial aggregates tend to become lodged in the capillaries, especially in those of the lungs. These fixed masses are attacked by the phagocytes and are more readily phagocytized and finally eliminated.

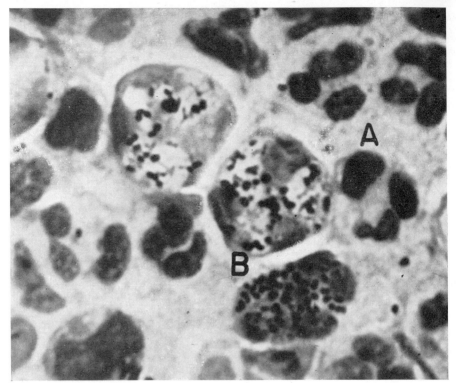

FIGURE 62.   Photomicrograph of pus, showing phagocytosis of diplococci by white blood cells (polymorphonuclear leucocytes). **A.** Leucocyte with no ingested bacteria. The cell wall and cytoplasm around the lobed nucleus are hard to distinguish. **B.** Leucocyte that has phagocytized large numbers of diplococci.

Considerable numbers of virulent bacteria, although taken up by phagocytes, may not be destroyed. Several hours following invasion, the number of bacteria in the blood stream may rise, indicating that the phagocytic and other secondary defenses have not been able to hold the infection in check. When the phagocytic function has successfully met the challenge of the invading bacteria by fixing or destroying a part or all of the invaders, there is only a slight secondary rise of organisms in the blood, or none at all. If pathogens become established in local areas, they may grow to produce foci or colonies from which massive invasion of the circulation may occur. Sometimes smaller numbers of organisms are required to induce a fatal generalized or systemic infection in this manner than are necessary when early infection occurs by way of the lymph or blood stream.

While phagocytosis is one of the means the host has for removal of or destruction of bacteria, it should be noted that the invading microorganisms may not be altogether passive in submission to the phagocytes. It was pointed out in the previous chapter that invading pathogens may actively combat phagocytes by the production of **leucocidins,** which kill cells capable of phagocytic action. Possession of a capsule also helps to protect pathogens against destruction by phagocytes.

Antibodies, the Humoral Defense

The **antibodies** are serum proteins manufactured by the host when **foreign proteins** called **antigens** are introduced into the tissues. Organisms, of course, contain proteins which are foreign to the host; antibodies, therefore, are formed against invading organisms. Antibodies are also formed against other proteins, including the toxins produced by some microorganisms. The serum from a person who has recovered from the effects of an invasion by organisms contains antibodies, i.e., it is an **antiserum.** Such an antiserum is necessarily complex, since organisms are made up of so many substances; part of the antibodies in the antiserum will react with the toxins produced by the organisms and part will react with the organisms themselves. The **antitoxin** (that part of the antiserum which acts against the toxins) is known to combine with the toxin according to chemical laws; the combination results in the neutralization of the biological activity of the toxin but does not destroy it. Just how the antibodies fight the organisms themselves is not completely understood. It is assumed, however, that these antibodies are powerful, because persons or animals whose blood serum contains them usually do not become infected with the organisms against which the antibodies were formed, and also, because this immunity can be transferred to other individuals by injecting them with the antiserum.

The antibodies in the antiserum are named according to their activity: **antitoxins,** if toxins are neutralized; **precipitins,** if substances are precipitated; **agglutinins,** if cells are clumped; **lysins,** if cells are lysed; **cidins,** if cells are killed; **opsonins,** if they increase the rate of ingestion of organisms by leucocytes; or **virus-neutralizing antibodies,** if a mixture of a virus and its antiserum is rendered noninfectious.

The presence of the antibodies in blood serum can be demonstrated *in vitro* (outside the body, in the test tube) in a number of ways. If a solution of homologous protein is added to the antiserum, a precipitate will be formed; and if whole cells of organisms are added, the cells may be agglutinated (clumped) or lysed (disintegrated) or killed without visible lysis. Also, *in vitro,* antiserum can be shown to affect the number of bacteria ingested by leucocytes. These reactions are specific, and can be used to detect the presence of certain antibodies in blood sera. It can be surmised, but not assumed, that the antibodies act similarly on proteins and organisms inside the body.

This does not mean that these antibodies can be distinguished chemically from one another, but only that under given conditions *in vitro* the antiserum will show a given activity; in fact the evidence indicates that one antibody may exhibit more than one activity when the conditions are varied. Important factors conditioning the activity of an antiserum are the proportional amounts of antigen and antibody and the size of the particles of antigen. In the reaction, the antigen first combines with the antibody. Then, other conditions being favorable, visible agglutination or precipitation occurs if an electrolyte such as NaCl is present. Or, with other conditions favorable, lysis, killing, or opsonification of cells will occur if a certain constituent of normal blood serum, called **complement,** is present. Complement (a substance present in the blood) may also be combined with an antigen-antibody complex where dead cells or pure chemical substances are the antigens, so that no visible reaction occurs: this is called complement fixation.

Any material, whether pure protein or organisms, which when injected inside the body of an animal gives rise to the formation of antibodies, is called an antigen. Almost all **antigens** contain proteins (or their degradation products). The **antibodies** formed are specific and will react only with the antigen injected, or with other substances of very similar chemical composition. For example, egg white proteins will react only with antisera from animals which have been injected with egg white proteins, and not with antisera from animals injected with milk proteins. A person who has recovered from measles will have antibodies formed during the disease which will neutralize the virus of measles but will not neutralize the virus of infantile paralysis. When antibodies react with substances of similar, but not identical, chemical structure to the antigens injected, the reaction will be less than with the homologous antigens, and the amount of reaction will vary directly with the number of similar reactive groups in the substances; that is, the specificity of the reaction is quantitative.

Connective Tissue as a Defense

The third and last defense of the invaded animal is connective tissue. Connective tissue is laid down to replace other tissues which have been destroyed. In infectious processes such as tuberculosis, connective tissue walls-in the diseased area produced by the interaction of the tissues and the bacteria, and thus prevents escape of bacteria to other tissues.

INFLAMMATION

The body may aid the action of its phagocytic cells and antibodies in one or more ways. Whenever foreign particles invade the tissues, inflammation occurs in the invaded area, with the result that increased quantities of blood are concentrated in the area. The blood brings migrating macrophages and leucocytes to the region, and also supplies antibodies to combat the invading pathogens. The antibodies which give direct aid to phagocytes in their action on bacteria are called **opsonins.** Other antibodies present in the blood may clump, kill, or lyse (dissolve) invading bacteria, and thus make possible more rapid and effective phagocytic action by the macrophages and leucocytes. Inflammation is manifest by heat, redness, swelling, and pain in the inflamed area; it is evidence that the secondary defenses of the body are being brought into action against invading pathogens or foreign particles. The inflammation may be localized, which is evidence that the bodily defenses are overcoming the invaders. However, if the microorganisms break through these defenses, and if other secondary defenses are inadequate, generalized infection may result.

RESULTS OF FAILURE OF DEFENSES

If the localized defenses fail to hold, the organisms get into the lymph vessels and thence travel to the lymph nodules or glands. Here they are filtered out and may be held from spreading further, at least for a time. When severe damage is done locally, the organisms may also get into the blood vessels, which distribute them to various parts of the body; the disease becomes generalized and the chances for fatality are considerably increased.

IMMUNITY

Immunity implies a state, natural or acquired, in which the body is resistant to disease. The degree of resistance is dependent not only upon the defense mechanism of the host but also upon the virulence of the invading pathogens. These factors have been discussed previously. However, the effectiveness with which the various defenses of the same individual work at different times is often assumed to be dependent upon such factors as fatigue, nutrition, and climate. In reality the evidence for such an assumption is largely circumstantial and often the result of rationalization: it is easier to think that an attack of smallpox or typhoid fever resulted from fatigue rather than from failure to be vaccinated or from drinking contaminated water. Some small amount of experimental evidence does exist, however, as to how much certain external factors affect the functioning of the defenses. A warm, moist climate considerably speeds the rate of death of animals experimentally infected with bacteria. Actual starvation must certainly result in lowered defenses, but the effect of the lack of such foods as vitamins is comparatively unknown. Lack of vitamin A or parts of the B complex results in an easier establishment of infection in experimental animals. Various evidence indicates that individuals with already established infections need more vitamins; at least more of A, C, and parts of the B complex. However, in some experiments, suboptimal diets have caused increased resistance to infection. Fatigue does lessen the speed of recovery from infectious diseases, but the evidence as to its effect on the establishment of infection is contradictory.

Inherited Immunity

The effectiveness of the defenses of the body against a particular organism varies with the individual host and with the species of host. Apparently the inherited constitution of the individual determines his resistance to some extent; for example, some families of the white race are known to be much more resistant to tuberculosis than are others. The existence of such inherited differences in resistance would seem logical considering other inherited differences in individuals, but have not been proved, nor have the specific factors responsible been determined. It has been proved experimentally that some inbred families of rabbits are much more resistant to tuberculosis than other inbred families, but the resistance cannot be definitely correlated with any one factor such as the ability to form antibodies. Also, families of rabbits have been developed that are much more resistant to brucellosis than the parent stock. This same type of resistance has been developed in mice against mouse typhoid. This type of inherited immunity is known as **racial immunity;** certain races of the same species are more resistant than other races.

Some species of animals are quite immune to infection by pathogens that are highly infectious to other species. Human beings are resistant to the virus of hog cholera, which is highly infectious for swine. The virus of measles is infectious for man, but lower animals are resistant to this virus. Indeed, the study of certain infectious diseases of man has been retarded because no suitable laboratory animal has been found to be susceptible. This type of inherited immunity is known as **species immunity.**

Acquired Immunity

An individual who is not naturally immune to an infectious agent may acquire an immunity. An individual who has recovered from measles, or from one of a number of other infectious diseases, has valuable antibodies which he may pass on to another individual by donating blood serum. The individual who has built up his own antibody proteins is said to have an **active** immunity; the second individual, who has received the antibodies from the first, is said to have a **passive** immunity. The significant differences between active and passive immunity which should never be forgotten, are that it may take from one or two weeks to several months to build up an active immunity, whereas passive immunity is effected as soon as the antiserum is injected; and the active immunity may last for months or a lifetime, but the passive for only a few days or weeks. The reason for the persistence of the active immunity is not fully understood, since the exact place and the mechanism of formation of antibodies in the animal are not definitely known. In some diseases caused by viruses, e.g., smallpox and measles, the active immunity may last a lifetime. It seems possible that after an attack of the disease some virus remains alive inside body cells in a place where it does no harm and yet where it can serve as a constant stimulation for the production of antibodies or in some way interfere with subsequent infection with the same virus.

A durable active immunity against any disease is preferable to a fleeting passive immunity, and man has learned to produce an active immunity against some diseases without the expense of a typical attack of the disease. An Englishman, Jenner, in the eighteenth century observed that persons who had contracted cowpox from cattle did not subsequently get smallpox. The same immunization could be artificially produced by inoculating the skin of a human being with a small amount of material from the skin sores of a cow with cowpox; the person had a slight attack of cowpox, which is usually a very mild disease in man. Jenner recognized that cowpox and smallpox were very similar diseases; it is now known that smallpox and cowpox are caused by two closely related but distinct viruses.

Immunization

After the discoveries of the causative agents of many infectious diseases in the late nineteenth and early twentieth centuries, methods of immunization against several diseases have been developed. This process of artificial **active** immunization is called **vaccination.** The basic principle of vaccination is as follows: the immunizing agent (antigen) is the virulent organism or the toxin of an organism, treated to reduce its virulence or toxicity as much as possible without too severe alteration of its chemical structure. Immunization against the virulent organism will not be effected, of course, if the antigens are changed too much chemically. Injection of the antigen results in formation of antibodies specific for the particular antigen.

The method of reducing the virulence of the pathogen varies with the organism. In vaccinating against bacterial diseases, the cells from cultures that have been weakened in some manner or killed by heat are now used. To produce effective heat-killed vaccines, virulent strains of the bacteria must be used, and the heating must be as gentle as possible. Typhoid vaccine is produced in this way. Vaccines for diseases caused by viruses are produced in various ways. For instance, a type of rabies vaccine is prepared by growing the virus in a series of rabbits and using the dried spinal cord of the last rabbit as the vaccine: the virus is attenuated for man and dogs by the passage through the rabbits and by the drying. Against another disease caused by a virus, namely hog cholera, the animals may be vaccinated by inoculating them with a small amount of the blood from a hog with an active case of the disease, together with some serum from a hog which has recovered from the disease: the blood contains the unattenuated virus and the antiserum is given with it to reduce its virulence. Vaccination against yellow fever involves use of a vaccine prepared from a relatively avirulent strain of the virus cultivated in embryonating hens' eggs. Vaccination against influenza in human beings has been attempted through the use of inactivated virus which has been grown in embryonating hens' eggs. The pictures in Figure 63 illustrate two of the procedures used in working with eggs to prepare influenza vaccine.

By analogous methods, artificial active immunization can be developed against the exotoxin of toxin-producing organisms such as the diphtheria bacillus. The toxin can be obtained free from the bacterial cells by filtering broth cultures of the diphtheria bacillus. This toxin may be treated chemically with formaldehyde, which reduces its potency; this nontoxic substance, called **toxoid,** is then used as the immunizing agent. Very small amounts of the untreated toxin may be injected together with a small amount of antitoxin to reduce its potency: this is called the toxin-antitoxin or T-(AT) method. Artificial active immunization against tetanus and botulinum toxins may be accomplished by use of toxoids prepared from the toxins of the causative organisms.

Animals may be actively immunized artificially against some diseases, and their immunity passed on to human beings or other animals. Horses, for example, are immunized against the diphtheria exotoxin, or against the toxin of the bacteria causing tetanus; and both horses and rabbits are vaccinated against the cocci causing pneumonia. Their antisera can then be used for the **passive** immunization of man. Such antisera are, of course, cheaper and more readily procurable than sera from human beings who have recovered from the disease (these latter antisera are called "convalescent sera"). Unfortunately from the standpoint of obtaining immune sera, animals other than man are not susceptible to some diseases, such as measles, so that human antisera must sometimes be used.

FIGURE 63. Top, these carefully protected technicians are inoculating embryonating hens' eggs with influenza virus. After inoculation the eggs will be returned to the incubator and the virus will multiply in this living environment. Left, harvesting the allantoic fluid from the eggs at the end of the incubation period.

This fluid which contains the virus will be used to manufacture influenza vaccine. For vaccines against other viruses, the embryonic tissues may be harvested instead of the allantoic fluid. (Courtesy of the Virus Production Laboratories, E. R. Squibb & Sons, New Brunswick, New Jersey.)

Passive immunity may be acquired by the fetus from the mother. This varies, however, among the species of animals, depending upon the complexity of the placental membranes. Obviously, only immunity against pathogens to which the mother is immune will be passed on to the fetus. Also, the first milk (colostrum) of the mother contains antibodies that may be absorbed by the young animal. The passage of antibodies from the hen through the egg yolk to the chick embryo is also an example of this type of immunity, which is called **congenital** immunity.

The ways in which immunity may be acquired by an individual can be summarized as follows:

Passive acquisition:
(few weeks duration at the most)

1. **Natural,** by passage of antiserum from mother to child before birth. In some animals, such as the cow, the antibodies are passed from the mother to the calf by means of the colostrum, or first milk produced
2. **Artificial,** by injection of antiserum from an immunized human being or other animal

Active acquisition:
(several months duration at least—may endure for lifetime)

1. **Natural** or **accidental,** by attack of the disease with either manifest or obscure symptoms
2. **Artificial,** by vaccination with: (a) an attenuated virus; (b) a virulent virus together with a small amount of antiserum; (c) killed or weakened bacteria; (d) a toxoid; or (e) a toxin together with a small amount of antitoxin

Hypersensitivity in Immunity

Obviously the reactivity of the blood serum against organisms or against toxins or other proteins is increased by immunization. This reactivity may actually be so great that a state called **hypersensitiveness** results in which the individual will have a noticeable reaction, of more or less violence, within a few minutes or hours after a second or subsequent introduction of the antigen. The symptoms of hypersensitiveness vary with the kind of animal and with several other factors. For example, the guinea pig may have a violent reaction resulting in death within a few minutes after a second injection of egg white. Such a reaction is called **anaphylaxis.** In a normal or nonimmune guinea pig, i.e., one which had not received the protein previously, such an injection would cause no noticeable reaction. In man, the following are probably hypersensitivities: serum sickness; hay fever; food "allergies," which may be manifested in the gastrointestinal tract by various symptoms, in the respiratory tract by rhinitis or by asthma, or in skin rashes such as hives; and drug "idiosyncrasies."

In some individuals the injection of serum from another species (horse serum carrying antitoxins, for example) results in serum sickness. Such persons have previously formed antibodies to the proteins (in horse serum) which differ from the proteins in human serum, and are therefore foreign to man. Then, when the antigen (horse serum) is again introduced into the person, the reaction of the antigens and their antibodies affects the tissues to produce the sickness. The symptoms are varied and appear from one to ten days following injection of the serum. An immediate reaction analogous to anaphylaxis in experimental animals may, on rare occasions, lead to death of the individual. In hay fever, the sensitizing agent or antigen complex is the pollen of various plants. Reactions to foods may follow the eating of some food such as egg white or strawberries; probably the egg white or strawberry proteins pass undigested through the intestinal wall into the body where they react with antibodies formed after a previous absorption of the same protein into the body. In all these cases of hypersensitiveness, the protein antigens have probably been previously introduced into the body without causing any symptoms but causing the formation of antibodies. Why certain human beings have the misfortune to be so easily sensitized to some proteins is not known, although the tendency is apparently inherited. The so-called "idiosyncrasies" to drugs are also apparently hypersensitivities, because the symptoms occur only in certain individuals and usually only upon repeated taking of the drug.

Environmental Immunity and the Defenses of Communities

Living conditions may determine to a large extent the immunity possessed by members of a community against certain infectious diseases. Such immunity is **environmental,** and exists in addition to the individual immunity which has been discussed previously.

Comparison of Acquired and Environmental Immunity

Acquired	Environmental
1. **Individual**	1. **Individual,** determined by:
a. Active	a. Occupation (e.g., stone cutters with silicosis have lowered immunity to tuberculosis)
b. Passive	b. Habitation (crowding increases opportunity for contacts)
	c. Personal habits (e.g., cleanliness)

Comparison of Acquired and Environmental Immunity (*Continued*)

2. **Community**
   All members of community protected to some degree if a majority of its members have acquired immunity

2. **Community,** determined by:
   a. Control of water supply
   b. Adequate treatment and disposal of sewage
   c. Sanitary production and handling of foods
   d. Control of insects
   e. Slaughter and proper disposal of infected animals
   f. Treatment of diseases such as syphilis and tuberculosis
   g. Isolation in diseases such as tuberculosis

The specific methods effective in bringing about acquired and environmental immunity to a given disease will depend upon the disease: for example, control of mosquitoes will prevent malaria and yellow fever but will have no effect upon the incidence of smallpox or diphtheria because they are not spread by mosquitoes. This difference in diseases is the answer to such familiar questions as, "Why can't they make a good vaccine for colds?" The cold virus is very different from the smallpox virus and therefore the disease is different: The cowpox virus can be grown in calves and used as a vaccine against smallpox, whereas the cold virus has not, as yet, been grown outside the human body; but more important, an attack of smallpox results in a naturally acquired immunity lasting for years, whereas an attack of the common cold confers only a very short immunity if any. This does not mean that we may not have a vaccine against colds some day; it does mean that it is a more difficult problem than was the development of the smallpox vaccine.

Against some diseases the community is relatively defenseless. In general, there are two reasons why a disease cannot be controlled: (1) it may be socially and economically impossible even though we know how it could be done; and (2) if it cannot be prevented by environmental immunity, acquired immunity must be used, and good methods of vaccination have not been developed for some diseases. Those diseases which cannot be prevented by an environmental immunity usually are those spread by moisture droplets or contact before the disease is diagnosed. Syphilis, measles, chickenpox, gonorrhea, whooping cough, pneumonia, scarlet fever, mumps, tuberculosis, and influenza have a high incidence in this country. Of these, syphilis, gonorrhea, and tuberculosis could be prevented from spreading if it were economically and socially possible to test every person and to isolate and treat all who have the disease. Of the other diseases, measles, chickenpox, pneumonia, scarlet fever, mumps, and influenza are all carried by moisture droplets from an infected person before he has obvious signs of the disease, and no very good methods of vaccination are known for these diseases. These diseases apparently can be controlled on a small scale by a type of environmental immunity: namely, irradiating, with ultraviolet light, the air in schoolrooms, barracks, and hospital wards. Control by this method on a large enough scale to provide a really effective environmental immunity is as yet, however, only an interesting possibility. Against whooping cough there is now an apparently good vaccine, but it is not yet universally used.

When the number of cases of a disease in a community rather suddenly increases and affects a relatively large proportion of the population, the disease is said to be **epidemic** in human beings or **epizootic** in animals. An **endemic** or **enzootic** disease is one which has a low incidence in the community and the number of cases is relatively constant.

REFERENCES

American Association for the Advancement of Science, *Aerobiology*. Lancaster, Pa., Science Press Printing Company, 1942.

Chapin, C. B., *A review of public health realities*. N. Y., Commonwealth Fund, 1934.

Cannon, P. R., "The functional significance of agglutinins and precipitins." *Phys. Rev.* (1940), *20*:89–115.

Dubos, R. J. (ed.), *Bacterial and mycotic infections of man*. Philadelphia, Pa., Lippincott, 1948.

Duclaux, E. (trans. by E. F. Smith and F. Hedges), *Pasteur, the history of a mind*, Parts 7 and 8. Philadelphia, Pa., Saunders, 1920.

Greenwood, Major, *Epidemics and crowd diseases, an introduction to the study of epidemiology*. N. Y., Macmillan, 1935.

Kelser, R. A., and Schoening, H. W., *Manual of veterinary bacteriology* (5th ed.). Baltimore, Md., Williams & Wilkins, 1948.

Landsteiner, K., *The specificity of serological reactions*. Springfield, Ill., C. C. Thomas, 1936.

Lurie, M. B., "Heredity, constitution, and tuberculosis: experimental study." *Am. Rev. Tuberc.* (1941), *44*:1–125.

Marrack, J. R., "The chemistry of antigens and antibodies." *Med. Research Council, Spec. Report Ser. No. 230* (1938).

Menkin, Valy, *Dynamics of inflammation*. N. Y., Macmillan, 1940.

Price, P. B., "The bacteriology of normal skin, a new quantitative test applied to a study of the bacterial flora and the disinfectant action of mechanical cleansing." *J. Infect. Dis.* (1938), *63*:301–318.

Rivers, T. M., "Viruses and Koch's postulates." *J. Bact.* (1937), *33*:1–12.

Rivers, T. M. (ed.), *Viral and rickettsial infections of man*. Philadelphia, Pa., Lippincott, 1948.

Rosebury, T., *Experimental air-borne infection*. Baltimore, Md., Williams & Wilkins, 1947.

Smith, T., *Parasitism and disease*. Princeton, N. J., Princeton University Press, 1934.

Wilson, G. S., and Miles, A. A., *Topley and Wilson's principles of bacteriology and immunity* (3rd ed.), Vols. I and II. Baltimore, Md., Williams & Wilkins, 1946.

30. TRANSMISSION OF INFECTIOUS DISEASES

Infectious diseases are transmissible because the bacteria, rickettsiae, viruses, molds, yeasts, or protozoa which cause them may be transferred from one individual to another. Transmission of some infectious agents may be accomplished by **direct contact** with infected tissues or with secretions or excretions from such tissues. Transmission of other infectious diseases may occur when the causative agent follows an **indirect,** often circuitous, route in its transfer from the infected host to a susceptible individual.

For infectious disease to occur, the inciting agent must be given the opportunity to reach susceptible tissues in sufficient numbers to become established and grow. The surest way to prevent infectious diseases is to remove or kill the pathogens before they can reach or enter a susceptible host; therefore, a consideration of the portals of entry into the body, of the possible channels of discharge of pathogens from the body, and of the means of transmission from infected to noninfected individuals is important.

Portals of Entry into the Body

Pathogens may enter the bodies of higher animals through the skin and exposed mucous membranes, or through the membranes of the eyes, the ears, the respiratory tract, the gastrointestinal tract, or the genitourinary tract. If invasion is to occur, the causative organisms first must reach those places on the outside of the body through which they have the peculiar ability to enter, and from which there is a path to the tissues in which they can grow. For example, micrococci, which are normal inhabitants of the

372

skin, usually cannot produce infection until the intact, healthy skin is injured in some way; *Clostridium perfringens* is a normal inhabitant of the intestinal tract, but when it gets into deep wounds it may produce gas gangrene; *Salmonella typhosa* causes typhoid fever only if it reaches and invades certain tissues of the intestinal tract. Many pathogens can enter the body through the membranes of the respiratory tract; some may produce infection in tissues of the respiratory tract, while others migrate from their point of entry to other susceptible tissues. Some pathogens have a high degree of specificity for certain tissues; others are comparatively nonspecific and will infect more than one kind of tissue.

Channels and Means of Discharge from the Body

Pathogens may leave an infected individual's body in secretions or excretions; the particular secretion or excretion which will carry the organisms, as well as the channel of discharge, will depend upon the place where the pathogens are growing in the body. Pathogens on or in the skin may escape if the skin is destroyed and the lesion becomes exposed; those in blood would leave if hemorrhages occur from any surface on the outside of the body, or if arthropods such as mosquitoes, lice, fleas, ticks, or blood-sucking flies remove blood; those present in open wounds in the intestinal tract would be expelled in the feces; those present in the kidney or other parts of the urinary tract would escape in the urine; pathogens in the genital tract would be discharged in its secretions. Not so obvious, is the fact that many pathogens may be present in the secretions of the upper respiratory tract during some stage of several diseases not considered to be diseases of the respiratory tract. For example, measles and smallpox are transmissible by means of moisture droplets ejected from the mouth or nose; in rabies, the seat of infection lies in the central nervous system, yet the causative virus escapes from a rabid animal in the saliva secreted by the salivary glands of the mouth.

The period of time during which pathogens are discharged from an infected individual, and the total number of pathogens discharged, depend to some extent upon the course of the disease. In acute cases of an infectious disease, death may occur so rapidly that comparatively few pathogens are discharged. In chronic infections, however, the disease lasts for a comparatively long time, during which the causative agents may be discharged continuously or intermittently, and consequently a large number of pathogens may be given off. Of course, in some chronic diseases such as tuberculosis, the infected area may be so located in the body or so walled off by bodily defenses that the causative bacteria cannot escape; in such cases, the pathogens are discharged only when they break through the defensive barriers and reach tissues from which they may readily be carried to the outside.

Some apparently healthy persons and animals are **carriers** of pathogenic agents and may disseminate pathogens for long periods of time. Carriers may be recovered cases of the disease, but in some instances the attack of disease which induced the carrier state was so slight that the individual was not aware of the infection. The carrier problem is great in such diseases as epidemic meningitis, typhoid fever, and poliomyelitis in human beings; brucellosis, hog cholera, and pullorum disease in animals. Recognition and control of carriers presents a great problem to public health authorities. Pathogens may be discharged from a carrier in the same manner that they depart from an individual recognized as a case of the disease.

Means of Transmission of Pathogens

Transmission by Direct Contact

The diseases of man transmitted chiefly by direct contact are syphilis and gonorrhea, diseases of the respiratory tract, and other diseases caused by pathogens which may be present in the upper respiratory tract. Examples of diseases of animals transmitted chiefly by direct contact are brucellosis and hog cholera. The meat or milk of an infected animal may be used as food by a human being or other animal and thus transmit pathogens directly. Diseases which may be transmitted by direct contact may also be spread by other means.

Transmission by Indirect Means

In the indirect transmission of pathogens, the vehicle which carries the organisms may serve only as a mechanical means of transmission, or it may play an active part in the process. The vehicle may be some inanimate substance or object, or it may be a living vector.

Transmission of pathogens by water and foods is so specialized and important a subject that it will be described and discussed separately in the latter part of this chapter.

Air is important as a temporary carrier of pathogens suspended in moisture droplets coughed or sneezed from the mouth and nose. Any pathogen present in the mouth, nose, or upper respiratory tract may be ejected into the air by coughing or sneezing, and may remain suspended in the air for considerable periods of time. Air currents may carry pathogens for some distances, but transmission through the air usually is more important indoors under comparatively crowded conditions than outdoors, where the dilution effect is great, and where ultraviolet light from the sun may strike

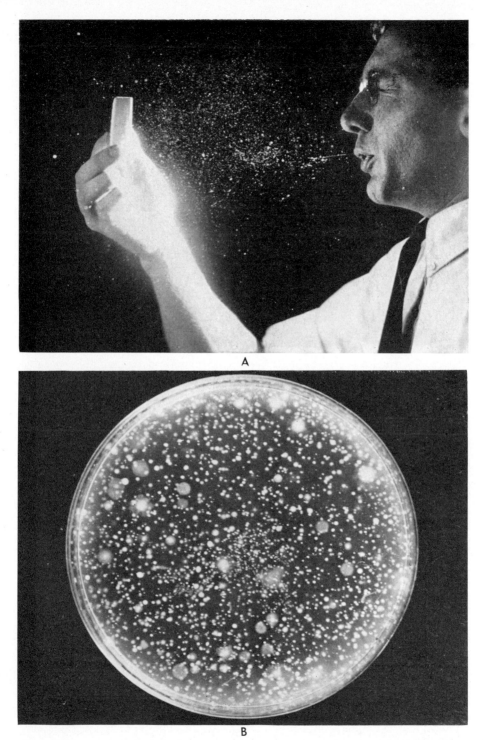

FIGURE 64. **A.** A high-speed photograph of an unstifled sneeze. Note the many droplets that have been atomized into the air. **B.** Colonies of bacteria have developed on the medium exposed to the sneeze droplets. (Jennison, S.A.B. Nos. 17, 18.)

the organisms. Rapid drying of the droplets which carry pathogens in the air tends to weaken or kill many of the organisms which may become airborne. Figure 64 illustrates the production of moisture droplets by sneezing and shows the bacterial colonies which developed on the medium that was exposed to the sneeze.

It is possible for many pathogens that are discharged from infected individuals to reach the soil, but because most of these organisms are parasitic they do not find conditions in the soil suitable for their growth or survival. However, those pathogens which are resistant to drying and other adverse environmental conditions either because of their innate properties, or because of protection afforded by organic matter, may survive in the soil for long periods of time. Some of the relatively saprophytic pathogens such as *Clostridium tetani,* may even grow in soils that are rich in organic matter.

It is also possible for pathogens to be transmitted by fomites (inanimate objects such as clothing, bedding, books, money, eating and drinking utensils, feed sacks, stock cars, etc.). Infectious agents may exist for varying periods of time on fomites. In general, those pathogens which are readily discharged from an infected individual may easily be transmitted by fomites. From the surfaces of contaminated fomites the pathogens may gain entrance to the body of a healthy person or animal through the usual portals of entry that have been described.

Arthropods (such as lice, ticks, fleas, flies, and mosquitoes) may serve as accidental carriers of pathogens, or in some cases as active, intermediate hosts for the organisms. Flies may carry pathogens on their feet or in their digestive tract, and thus serve as mechanical vectors without becoming infected. The *Aedes* mosquito may suck blood from an individual infected with the yellow fever virus and transmit the virus to a healthy person. Similarly, lice, ticks, and fleas may transmit pathogens from one individual to another or from infected animals to human beings. In the transmission of the malarial parasite, the *Anopheles* and certain other mosquitoes serve as vectors in which the pathogen undergoes part of its life cycle. The first proof that arthropods could serve as vectors of disease was presented by Smith and Kilborne in the now classic United States Department of Agriculture, *Bureau of Animal Industry Bulletin No. 1* (1893). They proved that a tick served as the vector for spread of the protozoan which caused Texas fever in cattle.

DISEASES OF HUMAN BEINGS SPREAD BY WATER AND BY FOODS

Spread of disease-producing agents by means of water or foods may result in isolated cases of disease, in small outbreaks, or in epidemics, depending upon the extent of distribution to human beings after the water or food has been contaminated. Water and food may serve simply to transmit the infectious agent or, as in certain food poisonings, the organisms may grow and produce toxins in the food.

Most sizable communities make some effort toward sanitary control of the water supply through water purification plants and sewage treatment and disposal systems. Few communities, however, do much toward preventing the spread of diseases by means of foods other than milk. Sanitary control of foods is a problem not only of the community, but also of the distributor, vendor, family, and individual.

Water-Borne Diseases

It has been pointed out that the chief source of contamination of water with pathogenic microorganisms is sewage. The pathogenic organisms are eliminated in large numbers from the intestines of cases and carriers and may, therefore, be present in untreated drinking water into which untreated or inadequately treated sewage has been introduced. The obvious methods for controlling the spread of these diseases—namely, treatment of the water, and sewage treatment and disposal—have been used so well in the large cities of Europe and the United States that the case rate and therefore the mortality are now very low. In some parts of the world, however, these diseases are still endemic and they may become epidemic anywhere under stress of disasters such as war and floods. The more serious water-borne diseases are typhoid and paratyphoid fevers, bacillary dysentery, amebic dysentery, and cholera. Small outbreaks of all these diseases except cholera continue to occur in the United States because of the existence of carriers.

Typhoid and paratyphoid fevers and bacillary dysentery are all caused by bacteria very closely related to *Escherichia coli*, a common inhabitant of the intestinal tract and usually nonpathogenic. The causative agent of typhoid fever is *Salmonella typhosa; Salmonella paratyphi, Salmonella schottmuelleri,* or other *Salmonella* species may cause paratyphoid; and at least five distinct species of the genus *Shigella* may cause dysentery, including *Shigella dysenteriae,* the so-called Shiga type, *Shigella sonnei,* the Sonne type, and *Shigella paradysenteriae,* the Flexner type. In typhoid and paratyphoid fevers the organisms cause disease in the intestinal tract but also enter the blood stream rather early and affect various other organs; these diseases can be differentiated definitely only by the isolation and identification of the causative organism. Dysentery is mainly an inflammation of the lower parts of the intestinal tract.

Artificial active immunization is carried out against typhoid and paratyphoid fevers with a polyvalent vaccine (so termed because it contains the dead cells of both typhoid and paratyphoid bacilli). This vaccination is routinely done, however, only on individuals who expect to meet the pathogens often and may therefore accidentally imbibe them, e.g., soldiers who will live under crowded and insanitary conditions in times of war, those working in bacteriological laboratories, or those travelling in countries where typhoid fever is endemic. Even though vaccinated, individuals in places where typhoid is endemic should indulge only in beverages in which the typhoid bacilli have been killed by boiling, by the addition of chlorine, or by other suitable methods of disinfection.

The diagnosis of enteric infection depends to considerable extent upon isolation and identification of the causative organisms. To this end a number of highly selective media have been developed that will permit the growth of enteric pathogens and differentiate them from the normal intestinal flora. In the diagnosis of typhoid fever an agglutination reaction known as the Widal test is employed.

Cholera, caused by *Vibrio comma,* is an acute disease affecting the intestinal tract. The disease is endemic in some countries of Asia and large epidemics have occurred throughout the world.

The ameba, *Entameba histolytica,* is another agent which causes dysentery. The disease may be chronic, and in many cases apparently the symptoms never become noticeable. Investigations have shown that a small but definite percentage of persons who have never had an attack are found to carry the cysts of the ameba. In a small percentage of cases the disease may be acute and death may occur within a few weeks of the onset. The cysts, the infective form of the organism, are resistant to chemicals such as chlorine but are killed by the temperature of boiling water.

An epidemic of water-born disease is traced by testing water for *Escherichia coli,* the presence of which is assumed to prove the pollution of water with sewage. This organism will be present more regularly in polluted water and in far larger numbers than the pathogens.

Food-Borne Diseases

Food-borne diseases may be classified into two groups: (1) those caused by organisms unable to grow in the food as it ordinarily is handled, and (2) those caused by organisms able to grow in the food. In the spread of diseases of the first group, the food serves merely as an inanimate carrier of the causative organisms, much as a door knob, handkerchief, drinking cup or any other fomes would serve that purpose. The second group includes the diseases usually termed food poisonings, such as botulism and staphylococcus poisoning, or food infections such as *Salmonella* infections. Most of this discussion will be confined to the diseases of the second group.

Food will serve as the inanimate carrier of the same infectious agents as water, namely, organisms causing intestinal diseases; in addition, it is often subject to contamination with pathogens from the respiratory tract, such as those causing tuberculosis, scarlet fever, and diphtheria.

Food Poisoning

The term "food poisoning" commonly is applied to any sudden illness involving the gastrointestinal tract and therefore may include illness resulting from the ingestion of inorganic chemicals, poisons derived from animals or plants, and toxic products from bacteria or bacterial infections. Allergies and even over-eating may cause intestinal disturbances miscalled food poisoning. The symptoms of food poisoning consist of acute abdominal pains, nausea, vomiting, and usually diarrhea, which last from 12 to 24 hours and are followed by an uneventful recovery. The popular term for any such illness is "ptomaine poisoning," although ptomaines, which are amines resulting from the putrefaction of proteins, do not cause poisoning when taken by mouth and every case of so-called ptomaine poisoning that has been thoroughly investigated has been proved to have some other cause. This term probably is misapplied most often to staphylococcus poisoning.

Food poisoning caused by bacteria able to grow well in foods is of two types: (1) true poisoning, due to exotoxins of bacteria, with staphylococcus poisoning and botulism as examples; and (2) food infections, as exemplified by disease caused by species of the genus *Salmonella*.

Staphylococcus Poisoning

Staphylococcus food poisoning is caused by enterotoxin-producing micrococci, of which some strains of *Micrococcus pyogenes* var. *aureus* are examples. The term staphylococcus food poisoning is derived from the former genus *Staphylococcus*, the organisms of which are now included in the genus *Micrococcus*. The toxin is called enterotoxin because it produces the gastrointestinal symptoms mentioned in a preceding paragraph. These symptoms usually appear in about three hours, occasionally in one to six hours, after ingestion of the food. An uneventful recovery takes place in from one to three days and the mortality is zero. This, undoubtedly, is the most common type of food poisoning; probably nearly everyone has been subjected to staphylococcus poisoning one or more times and may expect to encounter it again. Some few may have escaped, however, due to the great variation in the susceptibility of individuals to the action of the toxin. Reliable data on the incidence of this type of poisoning are not available, for the disease is not reportable in most states. Individual cases seldom are reported or even diagnosed correctly and many small outbreaks probably pass unnoted. When large groups of people who eat together (as at luncheon clubs, church suppers, picnics, military camps, etc.) are poisoned, publicity is given to the outbreak, the cause is determined, and reports become available. Certainly thousands of cases of staphylococcus poisoning occur annually in this country.

The following conditions are necessary for production of an outbreak of staphylococcus poisoning: (1) the food must become contaminated with an enterotoxin-producing micrococcus, and (2) the food must be kept at a temperature that will permit growth of the micrococcus. The most common source of the organism is a food handler, who may carry it in his throat or nose, or on his skin (especially in boils, pimples, or carbuncles), although the udder of an infected cow may be the source of the coccus in dairy products. The micrococcus grows best at 37° C., and also very well at room temperature. Foods producing the poisoning usually have a history of storage for some hours at room temperature. On subsequent refrigeration the organisms continue to grow and produce toxin slowly while the food is cooling, but they will not grow in foods at the temperature of a properly cooled icebox or refrigerator.

The following foods are among those which have been incriminated as causes of outbreaks of staphylococcus poisoning: custard and cream filled cakes and pastries, cream sauces, precooked meats such as ham and tongue, meat salads and sandwiches, roast turkey and the dressing, chicken and ham paste, chicken salad, chicken gravy and stuffing, sausage, milk, cheese, butter, ice cream and cream. Frozen vegetables may be involved, but only if grossly mishandled. Cakes and pastries, hams, and roast turkey are incriminated so often that they warrant special mention. The custard and cream filled cakes and pastries are readily subject to contamination as usually prepared and seldom are refrigerated before sale and consumption. Tenderized and precooked hams often are handled as if they were cured, smoked hams, allowing plenty of opportunity for growth of the staphylococcus. The residue of roast turkey after the first meal from it frequently is too large for the refrigerator and consequently is held over for some time at a temperature permitting growth of the staphylococci.

Staphylococcus poisoning can be prevented by: (1) prevention of contamination of the food with micrococci, i.e., sanitary handling of food by healthy handlers; (2) proper refrigeration of the food at all times; and (3) heating of the food during preparation to kill the micrococci. The latter procedure is recommended for treatment of eclairs, puffs, and similar pastries after filling, with heating for 30 minutes at 375° to 425° F. (190.6° to 218.3° C.). The micrococci are not too difficult to kill by heat, but the enterotoxin produced by them is very heat stable and cooking or boiling of the food is not a reliable method for destroying the toxin, nor will refrigeration or freezing reduce its potency.

Botulism

Botulism is a true food poisoning due to toxin formed by an anaerobic sporeformer, *Clostridium botulinum* or *C. parabotulinum,* during growth in underprocessed canned foods or in sausage or ham. *C. parabotulinum* is the name applied to the proteolytic species of the organism, and *C. botulinum* is the nonproteolytic species. Five types of toxin are recognized: types A, B, and E affect human beings, with A the most potent; types C and D affect animals. The toxin is the most powerful poison known, so potent that the mere tasting of canned food containing it may lead to death.

Symptoms usually appear within 12 to 36 hours, but shorter and longer periods of incubation have been reported. The symptoms vary in different cases, but usually are mild at first with an indefinite feeling of fatigue, dizziness, and sometimes a headache. Gastric evidence usually is lacking, with constipation occurring more frequently than diarrhea. There is paralysis of muscles of the eyes and pharynx, resulting in interference with vision, swallowing, and speaking. Paralysis spreads to the respiratory system and heart, resulting in death within one to eight days, or perhaps in recovery if the patient survives for over ten days. Mortality averages about 65 per cent in the United States but is lower in Europe. In the United States, home canned foods have been responsible for the greatest number of cases, while in Europe most botulism has followed the eating of preserved meats. Antitoxic serum specific in its action against botulinum toxin is available, but usually is not effective in therapy because by the time the symptoms of poisoning appear the toxin has already combined with the nervous tissues.

Botulism receives much publicity because of the high mortality rate, but the incidence is very low. There are, on the average, only about ten outbreaks of botulism per year in this country, with an average of three cases per outbreak. Compared with staphylococcus poisoning, which affects most of us sooner or later, botulism is infrequently encountered.

The conditions necessary to an outbreak of botulism are: (1) presence of spores of the clostridium in the canned food; (2) a food in which the clostridium can grow; and (3) survival of spores due to underprocessing of the canned food, followed by their germination and by growth of the clostridium. The spores are found in soils throughout the country and enter foods from this source. The organisms can grow in foods belonging to the low or medium acid groups with a pH between 4.5 and 7.0. Such foods include: string beans, corn, beets, asparagus, spinach, peas, meats, and many others. Underprocessing of such foods is likely to result unless a steam pressure sterilizer is used according to directions. Most botulism results from consumption of home-canned foods that have been heat-processed with the hot water, flowing steam, or oven method. No outbreak of botulism has been traced to commercially canned foods since 1926.

Methods for the prevention of botulism involve: (1) the use of approved procedures for the heat processing of canned foods in order to kill all botulinum spores; (2) rejection of all cans or jars of food showing gas pressure or abnormality in odor; (3) refusal to taste a canned food about which there is any doubt; (4) avoidance of foods which have been cooked, held, and not again reheated, and avoidance of improperly cured and smoked ham or sausage; and (5) boiling a suspected canned food for 10 to 15 minutes to destroy the heat-labile toxin. Often a canned food containing the botulinum toxin gives little evidence of abnormality. Growth of the proteolytic botulinum organism in protein foods usually gives a putrefactive odor that would lead to rejection of the food, but growth of the nonproteolytic type in a food such as corn results in the production of potent toxin with very little detectable odor.

Poisoning Due to Other Bacteria

Streptococci occasionally are incriminated in outbreaks of food poisoning, with the alpha type of streptococcus involved. Symptoms are similar to those of staphylococcus poisoning. Other bacteria, such as *Escherichia coli* and *Proteus vulgaris*, have been accused, but probably were innocent bystanders.

Salmonella Infection ("Poisoning")

Infection by various species of the genus *Salmonella* produces symptoms in man typical of food poisoning, but no exotoxin is involved. Instead, illness follows infection, and any toxic effect must be due to an endotoxin formed by growth of the organisms in the gastrointestinal tract. A very large number of species and types of *Salmonella* have been found involved in outbreaks, but two species, *Salmonella typhimurium* (*aertrycke*) and *S. enteritidis*, that parasitize both man and animals, are most commonly encountered.

Symptoms appear within 12 to 24 hours in most cases, but may appear as soon as 7 or 8 hours or not until 24 to 30 hours. The longer incubation time helps differentiate this infection from staphylococcus poisoning. Preliminary symptoms are a headache, prostration, and chills; these are followed by nausea, vomiting, abdominal pain, diarrhea, and a low fever. The duration of the disease may be from a day or two up to weeks or months; however, the mortality is low, averaging about 4 per cent. The incidence of *Salmonella* infection is lower than that of staphylococcus poisoning.

The presence of virulent *Salmonella* bacteria in the food is, of course, essential for the production of infection. Important is the fact that *Salmonella* organisms can grow in foods and thus increase the size of the dose and the likelihood of infection. Sources of the organisms in food are: (1) meat or milk from animals with a *Salmonella* infection, and (2) human or animal carriers of *Salmonella* organisms. Animals subject to *Salmonella* infections transmissible to man include chickens, turkeys, cattle, horses, sheep, swine, rats, and mice. Federal inspection of animals and meat serves to eliminate much of the infected meat, but the best safety measure is thorough cooking of all meat to kill any pathogenic bacteria that may be present. The prevention of the contamination of foods by rodents is a problem of keeping these animals from stored foods. The housefly is an agent of spread of enteric diseases and should be kept away from food. The problem of the human carrier is more difficult of solution. It would be difficult and expensive to test all food handlers to find carriers of pathogens, but regulations should provide that handlers of food who are ill be kept away from work. Sanitary methods of food handling provide the best method of control at present.

The foods most often incriminated in causing *Salmonella* infections are meats, fish, or animal products such as sausage, milk, and cheese; vegetables and cereals are involved less often. Any warmed over food may be a source of infection.

The methods for the prevention of *Salmonella* infections have been suggested in the preceding paragraphs: (1) inspection of meat animals and meats; (2) thorough cooking of meats and animal products; (3) proper refrigeration of foods, especially those that have not reached a boiling temperature during their preparation; and (4) care and cleanliness in the handling and preparation of foods, with special reference to the prevention of contamination by human or rodent carriers.

Trichinosis

Early stages of trichinosis often have been confused with food poisoning. This disease is not bacterial. It is caused by a nematode worm, *Trichinella spiralis,* and usually is acquired by eating raw pork containing cysts of the larva of the worm. The worm develops through the whole of its life cycle in the pig, the rat, or man, finally becoming encysted in the muscular tissue. When the encysted larvae are eaten they emerge from the cyst in the intestinal tract to form worms, which invade the mucous membrane of the gastrointestinal tract. At this state, about 48 hours after ingestion of the pork, symptoms such as nausea, vomiting, sweating, and diarrhea appear. Later, larvae are produced and travel by the blood stream to the muscles, where severe pains are produced.

Trichinosis can be prevented by cooking all pork so that the innermost portion attains a temperature of 137° F., by quick freezing and storage at sub-zero temperatures, by freezing and holding for at least 20 days at 5° F., or by smoking and curing the pork according to federal specifications.

Spread of Pathogens by Eating Utensils

Eating utensils may become contaminated with pathogens and transmit them to food and drink or directly to the user of the utensil. Dishes used by patients with infectious diseases should be washed with hot water (170° F.) and soap to remove all food particles and then rinsed with boiling water. The careless methods of dish washing routinely used in many restaurants insure the presence of numerous organisms on the "clean" utensils. Recent figures of the U. S. Public Health Service show 23,765 **reported** cases of food-borne disease throughout the nation in 12 months, and it is estimated that only 5 per cent of all cases were reported. The U. S. Public Health Service has published an ordinance and code, listed at the end of the chapter, which makes recommendations regarding dish washing as follows: cleansing is by means of warm water (110° to 120° F.) plus soap or other detergent, with frequent changing of the wash water; the next step, an "approved bactericidal process," consists of immersion for at least two minutes in clean water at 170° F. or more or for 30 seconds in boiling water, or immersion for at least two minutes in a lukewarm chlorine bath containing at least 50 p.p.m. of available chlorine or equivalent, or exposure in a steam cabinet at 170° F. for 15 minutes or at 200° F. for at least five minutes.

REFERENCES

Burrows, W., Gordon, F. B., Porter, R. J., and Moulder, J. W., *Jordan-Burrows Textbook of bacteriology* (15th ed.). Philadelphia, Pa., Saunders, 1949.

Dack, G. M., *Food poisoning* (Rev. ed.). Chicago, Ill. University of Chicago Press, 1949.

Hagan, W. A., *The infectious diseases of domestic animals*. Ithaca, N. Y., Comstock, 1945.

Harvard School of Public Health Symposium, *Virus and rickettsial diseases.* Cambridge, Mass., Harvard University Press, 1943.

Kelser, R. A., and Schoening, H. M., *Manual of veterinary bacteriology* (5th ed.). Baltimore, Md., Williams & Wilkins, 1948.

Rosebury, T., *Experimental air-borne infection.* Baltimore, Md., Williams & Wilkins, 1947.

Smith, T., and Kilborne, F. L., "Investigations into the nature, causation, and prevention of Texas or southern cattle fever." *U. S. Depart. of Agric., B. A. I. Bulletin No. 1* (1893).

U. S. Public Health Service, "Ordinance and code regulating eating and drinking establishments." *Public Health Bulletin No. 280* (1943).

Wilson, G. S., and Miles, A. A., *Topley and Wilson's principles of bacteriology and immunity* (3rd ed.), Vols. I and II. Baltimore, Md., Williams & Wilkins, 1946.

31. INFECTIOUS DISEASES OF HUMAN BEINGS

Efforts of the medical profession and public health authorities to prevent and to treat infectious diseases of human beings may be aided materially by the intelligent cooperation of the lay population. Knowledge of the etiology, means of transmission, and procedures available for prevention and control of infectious diseases should help all of us to cooperate more effectively with medical and public health workers. In this chapter some important and representative infectious diseases of human beings are discussed. Diseases spread by water and food have been discussed separately in the preceding chapter.

Table 7 shows the numbers of deaths per 100,000 population in registration areas of the United States from 1900 to 1945. The death rates given in this table are estimates rather than absolute values because failures to report births and deaths make population figures inaccurate except in census years, and because diagnosis of the cause of death is not always correct. Despite these difficulties, the estimates presented in Table 7 indicate the **trends** of the mortalities, and show the progress being made in the United States toward prevention of deaths due to infectious diseases of human beings.

In Table 8, data are given on the incidence of cases of the notifiable diseases in the registration areas of the United States, and on the ratios of cases to deaths caused by these diseases. These data probably are more in error than those presented in Table 7 because all cases of any disease are not accurately diagnosed or reported. However, the data in Table 8 indicate the magnitude of the problem of disease prevention which now exists in this country.

TABLE 7. Trends in Mortalities from Selected Causes in the United States[1]

Cause of Death	Deaths per 100,000 Estimated Population in Registration Areas in:							
	1900	1910	1915	1918	1920	1930	1940	1945
(Diseases of the heart)[a]	137.4	158.9	163.9	171.6	159.6	214.2	292.5	321.5
(Cancer)[a]	64.0	76.2	80.7	80.8	83.4	97.4	120.3	134.5
Pneumonia	175.5	141.7	130.2	286.7	136.8	83.1	55.0	51.8
Tuberculosis	194.4	153.8	140.1	149.8	113.1	71.1	45.9	40.1
(Motor-vehicle accidents)[a]	—[b]	1.8	5.8	9.3	10.3	26.7	26.2	21.3
Influenza	26.7	14.2	15.7	301.8	70.5	19.4	15.3	7.7
Syphilis	12.0	13.5	17.7	18.7	16.5	15.7	14.4	10.7
Puerperal septicemia	5.8	7.0	6.0	6.4	6.5	4.6	2.8	1.5
Whooping cough	12.2	11.6	8.2	17.0	12.5	4.8	2.2	1.3
Dysentery	12.0	6.0	3.4	5.6	4.0	2.8	1.9	1.2
Typhoid and paratyphoid fevers	31.3	22.5	11.8	12.3	7.6	4.8	1.1	0.4
Diphtheria	40.3	21.1	15.2	14.0	15.3	4.9	1.1	1.2
Malaria	6.2	1.1	1.6	3.0	3.4	2.9	1.1	0.3
Poliomyelitis and encephalitis	—[b]	2.9	1.1	1.2	0.9	1.2	0.8	0.9
Measles	13.3	12.4	5.2	10.8	8.8	3.2	0.5	0.2
Scarlet fever	9.6	11.4	3.6	3.1	4.6	1.9	0.5	0.2
Cerebrospinal meningitis	—[b]	0.3	1.4	3.4	1.6	3.6	0.5	1.3

[a] ( ) cause of death not attributed to infectious disease; data included for purposes of comparison.
[b] — data not available.

From the standpoint of importance in public health, the diseases listed in Tables 7 and 8 may be ranked in four categories as follows:

1. diseases of highest mortality now (incidence will also be high, of course);
2. diseases of high mortality in the past but now of low incidence and mortality;
3. diseases of low incidence but high or fairly high ratio of death rate to reported case rate;
4. diseases of high or medium incidence but with death rate low in comparison to number of cases.

In the first category will come: pneumonia, tuberculosis, influenza, and syphilis. Note in Table 7 how much higher their death rates are than those of any other infectious diseases. The epidemiological problems in these four diseases are quite different because syphilis and tuberculosis are chronic diseases and the other two acute. It can be seen from Tables 7 and 8 that syphilis has the highest case rate reported for any infectious disease but has a lower mortality than tuberculosis. The case rates of both diseases must be considerably higher than statistics indicate because it is certain that many

[1] SOURCES: U. S. Dept. Commerce, Bureau of the Census, 1942; "Death rates for selected causes in registration states, 1900–1940." *Vital Statistics Special Reports*, 1942, 15:281; Federal Security Agency, U. S. Public Health Service, National Office of Vital Statistics. *Vital Statistics Special Reports*, 1947, 27:41–45.

TABLE 8.   Case Rates and Ratios of Cases Reported to Deaths Registered for Notifiable Diseases
in the United States in 1940, 1943 and 1945[2]

Disease	Cases per 100,000 Population			Cases Reported for Each Death Registered		
	1940	1943	1945	1940	1943	1945
Syphilis	347.6	380.4	265.3	—[a]	—[a]	—[a]
Measles	220.8	478.5	110.9	428	493	460
Chickenpox	216.3	229.3	207.4	3,172	2,955	2,941
Gonorrhea	147.6	235.7	237.4	—[a]	—[a]	—[a]
Whooping cough	139.4	145.4	99.9	64	56	76
Pneumonia	136.4	147.8	124.3	2.52	2.95	2.96
Scarlet fever	117.9	104.1	125.5	238	337	469
Mumps	115.1	181.4	162.8	1,267	2,663	3,063
Tuberculosis	84.0	97.7	91.5	1.86	2.27	2.31
Malaria	61.3	50.2	52.3	56	92	151
Bacillary dysentery	19.3	33.2	32.4	26	68	84
Diphtheria	11.8	11.5	15.1	11	13	12
Septic sore throat	9.9	7.9	11.9	12.60	11.34	17.99
Poliomyelitis	7.5	10.5	10.3	9.79	11.20	11.28
Typhoid and paratyphoid fever	7.4	4.3	3.8	6.82	8.03	9.38
Amebic dysentery	2.8	3.4	3.0	15	20	19
Undulant fever	2.5	3.1	4.0	27.93	38.44	50.23
Smallpox	2.1	0.5	0.3	186	116	33
Typhus fever	2.0	3.6	4.4	16.38	22.24	24.26
Encephalitis	1.4	0.8	0.8	2.53	3.72	2.26
Meningococcus meningitis	1.3	14.3	6.2	2.73	6.46	4.75
Tularemia	1.3	0.8	0.8	8.44	13.72	7.47
Spotted fever	0.6	0.5	0.4	5.57	3.94	3.64

[a] — data not given.

cases are never diagnosed. Pneumonia is our most serious infectious disease
because of its high incidence combined with a low ratio of cases to deaths.
The statistics on pneumonia are probably quite accurate because of the nature of the disease; although tuberculosis has a lower ratio of reported cases
to deaths than pneumonia, the ratio of actual cases to deaths must be higher.
Influenza must have a very high ratio of cases to deaths; yet its mortality is
high and so its incidence must be very high.

Some of the diseases listed in Tables 7 and 8 which fall into the second
category are: diphtheria, typhoid fever, and paratyphoid fever. It is believed
that immunization, more accurate diagnosis, and effective treatment have
brought about reduction of the incidence and mortality of diphtheria. Protection and purification of water supplies, efficient treatment and disposal of
sewage, and improved sanitation in the production and handling of foods
have been major factors in decreasing the incidence and mortality of typhoid

[2] SOURCES: Federal Security Agency, U. S. Public Health Service. "Notifiable diseases
in the United States, 1940." *Public Health Reports*, 1942, 57:234–237; "The notifiable
diseases. Prevalence of certain important communicable diseases by states, 1945." *U. S.
Public Health Service Reports*, Supplement 193, 1947.

and paratyphoid fevers. Diseases in this category, to which also might be added smallpox, yellow fever, and cholera, might increase in incidence and mortality if the preventive measures available were not effectively employed.

Those of the notifiable diseases in Tables 7 and 8 belonging in the third category are: dysentery (bacillary and amebic), septic sore throat, poliomyelitis, undulant fever, typhus fever, encephalitis, meningococcus meningitis, tularemia, spotted fever. Some of these, i.e., dysentery and typhus fever, are more important than others in that they have a much higher incidence in other parts of the world than in the United States and are restrained here largely by environmental immunity.

Those diseases belonging in the fourth category can be seen from Tables 7 and 8 to be as follows: measles, chickenpox, gonorrhea, whooping cough, scarlet fever, mumps, and malaria. Some of the diseases in this last group cause as many deaths per year as some of those in the third category.

The death rates from infectious diseases in general can be seen from the data in Table 7 to be constantly decreasing in times of peace in this country. In many diseases the death rate has declined gradually but markedly in the years since 1900. In some diseases, notably syphilis, the death rate has not decreased, but the remarkable fact is that in none of the infectious diseases has it increased. On the other hand, the diseases of old age such as heart disease and cancer are causing an ever increasing number of deaths.

As the specific diseases are discussed, consider the probable reasons for their present status as to the incidence and mortality. To prove statistically that any one factor is responsible for prevention is usually impossible; one must work with the data at hand and cannot do controlled experiments on human beings.

DISEASES CAUSED BY BACTERIA

Pneumonia

Pneumonia is an acute inflammation of the lungs. The causative organisms may grow so fast that even though the air spaces of the lung become plugged with white blood cells, the bacteria escape into the blood stream and the disease may be rapidly fatal. Within ten days to two weeks of its onset the battle is over. Death occurs in about 30 per cent of untreated cases.

The majority of cases are caused by *Diplococcus pneumoniae* (commonly called pneumococci), but streptococci and micrococci, as well as *Klebsiella pneumoniae* and *Hemophilus influenza,* may cause some cases. Pneumonia also may be caused by still other bacteria as well as by certain viruses. Virulent pneumococci isolated from human cases are heavily capsulated; the

capsules are mainly carbohydrate. More than 30 different types of pneumococci are recognized, each with a different kind of capsular material. The
noncapsulated, rough variants of all these types are identical but are nonvirulent for experimental animals. The pneumococcus is a small, lancet-
shaped coccus which typically occurs in pairs but is frequently seen to form
chains on laboratory cultivation. The organism is Gram-positive.

Treatment of pneumococcal pneumonia with penicillin and some of the

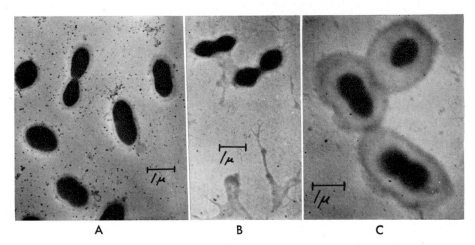

A   B   C

FIGURE 65.   Electron photomicrographs illustrating the "Quellung" or swelling
reaction of pneumococci. **A.** *Diplococcus pneumoniae*, Type III; **B.** *Diplococcus
pneumoniae*, Type III in Type I antiserum; **C.** *Diplococcus pneumoniae*, Type I
in Type I antiserum. The antiserum against the Type I pneumonococci will cause
swelling of the capsule of only the type I organism. (Mudd, Heinmets, and Anderson, S.A.B. No. 27.)

sulfonamides is highly effective and public health statistics now show a lower
mortality for pneumonia than in the past. Antisera against some of the types
of pneumococci may be used in conjunction with chemical therapy. The
antisera are made by injecting horses or rabbits with the capsulated organisms. The protein of the organisms must be present for the formation of
antiserum, but the kind of carbohydrate in the capsule will determine the
specific potency of an antiserum: that is, the antiserum formed against
Type I pneumococci will react only on pneumococci of Type I and not on
pneumococci of Types II, III, IV, etc. The carbohydrate or **haptene** determines the serological specificity of the organism, but the protein is necessary to make a complete antigen. The haptene will react specifically with
an antiserum *in vitro* but is not a complete antigen. Since more than 30
types of pneumococci exist, the type of antiserum to be used is of importance. This may be determined expeditiously by adding a drop of each kind

of antiserum to the patient's sputum, which contains the organisms; the specific antiserum will cause a marked swelling of the capsules of pneumococci that are of the same type. This is known as the Neufeld "Quellung" reaction, and is shown in Figure 65.

Cases and carriers spread the disease by moisture droplets, both directly and indirectly. As many as 50 per cent of the population of temperate zones may carry pneumococci in their mouths and upper respiratory tracts during the colder weather. Circumstantial evidence indicates that some pneumonias are caused by types of pneumococci which are most often acquired from another individual, whereas other pneumonias are caused by types of pneumococci which have probably spread from the patient's own upper respiratory tract. The evidence for this is that the incidence of the various types of pneumococci in carriers does not parallel their incidence in cases, certain types being found in a large percentage of cases and in only a very small percentage of carriers. The number of persons acquiring the disease is usually so low, as compared with the number of carriers, that individual resistance must be high. Occasionally epidemics do occur in groups living under crowded conditions and subjected to conditions which lower individual defenses. The bodily defenses against pneumonia are evidently lowered by subjection to sudden changes in temperature or to wet, or by other infections of the respiratory tract, such as colds.

The morbidity from this disease is difficult to control because of the high carrier rate. Persons who have infections of the upper respiratory tract should be isolated as much as possible, both to protect themselves against pneumonia and to protect others, since persons with other respiratory infections are more apt to be carriers than normal individuals. Since the families of patients are very frequently carriers, it would seem wise to isolate pneumonia patients and their contacts as much as possible and to carry on concurrent disinfection by burning receptacles used to collect sputum and by proper handling of the bed linens, dishes, and other fomites. Patients and those with other infections of the respiratory tract should cover their mouths with handkerchiefs when coughing or sneezing. Because of the high carrier rate, quarantine and disinfection measures can never be completely effective; and because individual resistance is usually high, the failure to carry out such measures does not result in epidemics as it would in such a disease as typhoid fever. Practically all persons must be considered susceptible. Those under one year of age and those over 45 have the highest mortalities, but the disease is an important cause of death in all age groups. Even individuals who have had an attack are susceptible again within a few months. Since mortality can be reduced by treatment, early diagnosis should be emphasized.

Tuberculosis

College students should seriously consider the disease tuberculosis because it is a leading cause of death in the group from 20 to 34 years of age. The disease usually lasts several years before it kills, or a cure is effected; during its course the infected individual should not come in close contact with others and should not engage in strenuous work.

The etiological agent of the disease is an aerobic, acid-fast, nonspore-forming, rod-shaped organism called *Mycobacterium tuberculosis*. Apparently because of its high fat content, it is very resistant to chemicals and thus can withstand many of the chemical defenses of the body, such as the acid in the stomach. It may enter the body through breaks in the skin or through any of the membranes and can establish itself in almost any of the tissues; but most frequently it has an opportunity to enter through the respiratory or the intestinal tract and the disease becomes localized in the lungs. However, tuberculosis can occur in the skin, meninges (the membranes covering the brain), genital tract, bones and joints, and in the lymph nodes. The organism grows very slowly *in vivo* just as it does *in vitro*. Usually the organisms will start growing in only one small focus in the lung; leucocytes will come to the area to form a tubercle; and connective tissue may later be laid down around the tubercle. Figure 66 illustrates a small tubercle in the lung. But if the organisms overcome these defenses of the body, more and more of the lung tissue will be destroyed until a cavity is formed in the lung. Then the organisms can easily travel to other parts of the lung, and may even be carried by the blood to other organs of the body; or sufficient numbers may be coughed up into the mouth and swallowed to cause intestinal tuberculosis.

Since tuberculosis may develop so slowly, symptoms may not be noticeable for several months or even years after the establishment of infection. The majority of the cases of tuberculosis found in an early stage can be cured, but the chances for cure become increasingly less with the length of time elapsing before the disease is discovered. The chances are very slight when the case is far advanced and shows all the symptoms such as fever, emaciation, characteristic cough, and contaminated sputum.

The primary method of controlling mortality depends upon finding cases in the early stages before symptoms appear. This can be accomplished by tuberculin testing, chest X rays of the positive tuberculin reactors, and the determination of the activity of the disease in those who show lesions upon X ray. The use of miniature film for X rays has greatly reduced the cost of this procedure, and many surveys are being made using chest X ray of all individuals without prior tuberculin testing.

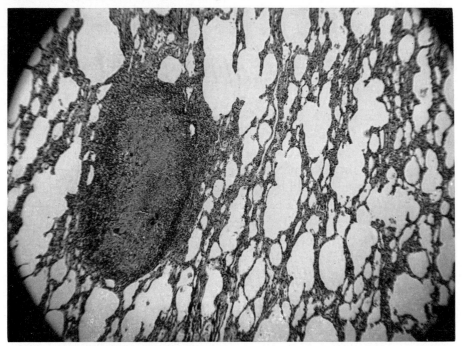

FIGURE 66. Photomicrograph of a section of a tubercular lung. Note the normal air spaces on the right. On the left is a tubercule caused by *Mycobacterium tuberculosis*. The air spaces have become filled with white blood cells and lymph cells which have come in to combat the infection. (Courtesy of J. J. Lalich, University of Wisconsin.)

Tuberculin is a derivative of a protein of the tubercle bacillus and is purified by various chemical procedures to increase its value in testing. Individuals who are infected with tubercle bacilli become hypersensitive to this protein, and when tuberculin is injected into the skin a reaction characterized by reddening and swelling occurs. But other individuals are also found to react, including those who have had tuberculosis at some time in the past, as shown by healed or calcified lesions found by X ray. Two doses of tuberculin are recommended because some individuals are so sensitive to it that if more than 2/10,000 mg. of tuberculin protein is injected into the skin, they will become mildly ill for a few days; yet this small dose does not elicit reactions in all tuberculous persons, hence the need for a second slightly stronger injection.

The tuberculin test, then, detects the tuberculous individuals but also causes reactions in many more individuals who do not have active tuberculosis. All the positive reactors to tuberculin should be X rayed to find which of them show signs of active or healed tuberculosis in their lungs. Some of the cases found on X ray have other symptoms of tuberculosis, but some of them found thus are early cases with no symptoms. In these latter cases the diagnosis of tuberculosis is confirmed by finding the tubercle bacilli in the gastric contents. The tubercle bacilli are coughed up into the mouth from the lungs and swallowed. The stomach contents are removed with a stomach pump, concentrated, and the material then is injected into a guinea pig or inoculated onto appropriate culture media. If the material from the stomach contains tubercle bacilli, the guinea pigs will usually show signs of tuberculosis within six weeks. The following facts explain why the test in guinea pigs is so much more effective than a microscopic search for the organisms; only one or two cells are needed to produce tuberculosis in the guinea pig and 500,000 bacteria would have to be present in every milliliter of fluid in order that one acid-fast cell could be found in each microscopic field. Cultures require several weeks' incubation before the tubercle organisms can be observed on the surface of the medium.

The occurrence of tuberculosis among 16,109 students at the University of Wisconsin examined from September, 1933, to March, 1938, is shown in Table 9.

TABLE 9.   Occurrence of Tuberculosis Among Students at the University of Wisconsin

Results of Tests	Percentage of Reactors	Percentage of Students
Positive tuberculin reaction		28.47
Negative tuberculin reaction		71.53
		100.00
No X ray evidence of pulmonary tuberculosis	91.00	
Healed lesions of tuberculosis found on chest X ray	6.30	
Positive reactors who failed to report for X ray	1.44 (231 students)	
Tuberculosis found on X ray and proved active	0.44 (71 cases)	
Tuberculosis found on X ray but found to be inactive	0.82	
	100.00	

Most tuberculosis is spread by the secretions from the respiratory tract either directly by kissing or indirectly by moisture droplets through the air in talking, sneezing, or coughing. Since acid-fast bacteria are more resistant to drying than other nonspore-forming bacteria, tubercle bacilli may remain viable in the dried state for several months and be acquired by the inhalation or ingestion of dust, or picked up from contaminated fomites.

Other animals also may be sources of infection for man. Higher animals are susceptible to infection with some kind of tubercle bacillus, either the human or the bovine variety (*Mycobacterium tuberculosis,* var. *hominis* or var. *bovis*) or the avian tubercle bacillus (*Mycobacterium avium*). The bovine variety is usually carried to man by milk. Less virulent for man than the human tubercle bacillus, it usually infects children to cause intestinal tuberculosis, or tuberculosis of the bones and joints, or scrofula (tuberculosis of the lymph nodes of the neck), although it may also cause tuberculosis of the lungs. The control of bovine tuberculosis will be discussed in the next chapter. The avian tubercle bacillus is of such low virulence for man that it is not an important cause of human disease under present living conditions in this country.

An inherited individual resistance of man to tuberculosis does exist. But a factor which determines whether infection of the susceptible individual will occur is the number of exposures—the size of dose is important in the production of the disease. In one of the rooming houses on a university campus a girl was discovered with advanced tuberculosis of the lungs. In that house were living 11 girls who had been previously negative to tuberculin; all were found to be positive when the case was discovered five months later, and one of the 11 had active tuberculosis. The girl who developed tuberculosis was susceptible. The other ten girls apparently had good resistance, or possibly some of them were susceptible but did not receive such large doses as the girl who developed tuberculosis.

Tuberculosis is an endemic disease, the incidence of which has gradually decreased in this country since the beginning of this century; the mortality in 1900 was 194.4 per 100,000 population; in 1945, it was 40.1. Control of the disease consists in finding early cases and in handling all cases of tuberculosis in such a way as to prevent the spread of infection. Treatment consists of adequate nutrition, and rest of the lungs, which is accomplished by bed rest with or without surgical treatment. This latter treatment may be either the simple introduction of air into the cavity surrounding one of the lungs (called pneumothorax) or a removal of part or all of one lung following removal of the protecting ribs. Various other procedures may be used but the principle is the same: namely, the collapse of a diseased lung so that it can rest while the remaining lung carries on the lung functions. Streptomycin and para-aminosalicylic acid have been used in treatment, with limited success. The value of streptomycin in therapy is further limited because the tubercle organism develops resistance to the antibiotic. During treatment the patient should be sufficiently isolated and the secretions from the respiratory tract should be destroyed so that moisture droplets do not carry the tubercle bacilli to noninfected individuals.

Various preparations have been used to vaccinate against tuberculosis. A bovine strain, which has been rendered avirulent by cultivation on a potato medium containing bile, is called the "BCG" strain, and is used as a vaccine.

At present, the BCG vaccine is undergoing extensive tests. However, whether any process of vaccination, or whether immunity acquired by an active case of the disease significantly increases resistance is hard to determine. Individuals who show healed lesions in their lungs, and vaccinated individuals, seem to be more resistant to subsequent infection, but are certainly not entirely immune.

Gonorrhea

This is one of the venereal diseases and is caused by a Gram-negative, biscuit-shaped diplococcus, *Neisseria gonorrhoeae*, known as the gonococcus. Even though low case rates are given in Table 8, it is estimated that in the United States about 10 per cent of the population is infected, and that a million new infections occur each year.

The gonococcus primarily forms local lesions on the mucous membranes of the genitourinary tract and usually remains localized, although it may persist for years. It may, however, invade the blood stream from these local lesions and be carried to various parts of the body forming extra-genital lesions. The organism may localize in the joints causing "gonorrheal rheumatism." In the newborn from an infected mother infection of the eyes may occur, and may cause blindness.

Laboratory diagnosis is made by direct observation of the gonococcus in discharges from primary lesions of the infected individual, and by cultivation of the organism from these discharges. In pus smears the Gram-negative gonococci are seen within the leucocytes; they have been phagocytized. (See Figure 62.)

The disease is spread primarily by direct contact, and by far the commonest method of infection is sexual intercourse. The mode of infection indicates clearly the ways in which the disease may be avoided. As has been pointed out so frequently, the problem is one of personal and social hygiene. Early diagnosis and effective treatment are absolutely necessary to prevent spread of the disease to noninfected individuals. Ophthalmia of the newborn is prevented by dropping a solution of silver nitrate into the eyes of the infant immediately after birth; this is required by state law, although it is permissible now in some states to use penicillin in place of silver nitrate.

Gonorrhea is now being treated successfully by the use of sulfonamides and penicillin. Immunity does not develop following infection.

Syphilis

This is another of the venereal diseases and is caused by a spirochete (higher bacterium), *Treponema pallidum*. Morphologically the microorganism is spiral-shaped and is motile not by means of flagella but through the rotation of the corkscrew-shaped cell. It is not readily stained and is best observed by use of the dark-field microscope.

Although the case rate for syphilis given in Table 8 is from 200 to 300 per 100,000 population, the actual number of cases is probably considerably higher. Jordan and Burrows estimate that 10 per cent of the adults in the United States will give a positive serological test for the disease. They estimate, also, that between 1 and 2 per cent of the children in this country have congenital syphilis.

Syphilis is a serious disease because it lasts for many years and affects many tissues of the body. As the disease progresses with the years in untreated cases complete physical and mental incapacitation may result. The primary lesion is a chancre which appears at the site of the infection, usually the exposed genitalia, about four weeks after exposure. Not until after another six weeks or more do symptoms of generalized infection appear, although experimental evidence shows that the organisms spread from the local area within a few hours after infection. These generalized symptoms usually include a rash progressing to open sores anywhere on the skin or the mucous membranes, and generally many of the internal organs show signs of infection. This stage may last for years, and then comes the last stage when the nervous system is affected and such symptoms as paralysis appear. When the spirochetes remain somewhere in the body, but no symptoms are evident, the disease is said to be latent. The spirochetes may go through the placenta of an infected female who is pregnant and infect a child before birth. The manifestations of congenital syphilis will, of course, be different since the route of infection is different.

Diagnosis can usually be made by examination for spirochetes in fluid from the primary chancre. The organism has not been grown outside the animal body, and therefore cannot be cultivated in the laboratory. Serological methods are used in diagnosis of the disease. The tests most commonly used are those of Wassermann and of Kahn which depend upon the discovery that the sera of syphilitic individuals have complement-fixing and precipitating antibodies for certain lipoids. These lipoids will not fix complement and are not precipitated in the presence of the serum of most nonsyphilitic individuals. They act in the complement fixation and precipitin reactions as nonspecific haptenes: nonspecific because they are obtained from the organs of normal animals and not from the spirochetes which cause the disease, and haptenes because they do not give rise to the formation of antibodies when injected into animals.

The organism causing syphilis is spread by direct contact; usually by sexual intercourse. The control of the disease depends upon the diagnosis and treatment of cases and the prevention of spread to noninfected individuals. The disease produces a questionable immunity to subsequent infection by the spirochete. There are no known methods of prophylactic immunity. The treatment of syphilis involves the administration of penicillin or of arsenical compounds at intervals until cure is effected.

Diphtheria, Whooping Cough, and Scarlet Fever

Diphtheria, whooping cough, scarlet fever, and measles are the four main childhood diseases; so called because the incidence is highest in childhood and the mortality is greatest in the first three years of life. Diphtheria, whooping cough, and scarlet fever are caused by bacteria and will be discussed here; however, measles is caused by a virus and will be considered under the section on diseases caused by viruses.

Diphtheria is potentially the most dangerous of the four main childhood diseases, but because of the discoveries, by bacteriologists and pathologists, of methods of producing artificial active and passive immunity, the mortality has been greatly decreased. The first symptom of infection with the diphtheria bacillus, *Corynebacterium diphtheriae*, is usually a severe sore throat. If the disease is suspected from the clinical symptoms, diagnosis can be confirmed by microscopic examination of stained smears prepared from throat swabs, and by cultivation of the organisms from throat swabs. The infection remains localized; but the organisms produce an exotoxin which may get into the blood stream and be carried to the peripheral nervous system and to the heart to cause damage. Mortality can be prevented, therefore, if antitoxin is present in the blood to neutralize the toxin as it gets into the circulation; once the toxin gets to the heart and nervous tissue it combines with them almost immediately and the antitoxin will have no effect. Antitoxin will be present in the blood of those who have recovered from an attack, or of those who have been actively immunized with toxoid or T-(AT) (toxin-antitoxin mixture), or it may be injected into the blood as antiserum from horses which have been immunized against the toxin, or it may have been passively acquired before birth.

The presence of antitoxin in the blood can be determined by means of the **Schick** test. A small amount of diphtheria toxin is injected into the skin; if the specific antitoxin is present it neutralizes the toxin so that no reaction occurs (Schick negative); but if antitoxin is absent, the toxin can act on the skin to produce a swelling and reddening (Schick positive). Thus, by means of this test the susceptible individuals (who should be actively immunized during an epidemic) can be selected. This test has shown that about 80 per cent of children have an immunity, passively acquired from the mother, which will last for about the first six months of life. Also many adults who have never had clinical symptoms of the disease or been actively immunized are Schick negative; the most probable explanation is that these individuals have had infections with symptoms so slight as to be clinically unrecognizable.

The disease is spread directly and indirectly by moisture droplets and by the mucous secretion. Since the organisms may live for days in either moist or dried mucus, precautions must be taken that the secretions from individuals with diphtheria bacilli in their noses and throats are not transmitted to other individuals by such objects as drinking glasses and pencils. Isolation of cases, however, does not prevent spread, because individuals may carry virulent diphtheria bacilli in their throats and noses for weeks after apparent recovery from the disease. The most important method of control, then, consists in the artificial active immunization of all children when eight to ten months old with toxoid; three doses are given at intervals of two to three weeks. The immunity lasts for several years and can be quickly restored by one small dose of toxoid or T-(AT). The mortality from the disease in non-immunized individuals can be greatly reduced if all cases of sore throat are examined by a doctor as early as possible so that a diagnosis of the disease can be made in time for antitoxin to be administered effectively. Death may occasionally occur from the blocking of the air passages with the products of inflammation at the site of infection.

Whooping cough is another disease which is not usually recognized to be as serious as it is. The case rate is still high but the mortality rate has declined greatly in the past 50 years. Of the deaths from whooping cough, 50 per cent occur before the age of one year. It is the secondary bacterial infection, especially of the lungs, which may cause death.

In this disease, the incubation period of from seven to fourteen days is followed by a catarrhal stage which is an inflammation of the upper respiratory tract characterized by mucous secretion, and then the peculiar paroxysmal cough appears which may last from two to six weeks. Colonies of *Hemophilus pertussis* are obtained when the infected person coughs onto a petri plate containing a special culture medium. All the evidence indicates that this organism is the cause of the disease, and growth of the characteristic colonies of *Hemophilus pertussis* on the plates is used for diagnosis during the catarrhal stage before the "whoop" appears. Epidemiological evidence indicates, however, that the disease is transmissible during almost any stage, and the child should therefore be isolated during the whole course of the disease. Such isolation will, of course, also protect the patient from the secondary invaders.

Vaccination has given some protection against the infection, and rendered the disease less severe if it did occur, when smooth, virulent strains of

H. pertussis were used in making the vaccines. Vaccines which have proved ineffectual may have been made from rough, avirulent strains. The vaccine should be given in three injections at weekly intervals to infants six months to one year of age, and, to be effective, must be given three months before exposure. Vaccination, although it leads to only a temporary immunity, is now considered by many pediatricians to be very much worth while in this disease to which susceptibility is practically universal, and in which the course is long and the complications possibly severe. Active immunity acquired by an attack is practically permanent.

Scarlet fever is caused by a number of strains of the hemolytic streptococcus, *Streptococcus pyogenes.* In fact, the same strain of hemolytic streptococcus may cause a number of diseases, including scarlet fever, erysipelas, "blood poisoning," pneumonia, tonsillitis, and puerperal sepsis, because of the differences in the portals of entry of the bacteria and because of individual differences in the defenses against organisms entering by the same portal. Scarlet fever starts with a sore throat but is further characterized by a rash. The incubation period is two to seven days. The rash lasts about two weeks. Exotoxins produced by the streptococci are responsible for the primary symptom of scarlet fever, the rash.

A **Dick** test can be used to test for susceptibility to scarlet fever. It is the same in principle as the Schick test, but is not so reliable in indicating resistance, again because antitoxic immunity is not the same as antibacterial immunity. The test shows that, as in diphtheria, a passive immunity acquired from the mother lasts for the first six months of life; and that most adults are immune to scarlet fever toxins, although many have never had a recognizable attack of the disease.

The **Schultz-Charlton** reaction can be used to differentiate scarlet fever from certain other diseases with a similar type of rash, such as German measles. Antitoxin is injected into an area of the skin where there is a rash and if the rash is due to the toxins of the hemolytic streptococci the erythema will fade.

The disease is transmitted by the secretions of the respiratory tract but not by contact with either the skin or the dead skin which peels. It is also possible for human beings to become infected with *Streptococcus pyogenes* by drinking milk from cows whose udders are infected with this organism. Carriers without clinical symptoms must exist, since cases develop from contact with individuals who have been released after several weeks of quarantine. The most important measure to control mortality consists in the treatment of cases to prevent bacteremia with its resulting complications. The use of antitoxin is discouraged, except in certain cases with symptoms of severe toxemia; antisera from animals other than man must be used with care because of the possibilities of serum sickness from foreign protein sensitization. Neither is active artificial immunization with toxoids or T-(AT) recommended, except for such persons as doctors and nurses who expect to be in close contact with patients having the disease. Recently, it has been shown that certain purified gamma globulin fractions of human blood serum have considerable value in the prevention and treatment of scarlet fever in infants. Injection of these substances confers a temporary, passive resistance. Certain sulfonamides and penicillin have been shown to be of value in the treatment of scarlet fever.

Puerperal Sepsis

Puerperal sepsis or childbed fever usually is caused by one of a number of varieties of hemolytic streptococci, that is, by streptococci which produce a substance which will lyse red blood cells. The streptococci get into the genital tract of the mother during childbirth. Before the advent of modern aseptic techniques, streptococci were carried on instruments, by attendants, and by the hands of the doctors who had attended other cases or had performed autopsies on those who had died of this fever. With modern methods of asepsis this source of the infection has been eliminated and the mortality from this disease has been greatly reduced. Sulfonamides and penicillin have been used successfully in the treatment of this infection.

Brucellosis

Members of the genus *Brucella* cause this disease, which is known also as undulant fever and Malta fever. The causative microorganisms, *Brucella abortus, Brucella suis,* and *Brucella melitensis* are small, Gram-negative, coccoid bacilli. The primary hosts are cattle, swine, and goats, respectively, but all three species of the genus *Brucella* are pathogenic for man.

The incubation period of the disease in man is highly variable and relatively long. The microorganisms cause a generalized infection, usually of low grade, with afternoon fever and general malaise as the usual symptoms, although in a few cases the disease may become more acute. Diagnosis is made by isolation of the causative organism from the blood. Agglutination tests for antibodies from the blood of the patient, as well as a skin test with an antigen prepared from *Brucella* cells, are of aid in diagnosis. An opsono-cytophagic test may also be used in diagnosis. Treatment by passive immunization or drugs is not effective, but, recently, the use of aureomycin or the combined use of sulfadiazine and streptomycin have shown some promise as therapeutic agents.

Because the primary hosts of this pathogen are animals, man nearly always acquires brucellosis from handling infected animals or through the use of milk or other dairy products from these animals. There are no reliable morbidity data, but Evans has estimated that between 40,000 and 4,000,000 cases occur in the United States each year. Jordan has collected data shown in Table 10 on the incidence of the disease according to occupation. These data show that the highest incidence is among packing house employees and the lowest among people who would not have occasion to handle animals. The cases among those not handling animals probably occurred from the use of unpasteurized dairy products.

TABLE 10.   Morbidity Rates on Undulant Fever in Relation to Occupation[3]

Occupation	Area	Per Cent Contact with Livestock	Per Cent Using Raw Milk	Cases 1936–1941	Population in Group	Annual Rate Per 100,000
Child	Rural	60	85	47	1,454,037	0.5
Farm wife	Rural	40	100	81	1,454,037	0.9
Farm workers (male)	Rural	100	100	320	311,776	17.1
Child & Teen age	Urban	23	77	26	1,084,231	0.4
Housewife	Urban	3	92	36	1,084,231	0.6
Merchant—Professional	Urban	25	84	154	1,621,500	1.6
Packing house worker	Urban	98	20	118	15,000	131.1

There is no good method of producing an artificial active immunity to brucellosis in man. The best prophylaxis is the use of pasteurized dairy products and careful handling of diseased animals. Eradication of the disease from the animal population would lead to elimination of the disease from the human population.

Tularemia

Tularemia or rabbit fever is another acute infectious disease in which the causative organism remains alive in an animal host, but to which man is susceptible. The chief animal hosts in this country are rabbits, but other animals including such widely different species as the wood tick, quail, and sheep also acquire the infection naturally. Man usually acquires the disease from handling infected rabbits; apparently the bacteria can penetrate the unbroken skin. The etiological agent is *Pasteurella tularensis*. Partial protection against the disease can be developed in human beings by injection of a vaccine containing attenuated causative bacteria. Cases of the disease have been treated successfully with streptomycin.

[3] From C. F. Jordan, *Proc. 46th Meeting of U. S. Livestock Sanitary Association,* 1942, p.137.

Bubonic Plague

This is an acute infectious disease carried by arthropods from rodents to man. Plague is caused by *Pasteurella pestis*, a small coccoid rod with polar granules.

The plague bacillus is harbored during interepidemic periods by several kinds of rodents including rats and ground squirrels. It is endemic in the western part of the United States. Epidemics are usually traced to rats, which frequent the habitats of man more than do the other rodent carriers. The flea carries the organism from rat to rat, from rat to man, or from man to man. The type of disease carried by the flea is called "**bubonic**" because of the formation of "buboes" or swollen glands in the affected human. The disease may also be transmitted from man to man by moisture droplets to cause a "**pneumonic**" plague, but this type usually composes only a small percentage of the cases during an epidemic.

Plague is successfully controlled by breaking the contact between the rodent and man. The extermination of all rats and other rodents is an enormous task and is impractical. The better solution is to rat proof all buildings, and, by strict hygiene and domestic cleanliness, to eliminate the flea transmission from man to man. In South Africa and Java a living, attenuated strain of *P. pestis* has been used as a vaccine for man with great success. An attack of the disease and recovery provides good immunity.

Neither immune serum nor drugs are too successful in treatment of plague.

Epidemic Meningitis

Epidemic meningitis is a disease with a high mortality in untreated cases but its mortality rate can be reduced to practically zero if sufficient quantities of penicillin, antiserum, sulfadiazine, or both antiserum and sulfadiazine are given as soon as the disease can be diagnosed. Early in the disease the causative organisms, *Neisseria meningitidis*, can be found in the spinal fluid. The disease is endemic, but epidemics occur in adults living under crowded conditions. The causative organisms are spread by cases and carriers through the secretions of the respiratory tract; the organisms die very quickly after leaving the body.

Tetanus and Other Wound Infections

The spores of several species of anaerobic rods are present in soil and are carried into wounds by splinters, clothing, skin, nails, etc.; the organisms are harmless when ingested or inhaled. These clostridia produce exotoxins which are absorbed and have various effects on the tissues; the toxin of *Clostridium tetāni* affects the nervous and muscular tissues to produce spasms, which first cause difficulties in swallowing and opening the mouth (lockjaw) and then extends to other parts of the body. An effective antitoxin for the tetanus toxin is produced in horses. Because of the prevalence in soil of the spores of *C. tetani,* this antitoxin may be administered when sizable wounds probably contaminated with dirt occur. As with the diphtheria antitoxin, the tetanus antiserum must be given as soon as possible after the wound has been inflicted, since it will be practically useless after the toxin has combined with the nervous tissue. It is possible to develop an active immunity against tetanus toxin in a human being or animal by injection of tetanus toxoid. Actively immunized individuals may be given an additional small dose of toxoid if they receive a wound which may be contaminated with *C. tetani;* such a "booster" injection is apparently as effective as antiserum in the prevention of tetanus in actively immunized individuals.

Infection of deep wounds with *Clostridium perfringens,* which is the most common cause of gas gangrene, is not so readily controlled. This organism produces several toxins, and antisera or toxoids have not been developed that will successfully combat all of them. In addition, *C. perfringens* and the other anaerobes frequently found growing with it in deep wounds, cause marked tissue destruction. Certain sulfonamides and penicillin have been shown to be effective in the treatment of gas gangrene.

Furuncles (Boils)

The boil is an acute, circumscribed inflammation of the skin, usually resulting in local suppuration. The tissues have been killed by the action of micrococci which have invaded the skin through a wound or hair follicle. This infected region is filled with the products of inflammation, the dead tissue, and the causative bacteria.

Often boils may be prevented in susceptible individuals by the use of autogenous vaccines. Micrococci may be isolated in pure culture from a boil on the patient, and the cells from this culture are killed and injected at intervals. Several such injections will usually render the individual immune for several months. Emphasis has been placed also on the use of toxoids from micrococcal toxins to produce immunity in susceptible individuals. Boils may be treated by the use of antibiotics such as penicillin and tyrothricin.

Dental Caries

Tooth decay (dental caries) is apparently caused by the action of acids produced by lactobacilli and enterococci normally inhabiting the mouth of nearly all individuals. When the diet is high in carbohydrates, and especially when sugar is allowed to remain in crevices in the teeth, acids are formed by the lactobacilli and enterococci which eat away the tooth substance to cause decay. Children on diets rich in vitamins D and C apparently have teeth which are more resistant in that the decay does not spread beyond a small original focus. Another factor which plays a role seems to be hereditary, since a small percentage of children can eat a great deal of sugar and yet not have dental caries. The addition of trace amounts of fluoride into the drinking water of children seems to prevent caries.

DISEASES CAUSED BY VIRUSES

Influenza

It is only within the last 20 years that this disease has been proved to be due to any one of several types of a virus. Influenza has caused the largest and most disastrous epidemics of recent times; in fact, in 1918–1920 it caused a pandemic (an epidemic spreading all over the world).

The symptoms of influenza are of a vague and nonspecific nature: fever; headache; loss of appetite; muscular pains, usually in the back, but moving from one muscle to another; and mild respiratory symptoms such as sore throat. In uncomplicated cases the fever dies down after a few days and the patient, although exhausted, makes an uneventful recovery. The disease can be diagnosed from the clinical symptoms only after it has run its course, or it can be diagnosed on circumstantial evidence during epidemics. Laboratory methods of diagnosis have not yet been fully developed. The disease is dangerous because it increases the susceptibility to bacterial infections of the respiratory tract, and it is in the epidemics of combined influenza and bacterial pneumonias that the mortality is high. *Hemophilus influenza,* a bacterium, is the most common secondary invader, and causes a severe pneumonia. An attack of the disease confers some immunity which, however, is of short duration. Vaccination against influenza is in the experimental stage. Treatment of the disease consists of rest and protection of the patient from respiratory infections caused by bacteria. The disease spreads from man to man, probably both directly and indirectly, by moisture droplets.

Measles

In view of the susceptibility of all persons to measles, it is surprising that the layman has so little appreciation of the epidemiological facts known about the disease; it is commonly and wrongly considered a rather harmless disease which is transmissible only when the characteristic rash is present.

But before the rash appears an incubation period of ten days and a prodromal period of four days intervenes, and it is during this latter period that the disease is most contagious. The symptoms during the prodromal period are fever, a "cold," and maybe bronchitis; during this time the disease is spread by moisture droplets. After the prodromal period a rash appears which lasts for ten days.

During the prodromal period the disease can be diagnosed by a physician from the clinical symptoms and signs. Since the disease is caused by a virus, it cannot be diagnosed easily by laboratory methods.

Treatment consists in keeping the patient in bed and protecting him from respiratory infections with bacteria, such as hemolytic streptococci, which may cause mastoiditis, pneumonia, etc.; for it is these secondary infections which may result fatally.

Passive immunization is effective. In fact, most infants are immune during the first few months of life because of immunity passively acquired from the mother before birth. Convalescent sera or immune globulin reduce the severity of the disease and prevent secondary complications. To be effective, however, they must be given during the incubation period, i.e., soon after the child has been exposed. Immunity actively acquired from an attack usually lasts for a lifetime, although a few cases of second attacks are on record.

Mumps

This highly contagious disease is caused by a virus. The usual symptom is swelling of the parotid or other salivary glands in the neck, although other tissues such as the pancreas or the testes may be involved. Convalescent human serum may be used in prophylaxis after known exposure, but there is no indication for use of immune serum in therapy. The disease is usually contracted in childhood, and it is spread by secretions from the respiratory tract of an infected individual. There is no method of vaccination.

Poliomyelitis (Infantile Paralysis)

This is primarily a disease of children, which occurs sporadically and epidemically, but in recent years the incidence is increasing among young adults. Many cases show only a fever, respiratory disorder, or gastrointestinal disturbance, but a few cases go on to exhibit the classical symptoms of flaccid paralysis.

The mode of transmission of the virus causing this disease is uncertain. The evidence available indicates that cases and carriers may transmit the infection and that the upper respiratory tract may be a means of exit and entrance for the virus. The virus has been found in sewage and in the feces of healthy carriers, and evidence exists that the virus may leave and enter the body by means of the alimentary tract. There is also evidence that insects may play a part in transmission of the infection.

No means of chemotherapy are available and the use of convalescent serum in therapy is not considered too helpful. It has been reported that convalescent serum may be of help if administered after exposure before symptoms occur. Methods of vaccination with the weakened virus have been attempted, but the dangers from the use of such vaccines are not compensated by a high degree of immunity. The best means of prophylaxis during an epidemic is to avoid crowds or close contact with possible carriers or latent cases.

Chicken Pox

This highly infectious disease of children is caused by a virus. The disease is usually mild and is characterized by skin eruptions. Individuals who recover from an attack of chicken pox possess an immunity which usually lasts for life.

Smallpox (Variola)

Smallpox is a virus disease characterized by skin lesions which may leave deep pitted scars. Transmission of the disease may be made by direct or indirect contact with carriers or cases.

The mortality from smallpox has been greatly reduced since vaccination has become a common practice. However, the incidence is increasing again in this country, although most of the recent cases have been of the mild type with a low mortality. This increase is a warning that an insufficient number of individuals is being vaccinated to make some communities immune and that, therefore, an epidemic of the severe type of the disease would be disastrous. Even the mild type of smallpox makes the patient extremely uncomfortable. The consensus of public health workers in this country is that vaccination with the virus of cowpox should be carried out on infants six months old and should be repeated at 18 to 20 years of age or during an epidemic.

Common Cold

The common cold is an acute infection of the upper respiratory tract. Its symptoms are well known, as most individuals suffer from a cold several times a year. The primary infection is by a virus and incapacitates the individual for several days; secondary bacterial infection may lead to pneumonia or other acute processes. Since the common cold is probably spread by droplet discharges from the infected individual, prophylaxis could be accomplished by isolation but this is not a practical solution. Attempts to immunize have been unsuccessful and most "cold vaccines" consist of killed bacteria for alleged protection against secondary invaders. Immunity produced by infection with common cold virus is transitory.

Yellow Fever

Yellow fever is a dreaded disease because of its high fatality. It is endemic in parts of South America and Africa and epidemics occurred in the United States until this century. The etiological agent is a virus which is carried from one host to another by several kinds of *Aedes* mosquitoes. Control consists in the elimination of the vector mosquitoes and in vaccination in regions where the disease is endemic. The vaccine, which has been developed recently, consists of a nonvirulent strain of the virus grown on chick embryos.

DISEASE CAUSED BY RICKETTSIAE

Typhus Fever

Typhus fever is an acute infectious disease caused by rickettsiae that are carried by anthropods from rodents to man or from man to man. Typhus is caused by *Rickettsia prowazeki*. This organism is carried by the rat, which is resistant to the disease. Sporadic cases of typhus occur in the human population when fleas from infected rats have an opportunity to bite human beings. The disease may be transmitted from man to man by the head or body louse. Therefore in a community of louse-ridden individuals an epidemic of typhus will probably occur if one case appears. The louse which lives on man succumbs to the disease but the rat flea and the rat louse do not, and apparently the rickettsiae remain alive in rats during interepidemic periods; the organism is carried from rat to rat by the rat flea or by the rat louse.

Typhus fever remains endemic in areas where the living conditions are poor and especially in climates where fleas and lice can survive for several days away from their hosts. The disease is successfully controlled by breaking the contact between the rat flea and man and by delousing human beings. The latter has been accomplished by the use of DDT.

An individual recovering from the disease is usually immune to subsequent infection. A vaccine prepared from artificially infected chick embryos has been used with some success.

Disease Caused by Fungi

Athlete's foot is a ubiquitous skin disease caused by molds belonging to the *Fungi Imperfecti.* Members of genera *Trichophyton* and *Epidermophyton* are most often involved. Parts of the body affected are the interdigital areas, areas between the thighs, hair and hair follicles, and the nails.

Various chemicals, such as undecylenic acid, are used to kill the organisms, which usually grow only in the superficial parts of the skin. But since these organisms grow where the skin is damp much of the time, the infections can often be controlled simply by keeping the skin dry. The organisms can live in damp places outside the body such as bath floors and wet towels. Because of the nature of the causative organisms, the individual can protect himself from acquiring the infection, and the infection can be prevented from spreading from one member of the family to another, but it is very difficult for school gymnasiums and such places to use public health measures to prevent spread of the fungus.

Fungi may also cause infections of the lungs. Invasion of other tissues or organs of the body is uncommon.

Disease Caused by Protozoa

Malaria

Malaria is a disease characterized by attacks of fever and chills at regular intervals; it may be chronic or acute. The disease is caused by several species of protozoa of the genus *Plasmodium,* which are carried from a case to the blood of another person by mosquitoes, chiefly those of the genus *Anopheles.* The disease is so named from the Italian words meaning "bad air" because it was formerly thought to be caused by the air from swamps and marshes. It is now known to be carried by mosquitoes of several species. Diagnosis is made by finding the parasites in the blood. The organisms grow in and destroy the red blood cells.

Treatment of the disease is with drugs such as quinine, atabrine, and plasmochin. An individual going into a region where malaria exists can protect himself against the development of the disease by the continued use of these same drugs.

Control consists mainly in destroying the breeding places of the kinds of mosquitoes which carry the disease and of destroying the mosquitoes. Recently a kind of mosquito hitherto indigenous only to Africa has been carried to Brazil by an airplane or fast ship, and has brought with it a particularly virulent species of malaria-causing *Plasmodium*. Agriculture was practically brought to a standstill in certain communities in Brazil, where almost the whole population acquired the disease and about one-tenth of the individuals died. Vigorous measures are being enforced to prevent transportation of this and other malaria mosquitoes.

REFERENCES

Burrows, W., Gordon, F. B., Porter, R. J., and Moulder, J. W., *Jordan-Burrows textbook of bacteriology* (15th ed.). Philadelphia, Pa., Saunders, 1949.

Dubos, R. J. (ed.), *Bacterial and mycotic infections of man.* Philadelphia, Pa., Lippincott, 1948.

Evans, Alice C., "Brucellosis in the United States." *Am. J. Pub. Health* (1947), *37*:139.

Huddleson, I. F., *Brucellosis in man and animals.* N. Y., The Commonwealth Fund, 1943.

Jordan, C. F., *Proc. of the 46th Meeting, U. S. Livestock Sanitary Assoc.,* 1946, p. 137.

Rivers, T. M. (ed.), *Viral and rickettsial infections of man.* Philadelphia, Pa., Lippincott, 1948.

Seibert, Florence B., *et. al.,* "The chemistry of tuberculin." *Chem. Rev.* (1944), *34*:107.

Smith, D. T., and Martin, D. S., *Zinsser's textbook of bacteriology* (9th ed.). N. Y., Appleton-Century-Crofts, 1948.

Stiehm, R. H., "A review of a five-year tuberculosis program among University of Wisconsin students." *Am. J. Med. Sci.* (1939), *197*:517.

Top, F. H., *Handbook of communicable diseases.* St. Louis, Mo., Mosby, 1941.

White, B., *The biology of the pneumococcus.* N. Y., The Commonwealth Fund, 1938.

Wilson, G. S., and Miles, A. A., *Topley and Wilson's principles of bacteriology and immunity* (3rd ed.), Vols. I and II. Baltimore, Md., Williams & Wilkins, 1946.

3²·. DISEASES
OF ANIMALS

All diseases of animals are of economic importance, and some are of public health significance because they are transmissible to human beings. Stringent measures that are not applicable in diseases of human beings may be employed in the prevention and control of diseases of animals. Infected individual animals or herds may be slaughtered, and regulatory procedures may be employed to prevent transportation or importation of diseased animals or animal products such as meat. In addition, vaccination or passive immunization may be widely used to prevent or to control outbreaks of disease among animals. Through the use of available preventive and control measures, it should be possible to eradicate many of the infectious diseases of animals which now exist.

Losses due to animal diseases are calculated not only on the basis of mortality, but also on the basis of morbidity. Financial loss due to death of an animal in an infected herd may be less than loss incured by unthriftiness and lowered production among survivors. The Bureau of Animal Industry, United States Department of Agriculture, estimated in 1942 that the livestock industry in the United States suffers an annual loss of $418,000,000 due to disease. This is a conservative estimate, and the actual dollar value in 1950 would be closer to $1,000,000,000. From Table 11 it is apparent that the major financial losses are due to parasites which do not cause great mortality but result in unthrifty stock of lowered production. Bacterial diseases of major importance are brucellosis, bovine mastitis, and tuberculosis. The most important virus disease of livestock is hog cholera.

Representative important infectious diseases of domestic animals are dis-

TABLE 11.   Average Annual Livestock Losses Due to Certain
Diseases[1]

Internal parasites	$125,000,000
External parasites in poultry	85,000,000
Cattle grubs	65,000,000
Poultry diseases (except tuberculosis and those caused by parasites)	40,000,000
Brucellosis of cattle (Bang's disease)	30,000,000
Mastitis	19,000,000
Hog cholera	12,500,000
Tuberculosis (cattle, swine, poultry)	10,500,000
Swine abortion	10,000,000
Stable fly and horn worm	10,000,000
Screw worms	5,000,000
Cattle and sheep scabies	1,000,000
Encephalomyelitis	1,000,000
Swine erysipelas	1,000,000
Anthrax	750,000
Johne's disease	500,000
Hemorrhagic septicemia	500,000
Goat lice	500,000
Cattle tick fever	400,000
Rabies	250,000
Anaplasmosis	100,000
	$418,000,000

cussed in this chapter with the chief purpose of describing the etiology,
means of transmission, and possibilities for control of each.

DISEASES CAUSED BY BACTERIA

Brucellosis (Bang's Disease in Cattle; Traum's Disease in Swine)

Brucellosis is caused by *Brucella abortus* in cattle, *Brucella suis* in swine,
and *Brucella melitensis* in goats. These relationships are not absolute because *B. melitensis* may cause infection in swine and cattle; *B. abortus* has
been isolated from goats, and *B. suis* from cows. Other animals that may be
infected by these organisms are sheep, horses, dogs, chickens, guinea pigs,
mice, and man. *Brucella* species are small, coccoid, Gram-negative rods.

The disease is of primary importance in causing abortion in cattle and
swine. The loss is not only in the calf and pig crop but also in lowered milk
production in cattle and unthriftiness in swine. During pregnancy the organisms are present in the uterus of the cow, but at the beginning of the
lactation period usually become established in the udder and may be ex-
creted in the milk.

Cows are probably most often infected by ingestion of infected discharges

---

[1] From United States Department of Agriculture, "Keeping livestock healthy."
Yearbook of Agriculture, 1942, Washington, D. C., U. S. Government Printing Office.

from aborting animals. Bulls that have serviced infected cows may spread the disease by mechanical carry-over of organisms or by becoming infected. Brucellosis in bulls is characterized usually by infection of the testicles, which results in discharge of *Brucella* in the semen.

Diagnosis of the disease in cows may be made by isolation of the bacteria from the suspected animal or from the aborted fetus. More often the diagnosis is made by an agglutination reaction known as a Bang's test. If a suspension of *B. abortus* is agglutinated by an animal's serum in dilution of 1:100 or more, the animal is Bang's positive (a Bang's reactor) and is considered to have the disease. If the dilution of serum that causes agglutination is between 1:25 and 1:100, the animal is classified as a suspect; if less than 1:25, the animal is negative.

Eradication of the disease by slaughter of all cattle found to be Bang's reactors has been attempted in this country. The program has not eradicated the disease but has reduced the incidence. Vaccination of calves is effective in protecting them through several gestations but the immunity is not complete in that all vaccinated calves do not become resistant to infection. Calfhood vaccination is practical because brucellosis in cattle is a disease of sexual maturity and the calf has some degree of resistance. A living culture of low virulence, *B. abortus* strain 19, is used in vaccination and a low grade infection is induced in the calf. In the process of overcoming the infection the calf becomes immune. Vaccination complicates the "test and slaughter" program because a few vaccinated calves become permanent Bang's reactors.

Control of brucellosis in cows may be accomplished by vaccination and proper herd management. The latter means adequate sanitation, isolation of cows that have aborted, prompt disposal of aborted fetuses and fetal membranes, purchase of calves only for herd replacements (never purchase adult animals for replacements), and the use of bulls known to be free from brucellosis.

Bovine Mastitis (Garget)

Chronic mastitis, or inflammation of the udder, probably affects up to 20 per cent of the milk-producing cattle in this country. Milk production is decreased by the disease, the milk may be so abnormal as to be useless, and the affected quarter or quarters of the udder may finally cease producing milk entirely.

A large percentage of the cases of bovine mastitis are caused by *Streptococcus agalactiae,* an organism usually harmless to man if ingested in contaminated milk. The organisms may be carried from animal to animal by the hands of the milker or by milking machines. The bacteria may be deposited on the teat of the cow where they then travel through the teat canal up to the milk cistern and thence get into the milk-producing tissues where they become established. The spread of the disease can be prevented by proper sanitary precautions, especially by separating the animals as to milking order, the infected ones being milked last, of course. More elaborate precautions can be taken; and include the milker washing his hands before milking each animal, and the teat cups of the milking machine being cleaned and freed from the streptococci by rinsing a minute or more in hot water (170° F.) or in chlorine solution (200 p.p.m. available chlorine) before use on each animal. Also, the segregation of the infected animals in a separate barn is effective.

The infection often can be diagnosed by the "strip" test, in which some of the fore-milk is strained through a dark cloth; "flocs" in the milk indicate the presence of garget. Before the stage of the disease where "flocs" can be found in the milk, certain laboratory tests, such as for pH, chlorine content, and leucocyte count, may show abnormalities in the milk.

Acute mastitis may also occur and is caused by a number of different organisms including coliform bacteria, *Micrococcus pyogenes* var. *aureus*, *Corynebacterium pyogenes*, *Pseudomonas aeruginosa*, and *Clostridium perfringens*. This type of disease may be caused on rare occasion by *Streptococcus pyogenes*, which is pathogenic for man. The acute type is, of course, much more serious than the chronic type and cannot be controlled in the same way.

Treatment of chronic mastitis with penicillin, streptomycin, or aureomycin will reduce the number of infected animals but will not entirely eliminate mastitis from a herd. Chemotherapy of acute mastitis depends upon the type of microorganisms causing the infection.

Tuberculosis

More kinds of animals are susceptible to tuberculosis than to any other disease; and all three types of tubercle bacillus, human (*Mycobacterium tuberculosis* var. *hominis*), bovine (*M. tuberculosis* var. *bovis*), and avian (*Mycobacterium avium*), may be infective for the same species of animal.

In cattle, tuberculosis was the most prevalent, serious enzootic disease in this country until the cooperative federal and state program for the eradication of bovine tuberculosis began in 1917. Progressive, generalized tuberculosis in cattle is caused only by the bovine tubercle bacillus. Tuberculin made from the human tubercle bacillus is used in testing cattle since the human and bovine tubercle bacilli are so similar that their tuberculins are practically identical. Use of the human variety reduces chances of infection which might be caused by improperly prepared tuberculin. The program has consisted of the tuberculin testing of all cows and the slaughter of all reacting animals. It has resulted in reducing the incidence of tuberculosis in cattle to a small fraction of 1 per cent in all counties in the United States. Wisconsin early was forced to participate because Milwaukee ruled that only milk from tuberculin-negative cows could be sold in that city. The courts upheld the city and judged that such a requirement was legal, and then Chicago and other cities followed suit in demanding milk from tuberculin-negative animals. Coincident with the eradication of bovine tuberculosis has been the consistent decrease in those forms of human tuberculosis caused by the bovine tubercule bacillus. Another obvious advantage in the eradication of this disease is that a nontuberculous herd is more profitable to its owner.

Without tuberculin the eradication could not have been accomplished. The test is remarkably accurate, in that over 99 per cent of tuberculous animals react. The error in the other direction, namely, the reaction of nontuberculous cattle to tuberculin, is becoming more and more of a problem. At the height of the program the ratio of nontuberculous reactors to tuberculous reactors was very low. Now the procedure should be modified since this ratio has risen sharply. Two reasons are known for this. The first is that some of the animals have skin lesions, which are probably caused by acid-fast bacteria other than tubercle bacilli, but which are of no significance in that the disease does not become generalized. The other reason is that some animals infected with or exposed to avian tubercle bacilli, become sensitized and react to the tuberculin used in cattle testing.

Nearly 25 per cent of the swine coming into the packing plants in Wisconsin show lesions of tuberculosis. This is not too important economically since most of the infection is localized in the lymph nodes of the neck and is caused by the avian tubercle bacillus. A small percentage of carcasses show generalized tuberculosis which may be caused by either the avian or the bovine tubercle bacillus, although the latter has become a negligible cause of tuberculosis in swine as the program for the eradication of tuberculosis in cattle has proceeded.

The amount of avian tuberculosis in swine is an indication of its prevalence in chickens. Testing surveys with avian tuberculin have shown that about one-half of the poultry flocks in the north central states are infected; the disease is present all over the country but fewer flocks are infected in the other areas. The avian tubercle bacillus is the only type causing progressive tuberculosis in chickens and other fowl—the infection is of importance economically, but not from a public health standpoint. The most effective method of control on most farms which have tuberculous chickens is to start a new flock from nontuberculous stock and keep them in a new yard which has not been used previously for chickens. The avian tubercle bacilli are even more resistant to adverse conditions in nature than the human and bovine types, and may remain viable in soil for several years.

Johne's Disease

This disease of cattle and sheep is caused by an acid-fast bacterium, *Mycobacterium paratuberculosis*. The disease can be diagnosed by the use of Johnin, a preparation similar to tuberculin. The symptoms of the disease are a prolonged gastrointestinal disturbance and gradual emaciation of the animal.

Pullorum Disease

Pullorum disease, often called bacillary white diarrhea, is an infectious disease of birds caused by *Salmonella pullorum*. This disease may cause serious losses of baby chicks, other poultry, and birds. Usually the disease is acute; but, as is the case with other *Salmonella* infections, the organisms may persist a relatively long time in carriers. Losses occur from decreased fertility and hatchability of the eggs from infected birds as well as from a high percentage of fatalities in the young chicks. The disease spreads in several ways: via the eggs from infected ovaries of adult birds, by ingestion of contaminated material, and by inhalation of contaminated material during hatching in the incubator. The disease is highly contagious, and may spread rapidly during the first few days after hatching.

Flocks can be freed of the disease and can be kept uninfected in the following way. The blood serum or the whole blood is tested for agglutinins against a known culture of *Salmonella pullorum*. The reacting birds are culled; the remaining birds are put in quarters which have been cleaned and disinfected; and replacements are made with birds, or eggs for hatching, from "pullorum-clean" flocks.[2] Hatcheries and incubators should be kept clean and should be disinfected. In fact, the spread of the disease from infected to the noninfected chicks in incubators can be controlled to some extent by having a rather high relative humidity, by fumigating periodically with formaldehyde during incubation, and by removing the chicks immediately after hatching to a clean, dry box.

[2] The Bureau of Animal Industry, U. S. Department of Agriculture, classes flocks in which testing has been done as: (1) U. S. pullorum-tested, (2) U. S. pullorum-passed, or (3) U. S. pullorum-clean. The pullorum-clean flocks are the most apt to be free from the disease and are essentially flocks in which no reactors have been found in two tests not less than six months apart; the standards for the other two classes are not quite so high, and therefore flocks in these classes might possibly contain infected birds.

The agglutination test is reliable in disclosing infected birds, according to both experimental data and practical results. Experiments show that *Salmonella pullorum* can be isolated from over three-fourths of the chickens reacting to the test. Practically, the value of the test is shown by the fact that in one state (Maine) where the test has been applied since 1925, the number of reactors has decreased to less than one-fiftieth of the number reacting at the beginning of the program. Those states which have promoted the eradication program for some years have far less of the disease than other states. Nothing can be done to treat diseased chicks; they should be killed and their carcasses burned.

Anthrax

Bacillus anthracis is a very successful and unique pathogen. It is the only aerobic spore-former of high virulence for man and other mammals. Its virulence lies in the ability of only a few cells to produce the disease, and in its relatively high invasive powers. Its ability to remain viable in the spore stage in soil for many years means that, unlike most other aerobic pathogens, the organism does not die out under natural conditions if the host animal dies. The most virulent strains of the organism apparently are those which produce a large amount of capsular material insoluble in the body fluids.

Anthrax has been the most serious disease in cattle and sheep in Europe; the fatality is very high and the susceptibility to the disease is common to almost all animals. In this country the losses have been less, although numerous sporadic outbreaks occur each year in enzootic areas. The spores when taken into the digestive tract of the animal probably germinate first and the vegetative cells produced then penetrate the membranes and become distributed throughout the body; they multiply very rapidly in most organs, quickly overcome the defenses of the animal, and get into the blood stream a day or so after invasion. In the stage where the organisms are numerous in the blood, the disease can be transmitted by biting insects to other animals. After the death of the animal the bacteria sporulate; and, unless the carcass is burned or buried deeply immediately, the spores and vegetative cells may be ingested by other animals in the herd; or the spores will become disseminated in the top-soil, where they remain as a source of infection.

Anthrax bacilli are transmissible to man from animals and will infect human beings if inhaled or eaten, or if they get into the skin through a small break. The spores may be inhaled since they remain viable on the wool and hides of animals just as in the soil. The disease acquired in this way is a pneumonia which may result in death, and is found most frequently in individuals who sort, card, and spin wool. Infection via the gastrointestinal tract is rather rare since the meat of infected animals is not usually eaten. Infection through the skin is the most common route in this country. But the appearance of the swelling caused in the skin is sufficiently characteristic and the organisms remain localized long enough for bacteremia to be prevented by treatment with antiserum, sulfonamides, penicillin, or combinations of these therapeutic agents. Prompt diagnosis of anthrax in man and early treatment with penicillin have proven highly successful in reducing mortality caused by this once dreaded disease.

Killed anthrax bacilli are ineffective as vaccines, but living organisms of low virulence may be used to vaccinate animals against anthrax. Pasteur discovered that nonspore-forming strains of low virulence suitable for use in vaccines could be obtained by growing virulent strains of the organism at 42° to 43° C. A suspension of these living bacteria is used as a vaccine for animals, but the acquired immunity lasts only from one pasture season to the next. Animals may be passively immunized with antiserum from immune animals. Such protection, however, although conferred immediately, lasts but a short time. There is evidence to show that infected animals may be treated successfully with penicillin and sulfonamides.

Diseases Caused by Viruses

Hog Cholera

Epidemics of hog cholera have in the past been responsible for the greatest losses resulting from any disease of swine, and costly outbreaks still occur. The symptoms are those of an acute generalized infection. Diagnosis of the disease can be established by the macroscopic and microscopic tissue changes seen at autopsy. This highly infectious disease is caused by a virus.

The disease is spread chiefly by the secretions and excretions from an infected animal to the food and drink of the noninfected. Garbage-fed swine may contract the disease through ingestion of infected pork. The virus may spread from one farm to another on the shoes and clothes of human beings. In addition, infection may occur through improper handling of the virus used for immunization.

A lasting active immunity can be effected by the simultaneous injection of virus and antiserum; the antiserum is given to reduce the virulence of the virus. Recently, vaccines have been prepared by treating virus-containing blood or bone marrow with crystal violet and oil of eucalyptus to inactivate the virus. Such vaccines have given good results. A vaccine prepared from a rabbit-adapted strain of the virus also appears to be satisfactory. Animals can be passively immunized with antiserum from hogs that have recovered from a natural infection or that have been actively immunized; this treatment gives protection for a few weeks and can be used if symptoms are present or to protect healthy animals in an infected group.

The use of living virus for vaccination will protect swine, but will also keep the infection alive in the swine population. Better methods for control of hog cholera must be devised before the disease can be eliminated.

Newcastle Disease

This destructive virus disease of birds was first recognized as a separate entity, distinct from the closely related fowl plague, in 1926. Newcastle disease was introduced into the United States, possibly from the Orient, in about 1935. For reasons that are incompletely understood, Newcastle disease has not caused as high mortality among birds in the United States as it has in countries of the eastern hemisphere.

The virus of Newcastle disease affects the digestive, respiratory, and nervous systems. It causes a variety of symptoms, the most striking of which are lameness, paralysis, and disturbances in balance. The incubation period may be as short as three days, and the course of the disease usually is rapid, although some chronic cases may live for weeks. All of the body secretions and excretions of infected birds contain the virus, even during early stages of the disease before symptoms are apparent. The virus spreads rapidly, and may gain entrance to the body by inhalation or ingestion. The virus is relatively resistant to adverse conditions, and hence is destroyed with difficulty by disinfection procedures.

Newcastle disease has been eradicated in England on two separate occasions by quarantine and slaughter procedures similar to those employed in the United States to combat foot-and-mouth disease. In countries such as India, where the disease has become enzootic, the chief hope for control lies in a widespread, frequently repeated, program of vaccination.

Two types of vaccine, both grown on embryonating eggs, have been developed as a result of intensive work performed from 1943 to 1946. A killed virus vaccine, in which the infected embryo material has been treated with formalin, has been found to confer an active immunity in chickens which lasts for about 60 days. A living, modified virus vaccine, has been prepared by growing the virus in ducks or hamsters. The virus thus attenuated may be employed as a living vaccine, and induces a lasting immunity, but may cause occasional fatal cases of the disease among vaccinated chickens.

Young chicks hatched from eggs of actively immune hens possess a passive immunity that lasts for about one month. During this period the chicks cannot be actively immunized by vaccination. Use of antiserum from actively immune hens confers a weak passive immunity which has little practical value.

There is evidence that the virus which causes Newcastle disease may become adapted to mammals. It is possible that human beings may become infected with this virus, but the evidence in such cases is not clear-cut.

Equine Encephalomyelitis

Encephalomyelitis is an infectious disease of horses that may become epizootic under suitable conditions. In the United States, two strains of the causative virus have been found. The "eastern" strain originally was found east of the Appalachian Mountains, while the "western" strain existed in all other sections of the country. The virus affects the central nervous system of the horse, and the ensuing symptoms may vary from extreme lassitude to great excitability and "running wild." Mortality in untreated cases is about 20 per cent.

The epizooitology of this disease is not completely understood. The incidence of the disease in horses is higher in the summer months than during the rest of the year. It may be very prevalent one summer, and relatively few cases may appear the next year. Human beings may acquire the disease from infected horses. Mosquitoes (of the genus *Aedes*) and ticks have been found capable of carrying the virus, but whether or not they are the only vectors has not been established because other arthropods have been found to harbor the virus. The gopher and various birds may act as intermediate hosts and vectors.

The virus can be grown on the developing chick embryo in embryonating hens' eggs, and after treatment with formaldehyde may be used as a vaccine. Horses vaccinated six months previous to exposure to virulent virus have been shown to possess a fairly good immunity. Antiserum from immunized animals gives some degree of passive immunity, which lasts only a short time and is comparatively weak.

Rabies

The virus which causes rabies (hydrophobia) is introduced into other animals and man through wounds inflicted by the bites of infected animals. The animals chiefly responsible for keeping the virus alive in the United States are dogs, cats, foxes, and skunks; although the disease is transmissible to almost all animals.

The virus is present in the saliva of the rabid animal and is transmitted to the peripheral nerves exposed when another animal or a person is bitten.

The incubation period varies from six to eight weeks. It is shortest when the bites are deep and on the face or neck. In untreated cases the virus travels, apparently via the peripheral nerves, to the central nervous system and then the nervous symptoms appear. One of the most noticeable symptoms is inability to swallow (hence the name hydrophobia for the disease) and in the last stages a general paralysis appears. Death is inevitable in untreated cases if symptoms appear. Sometimes untreated persons bitten by rabid animals never have any signs of disease, probably because none of the virus reached the exposed tissues.

After a person has been bitten by a rabid animal there is a long period before symptoms develop. During this time the individual can be vaccinated if the dog or other animal which inflicted the bite is proved to have had rabies. If the animal does not show symptoms at the time, it should be held for observation for at least 15 days after the person is bitten. The first symptoms noticed in the dog may be those of a general nervous disturbance such as irritability, refusal to eat, and unwillingness to participate in any activity, and then, a day or so before death, are seen the characteristic symptoms of extreme irritability followed by convulsions. As soon as the animal shows definite signs, it should be killed and the head sent to a laboratory for diagnosis (the animal should never be killed by a shot through the head). The disease is diagnosed by finding the characteristically staining granules which occur within certain cells of the central nervous system and are most numerous in a particular area of the brain. These granules, the so-called Negri bodies, are composed of masses of the virus which has grown inside the cells. If the Negri bodies cannot be found, the brain tissue is inoculated into the brains of experimental animals and such animals observed for the appearance of the disease. If the inoculated animals do not show signs of rabies within 15 days, it can be assumed that the suspected animal was not infected with the rabies virus.

If infection of the suspected animal is established, the vaccination of the person who was bitten should be initiated. The rabies vaccine is one of the contributions of Pasteur. It consists of the spinal cords of rabbits which have been inoculated with the virus; the virus is attenuated by drying the cords over sodium hydroxide. Cord which has been dried for six to eight days is used for the first few injections because it contains the weakest virus to be used, and then stronger virus from cords dried for five, four, three, and two days is used for the following injections. The vaccine is given daily for about three weeks. Another type of vaccine requires the use of virulent virus —very small amounts of virus are injected at first, followed by a progressive increase in amount. Vaccines using virus killed with phenol or chloroform have been employed with success.

The case rate for human beings is low, partly because vaccination of exposed persons is effective. In some countries infection of man with rabies virus no longer occurs because the regulations governing the importation and supervision of dogs are strict and are effectively enforced. In the United States, vaccination of dogs, together with suitable restriction of their movements would serve to reduce the incidence of rabies in both man and animals.

Foot-and-Mouth Disease

Foot-and-mouth disease is one of the most contagious of infectious diseases. Cloven-footed animals, especially cattle and swine, are particularly susceptible. For example, in October, 1914, an outbreak was discovered in eight herds of cattle in Michigan. By March of the following year the disease had spread to 20 other states. Some 77,000 cattle, 85,000 hogs, 10,000 sheep, and 100 goats were slaughtered in order to stop this particular outbreak The Bureau of Animal Industry of the United States Department of Agriculture has developed means for eradication of this disease, and, starting in 1947, provided aid to livestock sanitation authorities who were confronted with the task of combating an outbreak in Mexico.

The following facts explain why the disease is so contagious. At the height of an epidemic the disease in cattle is an acute infection and is characterized by the formation of vesicles which are especially numerous in the mouth and on the hoofs but may occur on other membranes including the teats of the udder. The material from these vesicles contains the virus which is the etiological agent. The infected animal contaminates its environment from the lesions on the feet or from its saliva; the virus also is transmitted in the milk. The saliva, which is considerably increased in amount during the disease, is viscid and drools from the mouth. The virus may be present in the blood in the early stages of the disease and thus may be found in the meat from infected animals. But an epidemic may get started because the initial cases are mild and the symptoms therefore not very characteristic and easily confused with those of certain other diseases. The animal acquires the disease chiefly by the ingestion of contaminated food or water.

The virus is destroyed within a day by drying in air and sunlight but remains viable for a much longer time in the litter of the barn or in the soil. At temperatures around freezing it may stay alive in the soil for several months.

The measures which have proven effective in stopping outbreaks involve quarantine of all animals in affected areas, slaughter of all animals in a diseased herd, and disinfection of any fomites with which diseased animals may have come in contact. The carcasses of all animals are buried in a deep trench after treatment with chloride of lime; nothing can be salvaged, since meat or hide might carry the virus. One transmitting agent which is hard to control is the clothing of persons handling the animals. This is considered to be one of the biggest factors in the spread of the disease, and all inspectors engaged in the work of eradication wear rubber boots and coats which can be disinfected. The particular methods and regulatory measures used, and their rigorous enforcement by the federal authorities, are responsible for the control of the disease in this country. In many countries in Europe and in South America the disease has become enzootic because the authorities have compromised and tried to suppress the disease by quarantine, vaccination, and disinfection. Fresh meat from South American countries cannot be imported into the United States. The reason for the enforcement of this law is that the meat from just one diseased animal might be sufficient to start another costly outbreak in the United States.

Man may contract the disease but rarely does and therefore must have a good natural resistance. The disease is sometimes acquired by those working with infected animals but may be transmitted by milk. The virus is destroyed during the pasteurization of milk.

Like brucellosis, foot-and-mouth disease causes only low mortality, but is of great economic importance because meat and milk production are greatly lowered by infection. Once the disease is introduced into a herd it spreads to every animal which does not have an acquired immunity. An active immunity which lasts for several years is conferred by an attack. Vaccination against foot-and-mouth disease is in the experimental stage, but results obtained with certain types of vaccines appear promising.

REFERENCES

Brandly, C. A., *et al.*, "Epizooitology of Newcastle disease of poultry (and other studies of this disease)." *Am. J. Vet. Research* (1946), 7:243–333.

Bushnell, L. D., and Twiehaus, M. J., "Poultry diseases—their prevention and control." *Kansas Agr. Expt. Sta. Bulletin No. 284* (1939).

Hagan, W. A., *The infectious diseases of domestic animals.* Ithaca, N. Y., Comstock, 1945.

Hagan, W. A., *et al.*, "The relation of diseases in the lower animals to human welfare." *Ann. New York Acad. Sc.* (1947), Vol. 48, No. 6.

Huddleson, I. F., *Brucellosis in man and animals.* N. Y., The Commonwealth Fund, 1943.

Hull, T. G., *Diseases transmitted from animals to man* (3rd ed.). Springfield, Ill., C. C. Thomas, 1947.

Kelser, R. A., and Schoening, H. W., *Manual of veterinary bacteriology* (5th ed.). Baltimore, Md., Williams & Wilkins, 1948.

Merchant, I. A., *Veterinary bacteriology* (3rd ed.). Ames, Iowa, Iowa State College Press, 1946.

United States Department of Agriculture. "Keeping livestock healthy." *Yearbook of Agriculture, 1942*. Washington, D. C., U. S. Government Printing Office, 1942.

33. INFECTIOUS DISEASES OF PLANTS

A plant is diseased which is so impaired as a whole or in any of its parts that its usefulness to itself or to mankind is seriously reduced. Infectious diseases of plants are caused by living agents: fungi, viruses, bacteria (and to some extent by algae, seed plants, slime molds, protozoa, and nematode worms). Mechanical injuries, toxic substances, and either excess or deficiency of heat, light, moisture, or mineral nutrients may cause noninfectious plant diseases. Damage to plants caused by insects or large animals may also be important; in addition, insects frequently spread pathogenic organisms and cause injury which makes invasion by pathogens possible. It is estimated that in Wisconsin alone the annual loss caused by plant diseases amounts to $10,000,000.

A study of plant diseases is complicated by the fact that such a large number of different kinds of plants are grown for various purposes, and because each kind of plant may have many different diseases. For example, the apple is susceptible to approximately 40 different diseases; the plum is susceptible to some of the diseases of the apple and resistant to others, but it may become afflicted with still other diseases which do not affect the apple. No attempt will be made to describe all of the infectious diseases of every important kind of plant.

It is the purpose of this chapter to describe briefly a few, representative examples of the many infectious diseases of plants, and to point out some of the procedures available for their prevention and control. A thorough study of plant diseases is made by workers in that branch of biological science known as **phytopathology,** or **plant pathology,** and references to books on this subject may be found at the end of the chapter.

Causal Agents of Infectious Diseases of Plants

Multicellular fungi cause the majority of infectious diseases of plants. Viruses are second in importance on the basis of numbers of different diseases produced, but bacteria are responsible for almost as many plant diseases as viruses. Algae, seed plants, slime molds, protozoa, and nematodes are the causal agents of relatively few plant diseases.

It is perhaps obvious, but nevertheless important, to remember that every plant pathogen is not universally distributed. The causal organisms of plant diseases always come originally from infected plants. From an infected plant they may be carried by wind, water, implements, soil, human beings and animals, or insects; or they may be transmitted from diseased to healthy plants by direct contact. Many kinds of plant pathogens are transmitted from one generation of plants to the next via the seeds or other reproductive units of the plants.

Factors Influencing Infection

The fact that a pathogenic microorganism in some way comes in contact with an uninfected plant does not necessarily mean that infection of the plant will occur. The organism must enter the plant and grow in order to produce injury. A brief discussion of some of the main factors influencing infection follows.

Virulence and Resistance

The virulence of the many different strains and races of each species of plant pathogen may vary tremendously; different varieties of any species of plant vary widely in resistance to infection. The virulence of a pathogenic microorganism cannot be predicted by simple laboratory tests; it must be determined by greenhouse or field experiments. It is also impossible to predict, without the aid of experimentation, whether or not any one variety of a species of plant is resistant to infection. The virulence of the pathogen may be influenced by the conditions under which it grows or to which it has been exposed. Adverse environmental conditions attenuate the virulence of the parasite; optimum conditions allow it to maintain its original virulence. The resistance of a plant may be changed by environmental conditions or by its rate of growth. In general, plants do not acquire immunity—

if they do not inherit a natural immunity it is not possible, on a large scale at least, for them to acquire either active or passive immunity. Comparatively little is known concerning the mechanism of immunity of plants to infection.

If the virulence of the pathogen is high, infection may occur with relative ease; if the virulence of the pathogen is low, or the resistance of the host plant is high, infection may not take place even though the parasite is in contact with the host.

Portals of Entry and Chances for Localization

In general, pathogenic microorganisms may enter a plant in one or more of three ways: (1) by growing through the unbroken epidermis of the plant; (2) through wounds caused by wind, hail, implements, animals or human beings, and insects; (3) through natural openings such as stomata, flower parts, hydathodes, and lenticels. As a rule, pathogenic bacteria and viruses can enter only through natural openings or through wounds; multicellular fungi use these portals of entry, and some pathogenic fungi can grow through the intact epidermis of the plant.

Some pathogenic microorganisms are able to grow in almost any part of the plant; others are more specific, and can grow only in certain tissues. The tissue-specific pathogens must enter the plant through a portal that will allow them to reach the desired tissues. When they enter a tissue in which they cannot grow, infection does not readily occur because no growth and injury results.

If the causal microorganisms are present in large numbers and the means for their transmission exist, if there is a large population of susceptible plants, and if environmental conditions are suitable for the parasitic organisms and for invasion of the plants, widespread infection results. Such outbreaks of infectious plant diseases are called **epiphytotics** or **epidemics.**

How Plant Pathogens Produce Injury

Diseased plants exhibit physiological or morphological abnormalities which are recognized as the symptoms of disease. Plant pathogens produce disease by causing either direct or indirect necrosis (tissue destruction). **Direct necrosis** may be localized in relatively small areas in such diseases as anthracnose of beans and alfalfa leaf-spot; or it may involve a general, progressive destruction of the entire plant as in damping-off of seedlings and in fire blight of apples. **Indirect necrosis** involves the death of parts or tissues which are not necessarily infected with the causal organisms. When the causal organisms grow in or destroy the vascular tissues of the host plant they cause wilting of the parts served by the affected vascular tissues; such is the case in Stewart's wilt of corn, and in cabbage yellows. When the causal organisms grow in the parenchymetous tissues of the plant they cause such indirect necroses as are found in corn smut, crown gall and tobacco mosaic.

Plant pathogens often produce products which are harmful to the host plant, but these products are not true exotoxins—they do not stimulate the formation of specific antibodies when injected into a plant or animal.

PRINCIPLES OF CONTROL OF PLANT DISEASES

Prevention of epidemics of plant diseases is based on the same fundamental principles as the prevention of epidemics of diseases of human beings or animals. The source of the causal organisms may be determined and either eradicated or isolated. The means of transmission of the causal organisms may be determined and destroyed or removed. The resistance of the population may be increased to the point that the majority will not be susceptible to infection. Little or no time is spent on attempts to treat diseased plants, or diseased parts of plants; they are destroyed in order to eliminate the source of the causal organisms. The emphasis in control of plant diseases is on prevention, and on cutting lines of transmission.

The following brief outline and discussion of control practices has been adopted in revised form from Melhus and Kent's book.[1]

I. **Temporary Control Practices.** These are control practices that permit the crop to reach maturity despite the presence of the causal agent in the environment.
   1. **Modified cultural practices.**
      a. Crop rotation. Many plant pathogens may live in the soil on dead organic matter for a year or more. If the organisms are specific for a certain crop, the growth of nonsusceptible crops on the land for several successive seasons may lower the numbers of pathogens because of lack of suitable food. The susceptible crop can then be grown again successfully. This practice is used in combating such diseases as potato scab, but is not satisfactory against cabbage yellows because organisms causing this disease persist in soils for long periods of time. Crop rotation cannot be used successfully to combat pathogens that are air-borne or insect-borne.
      b. Destruction of infected plants or infected parts of plants to eradicate the causal agents. This practice is used commonly in gardening, in the care of trees, and in many other cultural practices. It is similar in principle to the eradication of cattle infected with the tubercle bacillus. Eradication, to be effective, must accomplish the destruction of the pathogenic organisms as well as the removal of infected plant tissues.

[1] Adapted from I. E. Melhus and G. C. Kent, *Elements of Plant Pathology*, pp. 68–113. Copyright 1939, by The Macmillan Company and used with their permission.

c. Sanitation. The practice of sanitation involves disinfection of implements and other equipment which might carry pathogens, disinfection of seed or fruit storage bins and houses, and elimination of insect carriers of pathogens. Sanitation is closely allied to the practice of eradication of infected tissues.

d. Partial sterilization of soil. Soils in greenhouses, cold frames, hot beds, and small portions of fields may be partially sterilized with heat to destroy pathogens which are present. In some cases, fungicides may be used in place of heat treatment. Steaming of the soil is the most commonly used method of applying heat, while formaldehyde is the most commonly used chemical disinfectant, but there are many other chemicals and special methods of applying heat available for the partial sterilization of soil.

e. Disease-escaping varieties of plants. Certain varieties of plants, though susceptible to a particular pathogen, may, when grown under conditions which favor the plant, or inhibit the parasite, escape infection. For example, Turkey Red winter wheat is susceptible to stem rust, but it may escape this disease when grown in northern Missouri and Kansas, southern Iowa and Nebraska. In these regions it may mature before the stem rust fungus multiplies sufficiently to cause infection.

2. **Disease-free seed and propagating stock.** There are many different kinds of plant pathogens which may be carried on seeds, bulbs, tubers and propagating stock. Oat smut is a good example of a seed-borne pathogen; the potato mosaic virus may be carried on tubers; gladiolus bulbs may carry the neck rot pathogen; apple nursery stock may carry the bacteria which cause crown gall. Disease-free seed and propagating stock may be sorted out for use or be purchased from agencies that certify their seeds and propagating stocks to be free from pathogens.

3. **Spraying and dusting.** Plants may be sprayed or dusted with some fungicide in order to prevent their infection. To be effective, spraying must be done with a fungicide known to be effective against the pathogen; the fungicide must be thoroughly applied at the proper time, and it must maintain its potency for a relatively long period of time. Effective spraying or dusting can be most readily accomplished if it is based on thorough knowledge of the kind and habits of the pathogen, and on the properties of the fungicide employed. Timeliness and thoroughness are the two most important factors controlling the effectiveness of spraying or dusting. Sulfur is the most commonly used fungicide applied as a dust. Solutions of lime sulfur ($CaS_2 \cdot S_x$), and Bordeaux mixture (4 lbs. $CuSO_4$ + 4 lbs. CaO dissolved in 50 gallons of water) are the most widely used fungicides applied by spraying.

4. **Seed Treatment.** Fungicides applied to seeds kill all forms of the pathogenic organism which may be present, and allow the development upon germination of healthy seedlings. Some fungicides when carried on the seed into the soil serve to kill or inhibit pathogens that are present in the vicinity of the seed. Treatment with hot water or with formaldehyde are common methods of seed disinfection, but the disinfectant action does not carry over into the soil when these practices are employed. Copper carbonate,

cuprous oxide, and organic mercury compounds are seed disinfectants which continue to act after the seed is planted.

5. **Wood preservation.** Fungus decay probably causes greater losses of stored wood and timber than all other causes combined. The practice of protection against fungus decay begins with the care and treatment of logs in the forest; it continues through the handling and manufacturing operations through which the wood goes to produce such products as structural timber, poles, props, ties, finished lumber, wood pulp, and paper. Damage caused by wood-discoloring or wood-rotting fungi can be prevented by: (1) proper time of cutting and peeling, (2) seasoning, (3) storage in water, (4) coating of cut surfaces of logs with fungicides, (5) rapid movement of logs to the mill. Proper drying, storage under dry conditions, and treatment of lumber with creosote, zinc chloride, or other chemicals, all aid in the prevention of discoloration or decay caused by fungi. The problems of wood preservation can be combated by the application of many of the same principles used to preserve the foods of man and of animals.

II. **Permanent Control Practices.** These are control practices that are designed to exclude, destroy, or reduce the prevalence of pathogens in the environment of a crop.

1. **Quarantine.** Plant quarantine is the legal restriction of the movement of plants or plant products between communities, states, or countries for the purpose of preventing or retarding the introduction and establishment of plant pathogens in those localities that are free from such organisms. Quarantine involves: (1) the regulation of plant importation; (2) the establishment of domestic plant quarantines and control practices; (3) inspection of plants and plant products at shipping and receiving terminals, and the destruction of infected plants or plants that may carry the pathogen. Effective quarantine measures can prevent the spread of pathogens carried on plants, seed and propagating stock, and on plant products.

2. **Eradication.** Eradication is a permanent control practice that involves the extermination of the host plants of a plant pathogen. Eradication of citrus trees infected with the citrus canker organism is one example of this control practice. Probably the most extensive eradication program in the United States involves the destruction of the common barberry, which serves as an intermediate host of the fungus which causes stem rust of cereal crops.

3. **Disease-resistant varieties and strains.** Varieties or strains of any species of crop vary widely in their resistance to different plant pathogens. When a resistant strain or variety of a crop can be selected, or bred by hybridization, it may be grown on a large scale in the presence of the pathogen without injury. Of course, it is necessary to select or to breed varieties that yield well and have other desirable qualities in addition to disease resistance. Selection, and production by hybridization of disease-resistant varieties takes advantage of the natural, heritable immunity of the plant. For example, Country Gentleman sweet corn is fairly resistant to Stewart's wilt disease; Golden Bantam corn is not resistant. If Stewart's wilt organisms are prevalent, the grower will get a greater return from Country Gentleman than from Golden Bantam corn. The yellows resistant cabbage, Wisconsin Hollander, was selected on the basis of field trials in soils where the

cabbage yellows organism was prevalent. An example of hybridization to produce a variety of oats that would be resistant to all races of rust and smut organisms is found in the work of the United States Department of Agriculture, in cooperation with the Iowa and Wisconsin Experiment Stations, which produced the Vicland, Forvic, and Clinton hybrid oats.

It is not possible on a large scale to give plants an acquired immunity by means of injection of vaccines or sera, but it is possible to select resistant varieties, or to breed resistant hybrids which have a natural, heritable immunity.

With the general principles of infection, immunity, and control practices in mind, it is possible to go on to a brief description of representative examples of plant diseases.

EXAMPLES OF DISEASES CAUSED BY MULTICELLULAR FUNGI

One of the Diseases Caused by *Phycomycetes*—Late Blight of Potato

The causal agent of this disease is *Phytophthora infestans*. The pathogen infects and causes necrosis of the edges and tips of the leaves of the potato plant. These necrotic areas enlarge until the whole leaf is destroyed. A white mass of conidiophores and conidia is produced on the infected area, which usually appears downy and may be yellowish in color. Figure 67 is a drawing of potato leaves infected with *Phytophthora infestans*. When conditions are favorable the necrotic area may extend to the stems. When the organisms infect the tubers they may cause them to rot, but if storage temperatures are low (below 5° C.), the organisms remain dormant in the tuber. The organism causes death of the plants by direct necrosis, and may cause rotting of tubers stored at temperatures above 5° C. The organism produces conidia which spread from leaf to leaf and from the leaf to the tubers.

Control of late blight may be accomplished by: (1) selection of healthy, uninfected seed; (2) modification of cultural practices (high hilling and delayed digging of the potatoes); (3) spraying the vines with Bordeaux mixture when environmental conditions appear to favor infection; (4) possibly through the use of resistant varieties and hybrids.

Phytophthora infestans does not remain viable for long periods in soil that is free from infected tubers. The organism is carried from one crop to the next through infected tubers that are used for seed.

One of the Diseases Caused by *Ascomycetes*—Apple Scab

The causal agent of this disease is *Venturia inaequalis*. The organism affects the leaves, flowers, fruit, and twigs of the tree. It causes reduction

FIGURE 67.   Potato leaves showing necrotic spots caused by the late blight fungus, *Phytophthora infestans*. The light fluffy sporulating mycelium appears here at the margins of the dead areas. (Courtesy of the Department of Plant Pathology, University of Wisconsin.)

in yield and in quality of the fruit, but is rarely responsible for the death of the tree. On the surface of the leaves, small, circular, brownish or gray spots develop and finally become olive green. The attacked tissues swell and bulge; this condition is followed by necrosis. The under surfaces of the lower leaves are affected first. Infected leaves curl and drop to the ground where they harbor the pathogen and become a source from which it may spread to other leaves. The pathogen may live over the winter in fallen infected leaves.

Flower bud leaves and flowers may become infected and be destroyed by necrosis; when this occurs little or no fruit is produced.

The fruit may be attacked at any time during its development, or at the time of harvest. If infection occurs early, the fruit is so deformed that it is of no value; late infection may cause but few scabby areas on the fruit. Necrosis of the fruit by *Venturia inaequalis* originates in small areas no larger than a pin point. These necrotic, scabby areas may enlarge and coalesce with others that are nearby; dry rot occurs in these areas when the fruit is stored.

The control of apple scab involves destruction of infected leaves, fruit, and twigs, spraying or dusting with a fungicide so as to prevent infection, and proper pruning to prevent the foliage from becoming too dense. Orchards should not be planted on low ground or in pockets where air circulation is poor, because in these locations the fungus multiplies to best advantage. There are no immune varieties of apples, but some varieties escape the disease better than others; it is necessary to use trial-and-error methods in order to determine which varieties are best suited for a locality.

One of the Diseases Caused by *Basidiomycetes*—Stem Rust of Wheat

The causal agent of this disease is *Puccinia graminis*. There are at least eight varieties of this species; one is pathogenic for wheat, barley, and many wild grasses; a second affects oats and some wild grasses; a third infects rye, barley, and still other grasses; other varieties attack timothy, brome grass, and other grasses. Within each variety there are many different races, or strains, which vary in virulence and in other properties.

The fungus attacks the young leaves and stems of the wheat or other grass fairly early in the growing season, or at any time when suitable environmental conditions (an abundance of moisture and a temperature of 15° to 20° C.) exist. When the humidity and temperature are relatively high, infection of the stems and leaves proceeds rapidly. First a red rust appears on infected leaves and stems, and later the rust becomes black. The fungus grows through the cells of the stem and leaves, and absorbs food that would normally be used to produce grain. As a result, the yield of grain is decreased, and the kernels shrink and shrivel when dried.

The life cycle of *Puccinia graminis* is complex, and cannot be described in the space available. It is possible for the parasitic organism to exist only on wheat; spores on infected wheat plants may spread to uninfected plants during the same growing season, or remain on the infected plants over the winter. Spores from infected wheat infect the common barberry, *Berberis vulgaris.* The mycelium which develops in the barberry produces new spores of a different kind that may be carried by the wind to susceptible wheat. Infection of the barberry does not destroy the plant, but is a necessary stage in the life cycle of the rust parasite in the northern United States.

In the northern United States, three control procedures may be employed to combat stem rust. First, and most important, is the eradication of the common barberry, the intermediate host of the pathogen. This is accomplished by putting at least ten pounds of common salt on the crown of the barberry plant. The second method of control is to grow disease-resistant varieties of wheat, but such varieties are not common, nor are they highly resistant to all races of the organism. The third method involves the application of sulfur dust to prevent infection, and the use of fertilizers and cultural practices designed to prevent lodging of the grain. Better control of this disease is needed, as shown by the fact that in 1935 it caused an estimated reduction of 121,882,000 bushels of wheat, 14,007,000 bushels of oats, and 26,414,000 bushels of barley from the normal yield in the United States.

One of the Diseases Caused by *Fungi Imperfecti*—Watermelon Wilt

The causal agent of this disease is *Fusarium bulbigenum.* The spores of this fungus may live on seeds, in dead plant material, and in the soil. When watermelon seedlings grow in the spring, the fungus may infect them through their root caps, and cause seedling necrosis which results in death of the plant. If the seedling grows sufficiently to reach the surface of the soil, the fungus may attack it and cause damping-off. Later infection may cause stunting or wilting of the plant. In some plants no wilting occurs, but the leaves become yellow, the plants are stunted, and the melons produced are few in number and small in size. This latter type of the disease provides an example of an indirect necrosis which is caused by growth of the fungus in the vascular system of the plant.

The control of watermelon wilt depends largely upon prevention. The fungus is able to live in the soil for long periods of time. Only resistant varieties of watermelon, such as the Pride of Muscatine, should be grown on contaminated soils. Seed to be planted on uncontaminated soils should be treated with some mercury dust, such as Ceresan or Semesan, to prevent contamination of the soil.

EXAMPLES OF DISEASES CAUSED BY VIRUSES

Common Tobacco Mosaic

The tobacco mosaic virus does not kill the plant, but it reduces the yield and quality of the crop. The virus enters the plant through broken hairs on the leaves, or through wounds. The leaves of infected plants may curl, become distorted and puckered, and show a mosaic pattern of two shades of green. Infected plants may be dwarfed, and their flowers distorted, blotched, and bleached; necrosis of infected parts may occur. Figure 68 is a photograph of a tobacco leaf which shows the damage caused by infection with the mosaic virus.

There are many strains of the virus; these vary widely in their effect upon the tobacco plant, and in the numbers of other kinds of plants which they are able to infect. More than 200 different species of plants, classified in 12 different families, are susceptible to one or more strains of the tobacco mosaic virus. The virus is very hardy, and can withstand drying and comparatively high temperatures. Because it can infect so many different kinds of plants, and because of its hardiness, it is almost universally distributed. Although only the leaves of a plant show symptoms of disease, the virus is present in all parts of the plant; therefore, any refuse of an infected plant harbors the virus.

FIGURE 68. Tobacco leaf showing the characteristic diseased mottling responsible for the name "mosaic." It is caused by a relatively stable filterable virus. Much of the basic work on viruses has been done with it. (Courtesy of the Wisconsin Agricultural Experiment Station.)

Control of tobacco mosaic disease depends largely upon destruction of infected plants and upon sanitation. Insects, implements, clothing, and the hands of workers may become contaminated with the virus and carry it to healthy plants. Chewing tobacco and some cigarette tobacco carry the virus and may serve as sources of infection if used in the vicinity of healthy plants. No satisfactory mosaic-resistant varieties of tobacco have as yet been developed.

Curly Top of Sugar Beets

The virus which causes this very destructive disease of sugar beets may also infect tomatoes, beans, squash, pumpkins, and spinach. At present, the virus is prevalent throughout the sugar beet growing regions west of the Rocky Mountains and in Argentina.

The curly top virus is transmitted largely by the beet leaf hopper, *Eutettix tenellus;* it is transmitted rarely by mechanical means. It is believed that the leaf hopper takes the virus into its digestive tract when it feeds on an infected plant. The virus then migrates to the insect's salivary glands, from which source it is ejected into the tissues of healthy plants. At least 24 hours must elapse between the time the insect ingests the virus and the time when it can be transmitted by the insect. The leaf hopper inoculates the virus into the crown or the petioles of the young beet seedling. The virus migrates to the phloem tissue and soon is carried to all parts of the plant. Within 4 to 18 days after inoculation symptoms of the disease appear.

The chief symptoms of the disease are clearing or transparency of the small veins on the younger leaves, followed by warty protuberances on the lower surfaces of the leaves. At the same time there is an increase in the number of rootlets, which results in a condition known as "hairy" root. The leaves curl, become darkened, thickened, and rough. Young beet seedlings are killed by the virus; older plants are dwarfed and blighted. The disease causes almost total loss of the crop.

The most practical control practices available are to plant disease-resistant varieties of sugar beets, such as U. S. 35 or 600, and to plant them early enough to allow the seedlings to develop their full resistance before infestation with leaf hopper occurs. The leaf hopper population may be decreased by destruction of weeds which harbor the insects.

Other Diseases Caused by Viruses

There are at least 100 other plant diseases caused by viruses. Most of these diseases involve yellowing of the leaves and stems, dwarfing of the plant and its fruits, or over-growth of infected parts. Smith's and Bawden's books, to which reference is made at the end of the chapter, contain descriptions of the more important virus diseases of plants.

EXAMPLES OF DISEASES CAUSED BY BACTERIA

Fire Blight of Apple and Pear

The causal agent of this disease is *Erwinia amylovora*. These bacteria invade many members of the plant family *Rosaceae*, but are most destructive in orchards where apples, pears, and plums are grown. Invasion of the plant may occur through natural openings in the flowers or young leaves, or through wounds. The bacteria are transmitted by insects which aid in pollination, by rain and wind, and by implements used in pruning. The symptoms of the disease depend upon the parts of the plant that become invaded by the causal bacteria. In young leaves, leaf blight occurs, and the leaves look as if they have been damaged by fire. Infected blossoms wilt and turn brown. Young fruits soften and blacken when infected. Twigs and young branches wilt and blacken. And when the pathogen enters the body of the tree, necrosis of the bark occurs, and results in a dried, cracked area through which a sticky exudate may exude. The disease causes loss of the crop and and in time kills the trees.

The bacteria cannot live in the soil for more than two or three months, but may survive through the winter in infected bark or twigs. The disease may be controlled by destruction of infected trees or parts of trees, by thorough sanitation, by spraying when about 80 to 90 per cent of the flowers are in bloom with a weak Bordeaux mixture, and by utilization of relatively resistant varieties. Eternal vigilance on the part of the grower is needed to cut out and destroy infected tissues and fruits, and to spray at the proper time. Sodding the orchard and avoiding the use of excessive quantities of nitrogenous fertilizers prevent rapid growth of the trees during June and July, and make them more resistant to infection.

Control of fire blight is not easy, and simple rules cannot be laid down that will enable the grower successfully to combat the disease under all conditions. For example, control measures which are successful in Wisconsin must be modified for use in California. Phytopathologists of the United States Department of Agriculture and of the agricultural experiment stations in the different fruit-growing regions of the country have developed special control measures for each region.

Soft Rot of Vegetables

The causal agent of this disease is *Erwinia carotovora*. It causes a wet rot of carrots, turnips, rutabagas, radishes, potatoes, cabbage, lettuce, tomatoes, peppers, and other vegetables. The disease occurs in the field and in stored vegetables. Figure 69 illustrates soft rot of cabbage.

The pathogen overwinters in stored vegetables, or in plant refuse, manure,

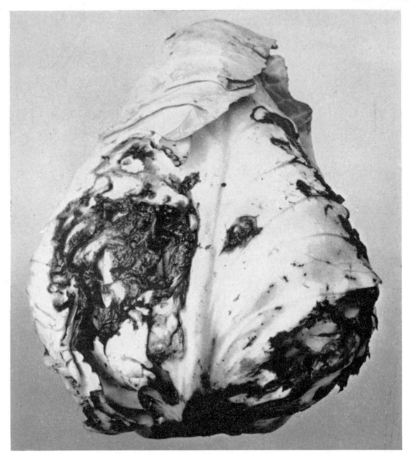

FIGURE 69.   Cabbage head with soft rot caused by *Erwinia caroto-vora*. Many fleshy vegetables are turned rapidly into soft bad-smelling pulp by this organism. (Photograph from the United States Department of Agriculture.)

and in the soil. It is spread very easily by contact, by implements, by insects, and by handling. The bacteria enter the plant or root through natural openings, or through wounds, and cause a rapid, wet rot of the tissues.

The disease may be controlled by crop rotation; by drying the surfaces of root-crops and exposing them to the sun before storage; by storage under comparatively dry conditions at a temperature below 5° C.; by destruction of infected tissues; and by sanitation in the cultivation and handling of the crop.

Stewart's Disease of Sweet Corn (Stewart's Wilt)

The causal agent of this disease is *Bacterium stewarti*. It causes wilting of sweet corn, but may also attack field corn in a similar manner.

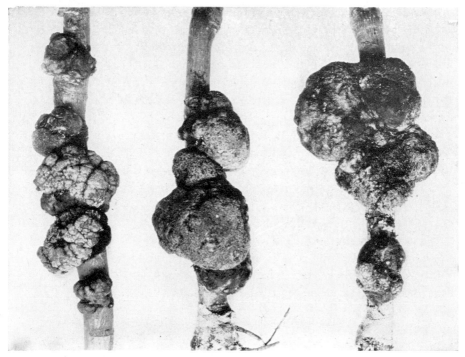

FIGURE 70. Crown gall on nursery apple trees. These galls were induced by wound inoculations with *Agrobacterium tumefaciens*. From left to right they have incubated 8, 10, and 12 weeks. (Courtesy of the Wisconsin Agricultural Experiment Station.)

The pathogen may live in the soil, on seed, in infected plant refuse, in manure, and in the flea beetle (*Chaetocnema pulicaria*). The bacteria may enter the young seedling through wounds or with the aid of insects. Infection is evidenced by the appearance of streaks on the foliage, and by wilting of the plant. The organisms infect the vascular system, and may be carried to all parts of the plant. If they do not kill the seedling, and the plant produces seed, the bacteria are often present on the seed. The bacteria do not spread rapidly from one infected plant to another.

Control of Stewart's wilt of corn may be effected through the use of resistant varieties, such as Country Gentleman; by crop rotation; and by destruction of infected plants.

Crown Gall of Fruits

The causal agent of this disease is *Agrobacterium tumefaciens*. It infects apples, peaches, raspberries, grapes, and other fruits.

The pathogen may live in the soil, and in galls. It enters the plant through wounds in the roots and other underground parts of the plant. Once in the plant the bacteria stimulate excessive proliferation of cells, with the resulting formation of tumors or galls. Young galls are soft, whitish, and spongy; later they turn yellowish, and finally become dark brown and comparatively hard. The gall is not covered by bark and may become invaded by saprophytic soil organisms which cause decay. Galls on apple tree nursery stock are shown in Figure 70. The organism rarely spreads from the primary galls to other parts of the plant to form secondary galls, or directly to other plants. Because they replace normal, nonabsorbing root tissues with nonabsorbing tissues, and because they may interfere with transfer of nutrients in the plant, the galls cause dwarfing, reduction in yield, and eventually death of the plant.

The disease may be controlled by use of land known to be free from the causal organism, by surface disinfection (with 1:1,000 aqueous mercuric chloride) of stocks used in grafting, and by wrapping grafted unions with nurseryman's adhesive tape. Sanitation during grafting operations and avoidance of injury during cultivation also help to prevent the disease.

Potato Scab

The causal agent of this disease is an actinomycete, *Streptomyces scabies*. It is a facultative parasite which exists naturally in fertile soils that are near neutral in reaction; and is less prevalent in wet, cool soils than in rather dry, warm soils.

The organism attacks young tubers, roots, and other underground parts of the plant. The lesions are first reddish in color, and later become brown and scabby. Infection causes not only decrease in yield, but reduces the quality of the crop.

Potato scab may be controlled by the use of scab-free seed; by utilization of new soil, or soil that has been made acid through the addition of ammonium sulfate and green manures (sulfur added at the rate of from 400 to 1,000 pounds per acre may also be used to cause soils to become acid); by avoidance of the application of lime and stable manure to land that is to be used for potatoes; and by the use of the relatively thick, rough-skinned varieties of russet potatoes. Seed potatoes should be treated with hot formaldehyde, mercuric chloride, or organic mercury compounds before they are planted, in order to kill the organisms on the surfaces of the tubers.

DISEASES CAUSED BY OTHER AGENTS

In the United States, there are about 250 species of parasitic seed plants, examples of which are the mistletoe and the dodder. These agents may parasitize other seed plants such as the tomato, alfalfa, and various species of trees.

Nematodes (round worms or eel worms) of many kinds may infest and injure a wide variety of plants. They are particularly important in the southern United States, but are becoming common in those northern states which have a long growing season; they also cause extensive injury in greenhouses.

Damage to plants by wild animals such as deer and rabbits may be serious in some regions of the United States. Such damage usually is of greatest importance in orchards and in forests or forest tree nurseries.

REFERENCES

Bawden, F. C., *Plant viruses and virus diseases*. Waltham, Mass., Chronica Botanica, 1943.

Boyce, J. S., *Forest pathology*. N. Y., McGraw-Hill, 1938.

Chester, K. S., *The nature and prevention of plant diseases* (2nd ed.). Philadelphia, Pa., Blakiston, 1947.

Dickson, J. G., *Diseases of field crops*. N. Y., McGraw-Hill, 1947.

Heald, F. D., *Manual of plant diseases* (2nd ed.). N. Y., McGraw-Hill, 1933.

Heald, F. D., *Introduction to plant pathology* (2nd ed.). N. Y., McGraw-Hill, 1943.

Leach, J. G., *Insect transmission of plant diseases*. N. Y., McGraw-Hill, 1940.

Martin, H., *The scientific principles of plant protection with special reference to chemical control*. London, Edward Arnold & Co., 1936.

Melhus, I. E., and Kent, G. C., *Elements of plant pathology*. N. Y., Macmillan, 1939.

Riker, A. J., and Riker, R. S., *Introduction to research on plant diseases*. St. Louis, Mo., John S. Swift Co., Inc., 1936.

Smith, K. M., *Virus diseases of farm and garden crops*. Worcester, England, Littlebury and Co., Ltd., 1945.

Walker, J. C., *Diseases of vegetable crops*. Ann Arbor, Mich., Edwards Bros., 1936.

PART IX

An Outline of the
History of Microbiology

34. THE ORIGIN AND DEVELOPMENT OF MICROBIOLOGY

Bacteria were first described by Antony van Leeuwenhoek of Delft, Holland. His findings were reported to the Royal Society of London in a letter dated October 9, 1676.

Antony van Leeuwenhoek was born in Delft, Holland, on October 24, 1632. At the age of 16 he entered the shop of a linen-draper in Amsterdam to learn the trade. There he became acquainted with the use of magnifying glasses for the examination of threads and fabrics. Possibly, as E. B. Fred has stated, ". . . this introduction to the microscopic world . . . stimulated his imagination to go beyond the thread counter and delve into mysteries as yet unheard of." Upon completion of his apprenticeship he returned to Delft where he opened a clothing store. He soon became interested in mathematics, and after a brief course of study was qualified as a surveyor. His knowledge of mathematics enabled him to be elected wine gauger for the city of Delft; he also was appointed Chamberlain to the Sheriffs of Delft. The income from these positions made him fairly independent of his trade, and enabled him to spend more time on his chief avocation, the grinding of lenses and the manufacture of simple microscopes.

Leeuwenhoek's microscopes consisted of a single biconvex lens which he ground and mounted between small apertures in a two-piece metal holder. The fluids to be observed under these microscopes usually were contained in thin glass capillary tubes, and when the instrument was held close to the eye, the microscopic objects in the fluid were viewed through the single lens. The magnifying power of his lenses was never greater than 300 diameters, but with these simple microscopes Leeuwenhoek was able to see bacteria and other microorganisms. Of his exact methods, Leeuwenhoek wrote in his most significant letter of October 9, 1676: "My method for seeing the very smallest animalcules and minute eels, I do not impart to others; nor how to see very many animalcules at one time. That I keep for myself alone." Dr. Barnett Cohen has described two methods that Leeuwenhoek might have used in his observations. The first of these involves placing the liquid to be examined in a spherical bulb, 1 to 3 mm. in diameter, blown on the tip of a capillary tube. The second procedure involves placing the drop of liquid to be examined on the lens, thereby taking advantage of the curvature of the drop to obtain added magnification. Both of these methods have yielded satisfactory results in the hands of Dr. Cohen, and perhaps explain how Leeuwenhoek was able to see bacteria with his simple microscopes; both methods provide an "objective" lens of glass or liquid to give added magnification.

Leeuwenhoek was most industrious, and constructed more than 400 microscopes. His insatiable curiosity led him to focus his lenses on substances of all sorts. The objects and microorganisms that he saw in rain water, wine vinegar, pepper infusions, scrapings from his teeth, and many other materials were described at great length, drawn with painstaking accuracy, and measured by comparison with such objects as a grain of sand, or the hairs on the leg of a louse. He discovered, and described in his letters to the Royal Society: spermatazoa, blood corpuscles, yeasts, protozoa, and many different kinds of bacteria.

The death of Leeuwenhoek in 1723 brought to an end a career of accurate, painstaking observation of the newly discovered world of microorganisms.

The discoveries of Leeuwenhoek stimulated others to study the microscopic forms of life, and much work of a descriptive nature followed. The compound microscope had been invented in 1590 by Janssen and his son in Middleburg, Holland, and compound microscopes of various types were used by the naturalists who studied the microorganisms that Leeuwenhoek had discovered with his own simple microscopes. Nearly all of this early work involved characterization and classification of microorganisms; their relations to natural processes and to the production of disease were unknown at that time.

ORIGIN OF THE SCIENCE OF MICROBIOLOGY

Louis Pasteur (1822–1895), the great French scientist, was the founder and originator of the science of microbiology. He was trained as a chemist and physicist, and became interested in the activities of microorganisms through his studies on tartaric acid. He believed microorganisms to be responsible for fermentation, and from 1855 to 1860 was busily engaged in the task of proving this theory. He showed that certain microorganisms produce one kind of fermentation, whereas others are responsible for different fermentations; that bacteria cause lactic acid, acetic acid, and butyric acid fermentations, whereas yeasts cause alcoholic fermentation.

While engaged in this work Pasteur and his assistants developed new techniques that made his studies possible and his results incontestable. The first of these new methods was the use of steam under pressure in an autoclave to sterilize liquids and other materials. Prior to Pasteur's time, steam under pressure had been used to sterilize foods, but Pasteur probably was the first to employ the autoclave in microbiological research. The second sterilization procedure he adopted involved the use of an oven to sterilize dry glassware. Pasteur also invented the practice, known today as pasteurization, which involves heating a liquid to a temperature considerably below its boiling point for a length of time sufficient to kill undesirable types of microorganisms without completely sterilizing the material or injuring it with heat.

Pasteur demonstrated the fact that certain microorganisms prefer to grow in an acid medium, while others grow best in an alkaline medium, and most prefer a near neutral medium. In connection with this work he showed that liquids which are acid in reaction may be sterilized more easily than those which are neutral or alkaline in reaction. That some microorganisms use sugars as their main foods, while others prefer proteins or protein derivatives was another fundamental discovery of Pasteur in the field of microbial nutrition.

One of Pasteur's most significant achievements was the demonstration that certain microorganisms, which he named "anaerobes," prefer to grow and live in the complete absence of free oxygen; others, which he termed "aerobes" can develop only in the presence of free oxygen; a third group, now termed "facultative," can live and grow in the presence of free oxygen, or can get along without it. In addition, he found that under aerobic conditions, microorganisms produce more completely oxidized products than do the facultative types and anaerobes which are grown in the absence of free oxygen. It is also significant that he had to develop special methods to provide anaerobic conditions for the anaerobic bacteria; development of these methods made this work possible.

It is typical of Pasteur's work that these fundamental discoveries were made while he was engaged in attempts to improve the qualities of French wines and beer, and to put the manufacture of vinegar on a scientific basis.

He was intensely interested in the practical problems of agriculture and industry. To him, the discovery of a fundamental fact, or the development of a new method were incidental to the solution of the broader problem which he was trying to solve. In the late 1850's, however, he was drawn into a controversy of great scientific importance, which at the time seemed to have little practical application: whether or not microorganisms could generate spontaneously from nonliving material.

Disproof of the Theory of Spontaneous Generation

For many years before Pasteur's time, a controversy had been raging over the theory that life could arise spontaneously from inanimate material. Bit by bit, over a long period of time, various investigators had shown conclusively that microscopic forms of life cannot be generated spontaneously from inanimate substances; but the discovery of microorganisms provided a new form of life for the believers in this ancient theory to investigate.

In 1745 Needham stated that flasks of meat broth that had been boiled and then corked underwent putrefaction, and that microorganisms could be found upon microscopic examination of the spoiled broth. This, he stated, was evidence that the microorganisms arose spontaneously from the broth; for had not the heating destroyed all living things that were originally present?

Spallanzani read Needham's reports, and between 1765 and 1776 published the results of his own investigations which demonstrated that a longer period of boiling, followed by sealing of the necks of the flasks before any air could be drawn back into the boiled broth, would preserve the broth. Needham claimed that sealing the flasks prevented the normal operation of the "vital force" of the broth because air was needed to aid in the "creation" of microorganisms from the constituents of the liquid.

Following this early controversy, many attempts were made to determine whether Needham or Spallanzani was correct. In 1810, Appert, a French confectioner, used Spallanzani's method to preserve foods, and thus laid the foundation for the modern canning industry. Franz Schulze, in 1836, passed the air that returned to a flask of boiled broth through solutions of caustic potash and sulfuric acid, and showed that boiled broth protected in this manner remained sterile. In the same year, Schwann passed the air that returned to a flask of boiled broth through a heated tube; broth exposed to heated air remained sterile, while broth in other flasks, exposed to unheated air, spoiled. In 1854 Schroeder and von Dusch showed that a flask of broth that had been boiled for a long period of time, and then fitted with a tube containing sterile cotton through which air returning to the flask had to pass, remained sterile. Later, Schroeder simply plugged the necks of the flasks of broth with cotton, boiled the broth, and found that it remained sterile because the cotton filtered the microorganisms from the incoming air.

But those who believed in the spontaneous generation of microorganisms were still unsatisfied; they claimed that all of the procedures used to sterilize the air had robbed it of its powers to initiate the generation of microorganisms from the broth. Pouchet, a well-known naturalist and member of the French Academy of Sciences, became the leader of the believers in the theory of spontaneous generation. This brought the controversy squarely before Pasteur, who believed that the microorganisms responsible for fermentation and putrefaction came from the air, and were not generated spontaneously in broth. He was forced, in order to prove his own theory, to devise a method which would demonstrate conclusively that microorganisms are generated only from pre-existing microorganisms. He accomplished this proof by drawing out the necks of flasks in which he had placed broth into long, goose-necked, capillary tubes, boiling the broth to sterilize it, and then allowing the flasks to stand undisturbed. The broth in these flasks remained sterile because the microorganisms in the air which returned to the flasks after boiling were held on the walls of the tubes, and could not reach the broth. The air which returned to the flask of boiled broth was unchanged by heating, chemical treatment or filtration, and the broth remained in constant contact with air. He showed that the microorganisms present in the air were present in the tubes, and thus demonstrated that microbes, like other forms of life, arise only from pre-existing, similar living things. Thus it may be seen that the work done to disprove an erroneous theory was of fundamental importance in the establishment of the science of microbiology.

One of the first to recognize the significance of Pasteur's work on the origin of microorganisms and the production of fermentation and putrefaction by microorganisms, was Sir Joseph Lister, a Scottish surgeon. Lister was also cognizant of the findings of other investigators who had proved the relative sterility of normal animal and plant organs and tissues. He believed that postoperative wound infections were caused by microorganisms, and in 1867 showed that treating everything used in surgery with disinfectants would almost eliminate such infections. He sprayed the air of the operating room with phenol, soaked the instruments and dressings in phenol, and thereby founded the practice of **antiseptic surgery.** This technique has given way to the more exact procedures of **aseptic surgery,** but unquestionably Lister's findings laid the foundations for the modern practices.

But we must return to the work of Pasteur to follow further developments in microbiology. He had shown that microorganisms arise only from pre-existing, similar living cells, and that these organisms are the cause of fermentation, putrefaction, and decay. In his work he had developed the practices and procedures of sterilization and pasteurization. He had learned that microorganisms require certain foods, that their oxygen demands are quite definite, and that the reaction of the surrounding medium influences their ability to grow. These, as we know today, are fundamental facts of microbiology, and having found them, Pasteur went on to apply them to new fields.

Production of Disease by Microorganisms, and Immunity to Disease

About the middle of the 19th century, the silkworms in southern France became afflicted with a disease, known as pébrine, which almost wiped out the production of silk in that region. In 1865 the problem of eradicating and controlling this disease was turned over to Pasteur, who had proved his eligibility for such a task by showing the vintners how to control, through pasteurization, the "diseases" of wines. With characteristic thoroughness and vigor he promptly set about the task of finding the cause of pébrine. He found that a microorganism was present in diseased silkworms, but not in healthy ones, and that this organism was carried from animal to animal through the egg. Thus he proved what others had suspected: that microorganisms may cause disease. Furthermore, he showed that by starting with disease-free stock, and growing the worms under conditions that prevented infection, the disease could be avoided.

The strain of overwork began to tell on Pasteur and he suffered an attack of paralysis, but upon recovery, he turned toward the study of another, even more serious disease: anthrax. Davaine had demonstrated that the blood of animals dead of this disease contained rod-shaped bacteria, and that the disease could be transmitted to a healthy animal by inoculation with blood containing these organisms. Pasteur, in 1877, isolated the bacteria we now know as *Bacillus anthracis* in pure culture, carried them through many successive transfers in artificial media, and reproduced the disease by inoculating healthy animals with pure cultures of the bacteria. Thus he demonstrated conclusively that certain bacteria are capable of causing disease.

In 1880 Pasteur was working on a disease known as fowl cholera. He had isolated the causative bacteria, and had them growing in pure culture. Upon returning from a vacation, he found that his cultures had become attenuated; they had lost their ability to cause disease when inoculated into healthy fowl. He obtained fresh, virulent cultures and inoculated these into chickens that had been inoculated with the attentuated cultures; at the same time he inoculated other chickens that had received no previous inoculation. He found that the chickens inoculated previously with the attenuated cultures did not contract the disease, while those receiving no previous inoculation became infected. In this way he stumbled onto the principle of immunizing by protective inoculation with the weakened causative agent of the disease. This was not exactly new because Jenner, nearly 100 years previously, had noticed that inoculation of human beings with cowpox prevented the more serious disease of smallpox. However, Jenner's observations were quite empirical, while those of Pasteur were based upon experiments conducted with pure cultures of a known bacterium.

Pasteur immediately went to work on a method to attenuate the causative agent of anthrax, and found that cultivating the bacteria at 42° to 43° C. greatly reduced their virulence. These weakened cultures, when inoculated into a susceptible animal would, after a short time, protect the animal against infection with a virulent strain of the organism. This fact he demonstrated publicly in 1881 in a dramatic experiment conducted on 50 sheep.

Pasteur then turned to a study of rabies, or hydrophobia, and although he was not able to find the causative agent of the disease, he succeeded in developing a system of immunization against it. Once again he applied the principle of attenuating the causative agent; but, since rabies is caused by a virus, he had to develop new techniques to accomplish his goal. The virus, which he obtained from the saliva of rabid dogs, was grown in the spinal chord of a rabbit. Upon death of the animal, the spinal chord was removed and desiccated under aseptic conditions. A series of injections with the desiccated virus-containing material, if started promptly enough after the bite of a rabid animal, was found to protect humans against hydrophobia. The symptoms of rabies do not, as a rule, appear in man till about two months after he has been bitten by a rabid animal. Starting the Pasteur treatment as soon as possible after being bitten enables the individual to build up an immunity rapidly enough to prevent the onset of this terrible disease.

Pasteur died in 1895; he will always be known as the father of microbiology, and as one of the greatest benefactors of mankind.

DEVELOPMENT OF MICROBIOLOGY

The early development of the technical aspects of the science of microbiology was due largely to the work of Robert Koch (1843–1910). In 1876 he published a complete description of the anthrax bacillus (known today as *Bacillus anthracis*) together with incontrovertible evidence that it caused anthrax. In 1877 he published his methods of preparing, fixing, and staining with aniline dyes film preparations of bacteria in infected tissues and in cultures. The introduction of staining greatly facilitated microscopic observations which formerly had been made on unstained preparations. In 1881 he described his methods for the production and use of liquefiable gelatin media on which colonies of bacteria could be grown. This work provided a technique which enabled the isolation of pure cultures of bacteria without resorting to the use of Lister's method of dilution in liquid media; a method which at its best was haphazard. Later, Frau Hesse, the wife of one of Koch's students, suggested the use of agar in place of gelatin; and Petri introduced the culture dish, which now bears his name, to replace the flat glass plates on which Koch originally made his plate cultures with liquefiable solid media.

In 1882 and 1884 Koch published his classical papers on the tubercle bacillus, and proved it to be the cause of tuberculosis. In 1883 he discovered the cholera vibrio. Later, he produced and used tuberculin for the first time. He was also the inventor of the hanging drop method for the microscopic examination of microorganisms in liquids, and developed ingenious procedures for testing the action of disinfectants. In addition to being one of the first to prove definitely that pure cultures of certain bacteria cause disease, Koch developed many of the fundamental techniques of bacteriology. Pasteur founded the science of microbiology, but Koch contributed more than anyone to its early development along technical lines.

In the space available it is impossible to give more than a brief outline of the fundamental discoveries and developments in microbiology during the later part of the 19th century and the early part of the 20th century. For purposes of convenience the developments which have occurred in different branches of microbiological science are described separately.

Infectious Diseases of Man and Animals

Discoveries of the causal agents of many of the infectious diseases of humans and animals were made in rapid-fire order during the later part of the 19th century. Of particular significance were the discoveries by Roux and Yersin (1889) of diphtheria toxin, and of Behring and Kitasato, and Fraenkel (1890) of the diphtheria and tetanus antitoxins; the elucidation of the humoral theory of immunity by Ehrlich, and of the cellular theory of immunity (phagocytic action) by Metchnikoff; the proof that arthropods are vectors of pathogens (ticks spread Texas fever) by Theobald Smith; the proof by Loeffler and Frosch that hoof-and-mouth disease is caused by a virus.

In the 20th century, comparatively few new causal agents of disease have been discovered. Some of the most significant work of this century is the discovery in 1915–1917 of bacteriophages by Twort and by d'Herelle, working independently; the development of public health bacteriology by Sedgwick, Park, Rosenow, Winslow, and others in the United States; fundamental work on immunology by Landsteiner; and the work on viruses by Stanley and his associates. Although Theobald Smith was the only American bacteriologist to make important contributions to the early study of disease, and most of the first work on this subject was done in Europe, the United States is now the center of research on diseases of human beings and animals. A discovery of fundamental importance was the finding (1931) by Goodpasture and his associates that many viral and rickettsial agents can be cultivated in embryonating hens' eggs. This method is now used to produce viruses and rickettsiae that are to be employed as vaccines; its discovery and development are of great significance to human welfare.

As pointed out in Chapter 10, the sulfonamides were first discovered to have chemotherapeutic value in 1935. The manufacture and use of a great variety of sulfonamides has been a major factor in improvement in the treatment of infectious diseases. Discovery of penicillin (1929) by Sir Alexander Fleming was another finding of tremendous importance in man's efforts to combat infectious diseases.

Infectious Diseases of Plants

In 1853 Anton De Bary demonstrated that smuts and rusts of certain plants are caused by fungi. In 1861 he discovered the cause of late blight of the potato, and in 1865 showed that the common barberry is the intermediate host for rust fungi. In 1878 T. J. Burrill demonstrated that fire blight of apples and pears is caused by bacteria. In 1887 the control of smut by hot water treatment of seed was introduced by Jensen. In 1888 the mosaic disease of tobacco was shown by Beijerinck to be caused by a virus. The study of plant pathology in the United States was developed largely through the efforts of T. J. Burrill of Illinois, E. F. Smith of the U.S.D.A., L. R. Jones of Wisconsin, and their many colleagues.

Agricultural and Industrial Microbiology

The early work in agricultural and industrial microbiology was performed by Pasteur, who was the first to demonstrate that microorganisms cause fermentation, putrefaction, and decay. In 1877 it was shown by Schloesing and Muntz that nitrification in soils is due to the action of microorganisms; Warington later demonstrated that the process occurs in two stages; Winogradsky, in 1890, isolated and described the bacteria responsible for nitrification. In 1886 Hellriegel and Wilfarth described the bacteria which form nodules on the roots of leguminous plants and cooperate with them in the fixation of nitrogen; these bacteria were isolated and described by Beijerinck in 1888. Anaerobic, nonsymbiotic nitrogen-fixing bacteria were isolated by Winogradsky in 1893. The aerobic, nonsymbiotic nitrogen-fixing bacteria (*Azotobacter*) were isolated by Beijerinck in 1901. Soil microbiology has been developed in the United States largely through the work of Löhnis, Fred, Waksman, Thom, Smith, and their many colleagues.

Industrial microbiology was originated by Pasteur, and he was responsible for many of the early developments in the industrial uses of microorganisms. Weizmann's isolation of *Clostridium acetobutylicum*, and the use of this organism to produce butyl alcohol and acetone from corn or molasses, has been a succesful industrial venture. Modern methods for the production of compressed yeast have been developed by Frey and others. Fred and Peterson and their co-workers at Wisconsin have done much toward the development of industrial microbiology in the United States. The production of antibiotics, particularly penicillin, has become a large branch of industrial microbiology.

The microbiology of milk and dairy products was studied first in Europe by Metchnikoff, von Freudenreich, and Orla-Jensen. Work in the United States on this subject was started by H. W. Conn, H. L. Russell, and E. G. Hastings. Much of the fundamental work in this field was done by these investigators during the 1890's, and since that time L. A. Rogers, H. A. Harding, J. M. Sherman, R. S. Breed, B. W. Hammer, and many others have continued to develop this important branch of microbiology.

Work in food microbiology has progressed rapidly since the 1890's, when H. L. Russell showed that spoilage of canned foods was caused by bacteria. In the United States, H. L. Russell, S. C. Prescott, E. B. Fred, Charles Thom, E. O. Jordan, F. W. Tanner, and many others have been active in the development of food microbiology.

Methods and Classification

Advances in microbiology have been made most rapidly following the introduction of new methods. The best example of this may be found in the tremendous strides made during the 1880's and 1890's following the development of Koch's techniques for the isolation and study of pure cultures.

The Pasteur-Chamberland filter, made of unglazed porcelain, and the Berkefeld filter, made from Kieselguhr by Nordtmeyer, were used to obtain exotoxins of the bacilli which cause diphtheria, tetanus, and botulinus poisoning. Use of these filters also led to the discovery of viruses and bacteriophages.

Between 1888 and 1918 at least 300 different types of apparatus were developed for the cultivation of anaerobic bacteria. Use of these new techniques facilitated the isolation and study of anaerobes.

Methods for the isolation of single cells of bacteria were introduced by Barber in 1908. Improvements of the original technique have made it possible to isolate single cells of microorganisms of all kinds. This technique has enabled bacteriologists to obtain cultures of unquestionable purity. The development and use of the electron microscope is revealing many of the facts of microbial morphology and structure.

New methods for sterilization of media and equipment, for counting the cells of microorganisms, for making photomicrographs and microscopic examinations, for the study of thermal death time, for testing the efficacy of disinfectants, and for the isolation and cultivation of microorganisms are being developed constantly. The expression of hydrogen-ion concentration of aqueous solutions in terms of pH units by Sorensen, and the application of this concept by W. M. Clark to measurement of the reaction of culture media has enabled bacteriologists accurately to measure the true reaction of culture media. W. M. Clark's and Barnett Cohen's fundamental work on oxidation-reduction potential measurements has made possible the use of quantitative methods in the study of the oxidation-reduction characters of culture media and of cultures of microorganisms. The use of these, and of other methods which are constantly being developed, makes microbiological work more exact and more effective.

Attempts to classify bacteria have been made at frequent intervals by many different workers since the time of O. F. Muller, who published in 1773 the first classification of the microorganisms. Ehrenberg, Ferdinand Cohn, Zopf, Migula, Lehmann and Neumann, and Orla-Jensen have been the chief European contributors to the subject of classification. In the United States and Canada, C.-E. A. Winslow, R. E. Buchanan, D. H. Bergey, A. P. Hitchens, E. G. D. Murray, and R. S. Breed have contributed much to the knowledge of this subject. There are many workers who have specialized in the classification of certain groups of bacteria; for example, the streptococci have been studied extensively by W. D. Frost, Mrs. Lancefield, J. M. Sherman, J. H. Brown, and many others; E. B. Fred, I. L. Baldwin, E. McCoy and others have worked on the classification of root-nodule bacteria; still other groups of microorganisms have been studied by other workers too numerous to mention. The classification of bacteria is a never-ending task which must be continued as new methods and new criteria for characterization are introduced.

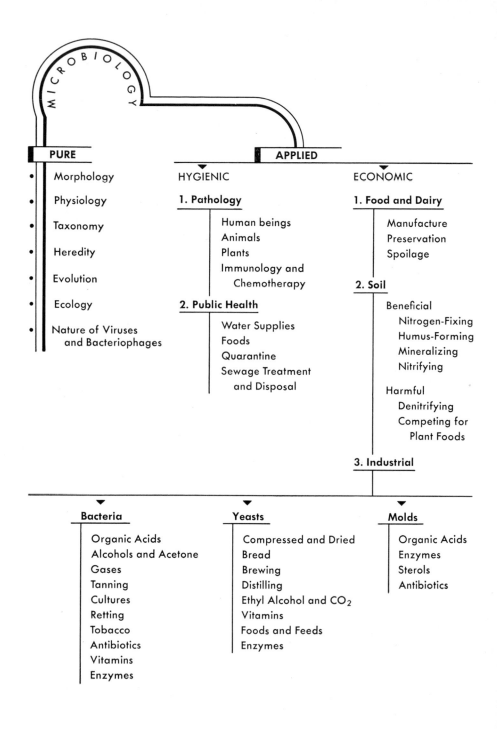

MICROBIOLOGY

PURE

- Morphology
- Physiology
- Taxonomy
- Heredity
- Evolution
- Ecology
- Nature of Viruses
  and Bacteriophages

APPLIED

HYGIENIC

1. Pathology

Human beings
Animals
Plants
Immunology and
Chemotherapy

2. Public Health

Water Supplies
Foods
Quarantine
Sewage Treatment
and Disposal

ECONOMIC

1. Food and Dairy

Manufacture
Preservation
Spoilage

2. Soil

Beneficial
Nitrogen-Fixing
Humus-Forming
Mineralizing
Nitrifying

Harmful
Denitrifying
Competing for
Plant Foods

3. Industrial

Bacteria

Organic Acids
Alcohols and Acetone
Gases
Tanning
Cultures
Retting
Tobacco
Antibiotics
Vitamins
Enzymes

Yeasts

Compressed and Dried
Bread
Brewing
Distilling
Ethyl Alcohol and CO_2
Vitamins
Foods and Feeds
Enzymes

Molds

Organic Acids
Enzymes
Sterols
Antibiotics

Present Status of Microbiology

From this brief, and admittedly incomplete review of the history of microbiology, the student may well gain the impression that microbiology is a science which has many ramifications. The diagram on page 456 shows the relationships of the many lines of microbiological work which exist today.

REFERENCES

Bulloch, W., *The history of bacteriology*. London, Oxford University Press, 1938.

Clay, R. S., and Court, T. H., *The history of the microscope*. London, Charles Griffin and Co., Ltd., 1932.

Cohen, B., "On Leeuwenhoek's method of seeing bacteria." *J. Bact.* (1937), *34:*343–346.

Compton, P., *The genius of Louis Pasteur*. N. Y., Macmillan, 1932.

De Kruif, P., *Microbe hunters*. N. Y., Harcourt Brace, 1926.

De Kruif, P., *Hunger fighters*. N. Y., Harcourt Brace, 1928.

Dobell, C., *Antony van Leeuwenhoek and his "little animals."* N. Y., Harcourt Brace, 1932.

Dubos, R. J., *Louis Pasteur, free lance of science*. Boston, Mass., Little, Brown, 1950.

Duclaux, E. (trans. by E. F. Smith and F. Hedges), *Pasteur, the history of a mind*. Philadelphia, Pa., Saunders, 1920.

Fred, E. B., "Antony van Leeuwenhoek on the three-hundredth anniversary of his birth." *J. Bact.* (1933), *25:*1–18.

Heald, F. D., *Introduction to plant pathology*. N. Y., McGraw-Hill, 1937.

Vallery-Radot, P., *Oeuvres de Pasteur* (6 vols.). Paris, France, Masson et Cie, 1922–1933.

Vallery-Radot, R. (translated by Mrs. R. L. Devonshire), *The life of Pasteur*. London, Constable, 1919.

Waksman, S. A., *Principles of soil microbiology* (2nd ed.). Baltimore, Md., Williams & Wilkins, 1932.

APPENDIXES

APPENDIX A

Kingdom. *Animal*
  Subkingdom I. *Protozoa*. Unicellular forms.
        "   II. *Metazoa*. Multicellular forms.

Kingdom. *Plant*.
  Phylum I. *Spermatophyta*. Seed plants.
    "   II. *Pteridophyta*. Ferns.
    " III. *Bryophyta*. Mosses and liverworts.
    " IV. *Thallophyta*. Thallus plants; simple, undifferentiated into leaves, stems, and roots;
      Subphylum I. *Algae*. Contain chlorophyll; may be unicellular or multicellular.
        Class I. *Chlorophyceae*. Green Algae.
        "   II. *Myxophyceae*. Blue-green Algae.
        " III. *Phaeophyceae*. Brown Algae.
        " IV. *Rhodophyceae*. Red Algae.
      Subphylum II. *Fungi*. Do not contain chlorophyll; may be unicellular or multicellular.
        Class I. *Basidiomycetes*. Smuts, rusts, mushrooms, and puffballs.
        "   II. *Phycomycetes*. Alga-like Fungi.
        " III. *Ascomycetes*. Produce sexual spores in an ascus (ascospores).
        " IV. *Fungi Imperfecti*. Do not produce sexual spores.
        "   V. *Myxomycetes*. Slime molds.
        " VI. *Schizomycetes*. Bacteria; unicellular; reproduce by fission.

NOTE: **Molds** are multicellular, filamentous Fungi classed as *Phycomycetes, Ascomycetes*, or *Fungi Imperfecti*.

    Yeasts. Nearly all "true" yeasts (those which form sexual spores) are *Ascomycetes;* "false" yeasts (those which do not form sexual spores) are *Fungi Imperfecti*.

    Slime molds are listed as *Myxomycetes* because they reproduce by spores borne on stalks. They are often classed as *Mycetozoa*, in the Animal Kingdom, because during the vegetative stage of their existence they are protozoan-like.

[1] This is not a recognized, technically accurate classification, but points out the chief relationships of protozoa, algae, yeasts, molds, and bacteria.

APPENDIX B

A CLASSIFICATION OF BACTERIA ACCORDING TO *Bergey's manual of determinative bacteriology* (6th ed.). Baltimore, Md., Williams & Wilkins Company, 1948.

This abbreviated outline follows the classification of bacteria in *Bergey's manual of determinative bacteriology*, 6th edition, by R. S. Breed, E. G. D. Murray, and A. P. Hitchens. The outline is not complete in all details but serves to present many of the principal characteristics of microorganisms which may be encountered by students beginning a study of microbiology.

Class. *Schizomycetes*
> Microscopic to submicroscopic unicellular Fungi which exist in one of four common shapes: spheroidal, cylindrical, spirillar, or filamentous. Reproduce asexually by fission; in addition, some of the filamentous forms may produce conidia.

Order I. *Eubacteriales*
> Simple, undifferentiated, rigid cells which usually do not branch or form filamentous structures. Cells found singly, in chains or masses. All reproduce asexually by fission. Some form endospores. Not acid-fast.

Suborder I. *Eubacteriineae*
> The true bacteria. Rigid, free cells which usually do not branch. Not attached by holdfasts or stalks. Do not form sheaths. Endospore formation in one family (*Bacillaceae*), rarely in others. Spheroidal, cylindrical, or spirillar shapes.

Family I. *Nitrobacteriaceae*
> Autotrophic (utilize CO_2 as only source of carbon; obtain energy by oxidation of elements or simple compounds).

Tribe I. *Nitrobactereae*
> Organisms deriving energy from oxidation of ammonia to nitrite or nitrite to nitrate.

Genus   I. *Nitrosomonas*
> Ellipsoidal cells which secure energy by oxidizing ammonia to nitrites. Two species. Found in soil. Type species: *Nitrosomonas europaea.*

Genus   II. *Nitrosococcus*
> Spheroidal cells which secure energy by oxidizing ammonia to nitrite. One species. Found in soil. Type species: *Nitrosococcus nitrosus.*

Genus III. *Nitrosospira*
> Spiral cells. Oxidize ammonia to nitrite very slowly. Two species. Found in soil. Type species: *Nitrosospira briensis.*

Genus IV. *Nitrosocystis*
> Ellipsoidal cells which group together to form cysts. Oxidize ammonia to nitrite for energy. Two species. Found in soil. Type species: *Nitrosocystis javanensis.*

Genus   V. *Nitrosogloea*
> Ellipsoidal or rod-shaped cells which oxidize ammonia to nitrite. Cells embedded in slime. Three species. Found in activated sludge. Type species: *Nitrosogloea merismoides.*

Genus VI. *Nitrobacter*
> Rod-shaped cells which secure energy by oxidizing nitrites to nitrates. Two species. Found in soil. Type species: *Nitrobacter winogradskyi.*

Genus VII. *Nitrocystis*
> Ellipsoidal or rod-shaped cells which oxidize nitrites to nitrates. Cells embedded in slime. Two species. Found in activated sludge. Type species: *Nitrocystis sarcinoides.*

Tribe II. *Hydrogenomonadeae*
> Short rods which derive energy from oxidation of hydrogen.

Genus I. *Hydrogenomonas*
> Short rods which derive energy from oxidation of hydrogen. Three species. Found in soil. Type species: *Hydrogenomonas pantotropha.*

Tribe III. *Thiobacilleae*
> Capable of deriving their energy from oxidation of sulfur or sulfur compounds.

Genus I. *Thiobacillus*
> Small Gram-negative, rod-shaped cells. Derive energy from oxidation of elemental sulfur, thiosulfate, or in some cases sulfide, sulfite, and polythionate. Sulfate is the principal product of oxidation, but free sulfur may be formed. Aerobic, but one species facultative. Five species. Found in soil, sewage, and water. Type species: *Thiobacillus thioparus.*

Family II. *Pseudomonadaceae*
> Straight or spirally curved Gram-negative, cylindrical, non-spore-forming cells. One genus has branched cells. Usually motile with polar flagella. Aerobic to anaerobic. Saprophytes, plant pathogens, and animal pathogens. Heterotrophic.

Tribe I. *Pseudomonadeae*

 Straight (or branching) rods. Usually soil or water forms, but some cause diseases of plants or animals.

 Genus I. *Pseudomonas*

  Rods, most of which produce a yellowish-green, green, or blue water-soluble pigment. One hundred and forty-eight species. Found in water and soil; some parasitic in animals and may become pathogenic. Type species: *Pseudomonas aeruginosa* (usually saprophytic or parasitic but frequently found as secondary invaders in old wounds where they give a bluish coloration to the pus).

 Genus II. *Xanthomonas*

  Usually monotrichous cells with yellow, water-insoluble pigment. Plant pathogens causing necrosis. Forty-seven species. Type species: *Xanthomonas hyacinthi.*

 Genus III. *Methanomonas*

  Short, monotrichous, rods which secure energy by oxidizing methane to carbon dioxide and water. One species. Found in soil. Type species: *Methanomonas methanica.*

 Genus IV. *Acetobacter*

  Secure energy by the oxidation of alcohol to acetic acid (with exception of one species), but are also capable of oxidizing other carbon compounds such as glucose and acetic acid. Cylindrical cells, which, as they age, become elongated, club-shaped, or branched. Seven species. Found in fermenting plant materials or fluids containing alcohol or acetic acid. Type species: *Acetobacter aceti.*

 Genus V. *Protaminobacter*

  Motile or nonmotile rods. Can attack lower alkylamines. Two species. Found in soil or water. Type species: *Protaminobacter alboflavum.*

 Genus VI. *Mycoplana*

  Cells branching, particularly in young cultures. Can use phenol and aromatic compounds as source of energy. Two species. Found in soil. Type species: *Mycoplana dimorpha.*

Tribe II. *Spirilleae*

 More or less spirally curved cells.

 Genus I. *Vibrio*

  Comma or S-shaped cells which may be short and cylindrical in early phases of growth. Gram-negative. Motile, with one exception and generally by means of a single flagellum. Twenty-two species. Many pathogenic for man and animals, some parasitic, and others found in water and soil. Type species: *Vibrio comma* (causes Asiatic cholera in man).

Genus II. *Desulfovibrio*

Slightly curved rods which reduce sulfates to hydrogen sulfide. Motile. Anaerobic. Three species. Found in sea water, marine mud, fresh water and soil. Type species: *Desulfovibrio desulfuricans.*

Genus III. *Cellvibrio*

Cellulose-decomposing bacteria which are long, comma-shaped cells, only slightly curved and with rounded ends. Gram-negative. Motile. Four species. Found in soil. Type species: *Cellvibrio ochraceus.*

Genus IV. *Cellfalcicula*

Cellulose-decomposing bacteria which are short, comma-shaped forms with pointed ends. Motile. Three species. Found in soil. Type species: *Cellfalcicula viridis.*

Genus V. *Thiospira*

Slightly bent rods, pointed at the ends with granules of sulfur within cells. Motile. Two species. Found in curative mud and sea and fresh waters. Type species: *Thiospira winogradskyi.*

Genus VI. *Spirillum*

Coiled cells, all motile and Gram-negative. Mostly saprophytes; one animal pathogen. Nine species. Found in fresh or salt water containing organic matter. Type species: *Spirillum undula.*

Family III. *Azotobacteriaceae*

Cylindrical or spheroidal, nonspore-forming, Gram-negative, aerobes; capable of fixing free nitrogen when supplied with carbohydrate or other suitable energy source. Heterotrophic.

Genus I. *Azotobacter*

Description same as that of family. Three species. Found in soil and in water. Type species: *Azotobacter chroococcum.*

Family IV. *Rhizobiaceae*

Usually cylindrical, nonspore-forming, Gram-negative, aerobes. Utilize glucose and other carbohydrates without producing much acid. Saprophytes, symbionts, and plant pathogens. Heterotrophic.

Genus I. *Rhizobium*

Cells capable of fixing free nitrogen when growing symbiotically in nodules on roots of *Leguminosae*. Widely distributed in soils where leguminous plants are grown. Six species. Type species: *Rhizobium leguminosarum.*

Genus II. *Agrobacterium*

Saprophytes, or plant pathogens causing galls or hypertrophies. Cannot fix free nitrogen. Widely distributed in soil, particularly around roots of plants, or in infected plant tissues. Four species. Type species: *Agrobacterium tumefaciens.*

Genus III. *Chromobacterium*

Produce a violet pigment soluble in alcohol but insoluble in water or chloroform. Produce acid from glucose and maltose but not from lactose. Liquefy gelatin. Saprophytic. Found in soil and water. Three species. Type species: *Chromobacterium violaceum.*

Family V. *Micrococcaceae*

Spheroidal cells which divide in two or three planes. Occur singly, in pairs, tetrads, packets, or irregular masses. Usually nonspore-forming. Heterotrophic. Usually Gram-positive. Aerobic to facultative or anaerobic. Carbohydrates frequently fermented to acid. Often liquefy gelatin. Facultative parasites and saprophytes. Often found on skin, in skin glands or skin gland secretions of vertebrates.

Genus I. *Micrococcus*

Spheroidal cells in irregular masses, never in packets or long chains. Usually Gram-positive. Facultative parasites and saprophytes. Twenty-two species. Type species: *Micrococcus luteus.*

Genus II. *Gaffkya*

Occur in infected animal tissues and in special culture media as tetrads, but in pairs or irregular masses in ordinary media. Aerobic to anaerobic, Gram-positive, parasitic. Two species. Type species: *Gaffkya tetragena.*

Genus III. *Sarcina*

Under favorable conditions, division occurs in three planes, producing regular packets of eight or more cells. Usually Gram-positive. Usually produce yellow to orange pigment. Saprophytes and facultative parasites. One species produces endospores. Nine species. Type species: *Sarcina ventriculi.*

Family VI. *Neisseriaceae*

Spheroidal. Gram-negative cells in pairs or in masses. Aerobes and anaerobes. Parasitic and difficult to grow in culture media. Heterotrophic.

Genus I. *Neisseria*

Paired, Gram-negative cocci with adjacent sides flattened. Grow poorly on culture media. Parasites of animals; some pathogenic. Produce catalase. Aerobes and anaerobes. Eleven species. Type species: *Neisseria gonorrhoeae.*

Genus II. *Veillonella*

Small, Gram-negative cocci occurring in masses, rarely in pairs or chains. All anaerobic. Grow well on culture media. Biochemically active. Parasites in mouth and intestinal tract of man and animals, but not pathogenic. Two species. Type species: *Veillonella parvula.*

Family VII. *Lactobacteriaceae*

Cylindrical cells or cocci which divide in one plane only to produce pairs or chains, but not tetrads or packets. Usually nonmotile. Gram-positive. Surface growth on media poor or absent; some species anaerobic. Carbohydrates essential to good growth, and are fermented to lactic acid or lactic acid with volatile acids, alcohol, and CO_2 as by-products. Gelatin rarely liquefied. Found regularly in the mouth and intestinal tract of man and animals, and in dairy products or fermenting fruit products. Heterotrophic. A few are pathogenic for man and animals.

Tribe I. *Streptococceae*

Cocci occurring singly, in pairs, and in chains. Some pathogenic species grow poorly without blood serum or other enrichment substances. Catalase negative.

Genus   I. *Diplococcus*

Parasites, grow poorly in artificial media. Cells usually in pairs, often elongated. May produce large capsules. Anaerobic species may occur in tetrads or clumps. Aerobic species bile-soluble; anaerobic species not bile-soluble. All parasitic; some highly pathogenic for man and animals. Six species. Type species: *Diplococcus pneumoniae*.

Genus II. *Streptococcus*

Spheroidal cells in pairs, or in chains; never in packets or irregular masses. Gram-positive. Some species form capsules. Facultative to anaerobic. Grow poorly on artificial media. Majority ferment glucose to lactic acid with production of little if any other products. Not soluble in bile. Common wherever organic matter containing sugar is found. Present in mouth and intestines of man and animals, dairy products, and fermenting plant products. Some species highly pathogenic for man and animals. Twenty-four species. Type species: *Streptococcus pyogenes*.

Genus III. *Leuconostoc*

Gram-positive cells which are spheroidal, but which may become cylindrical. Exist in pairs or short chains. Some species may form capsules and slime. Produce lactic and acetic acids, alcohol, and CO_2 from glucose. Fructose is changed to mannitol. Saprophytes found in milk and plant materials. Three species. Type species: *Leuconostoc mesenteroides*.

Tribe II. *Lactobacilleae*

Nonmotile, Gram-positive rods. Grow poorly on ordinary culture media. Facultative to anaerobic or microaerophilic. May produce lactic acid or lactic acid plus acetic, propionic and butyric acids, alcohol, and CO_2. Saprophytes, but may be found in intestinal tract of animals.

Genus I. *Lactobacillus*
Microaerophilic. Catalase negative. Rods, usually long and slender. Found in intestinal tract or in dairy products or fermenting plant materials. Fifteen species. Type species: *Lactobacillus caucasicus.*

Genus II. *Microbacterium*
Aerobic, catalase positive. Grow well on surface of culture media. Produce lactic acid. Found in dairy products and fecal material. Two species. Type species: *Microbacterium lacticum.*

Genus III. *Propionibacterium*
Aerobic to anaerobic. Ferment lactates, carbohydrates, and polyalcohols with formation of propionic and acetic acids and CO_2. Catalase positive. Found in dairy products, particularly in hard cheeses. Eleven species. Type species: *Propionibacterium freudenreichii.*

Genus IV. *Butyribacterium*
Anaerobic to microaerophilic. Ferment lactates and carbohydrates to acetic and butyric acids and CO_2. Usually catalase negative. Intestinal parasites. One species. Type species: *Butyribacterium rettgeri.*

Family VIII. *Corynebacteriaceae*
Rods, frequently banded or beaded, with metachromatic granules. Cells show marked diversity of form, but branching unusual. Generally Gram-positive; usually nonmotile. Aerobic to microaerophilic. Animal and plant parasites and pathogens. Saprophytic species found in dairy products, soil and water. Heterotrophic.

Genus I. *Corynebacterium*
Aerobic to microaerophilic, nonmotile rods of variable form. Animal and plant parasites and pathogens. Some saprophytes in dairy products, soil, and water. Twenty-five species. Type species: *Corynebacterium diphtheriae.*

Genus II. *Listeria*
Small, aerobic, motile rods. Cause a monocytosis in animals. Grow well on ordinary media. One species. Type species: *Listeria monocytogenes.*

Genus III. *Erysipelothrix*
Rods with tendency to form long filaments. Nonmotile, Gram-positive, catalase negative, microaerophilic, and grow well on ordinary media. Parasitic and frequently pathogenic on animals. Three species. Type species: *Erysipelothrix rhusiopathiae.*

Family IX. *Achromobacteriaceae*
Gram-negative, nonspore-forming rods characterized chiefly by lack of ability to ferment carbohydrates. Some are plant pathogens, but majority are found in soil or water; a few found in the intestinal tract of animals. Heterotrophic.

Genus   I. *Alcaligenes*
Nonchromogenic, no acid from carbohydrates, produces alkalinity or ropiness in litmus milk. Six species. Found in intestinal tract, water, and dairy products. Type species: *Alcaligenes faecalis.*

Genus II. *Achromobacter*
Nonchromogenic, but usually produces acid from glucose and may cause slight acidity in litmus milk. Twelve species. Found in water and soil. Type species: *Achromobacter liquefaciens.*

Genus III. *Flavobacterium*
Produce yellow to orange pigment; otherwise similar to *Achromobacter.* Twenty-seven species. Type species: *Flavobacterium aquatile.*

Family X. *Enterobacteriaceae*
Gram-negative, nonspore-forming rods that produce acid or acid and visible gas from glucose. Majority reduce nitrates to nitrites. Many are animal parasites; some highly pathogenic. Some are plant pathogens, causing blights and soft rots. Frequently occur as saprophytes and are widely distributed in nature. Heterotrophic.

Tribe 1. *Eschericheae*
Ferment lactose with formation of acid and visible gas in 24 hours at 37° C., or within 48 hours at 25° to 30° C. Some intermediate forms produce acid and gas from lactose slowly.

Genus   I. *Escherichia*
Produce indole from tryptophane. Methyl red positive. Do not produce acetyl-methyl-carbinol from glucose. May or may not use citrate as sole source of carbon. Found in feces and is occasionally pathogenic; widely distributed in nature as a saprophyte. Three species. Type species: *Escherichia coli.*

Genus II. *Aerobacter*
May or may not produce indole from tryptophane. Methyl red negative. Produce acetyl-methyl-carbinol from glucose. Use citrate as sole source of carbon. Widely distributed in nature as a saprophyte. Two species. Type species: *Aerobacter aerogenes.*

Genus III. *Klebsiella*
Capsulated forms from respiratory, intestinal, and genitourinary regions. Variable in production of indole, methyl red test, acetyl-methyl-carbinol production, and growth on citrate. May be pathogenic for man. One species. Type species: *Klebsiella pneumoniae.*

Tribe II. *Erwineae*
Plant parasites, causing blights or soft rots. Produce acid or acid and gas from lactose.

Genus I. *Erwinia*

Same characteristics as those of tribe. Twenty-two species. Type species: *Erwinia amylovora.*

Tribe III. *Serrateae*

Small, aerobic, saprophytic rods, usually producing a bright red or pink pigment on suitable culture media.

Genus I. *Serratia*

Liquefy gelatin rapidly. Cause proteolysis in milk. May hydrolyze fats. Liquefy blood serum. Five species. Widely distributed in nature as saprophytes. Type species: *Serratia marcescens.*

Tribe IV. *Proteae*

Ferment glucose with formation of acid or acid and gas. Do not ferment lactose. Decompose urea rapidly.

Genus I. *Proteus*

Actively motile at 25° to 30° C. Usually produce moist, spreading colonies on agar. Urea decomposed rapidly and trimethylamine oxide reduced by all species. Four species. Widely distributed in nature in decomposing organic matter and frequently found in intestinal tract. May be pathogenic for some animals. Type species: *Proteus vulgaris.*

Tribe V. *Salmonelleae*

Lactose rarely fermented within 30 days at either 37° C. or 30° C. Urea not decomposed rapidly. Attack many carbohydrates other than lactose. Parasites in warm-blooded animals and some reptiles. Many are pathogenic.

Genus I. *Salmonella*

Ferments glucose with formation of acid and, with few exceptions, gas. All known species pathogenic for warm-blooded animals. Cause food infections and enteric fevers. Complex antigenic structure. One hundred and fifty-one species. Type species: *Salmonella choleraesuis.*

Genus II. *Shigella*

Ferment carbohydrates with the formation of acid but no gas. Usually nonmotile. Difficult to separate from *Salmonella* except by determination of pathogenicity and serological tests. Eleven species. All parasitic on warm-blooded animals. Majority pathogenic, causing dysenteries. Type species: *Shigella dysenteriae.*

Family XI. *Parvobacteriaceae*

Small, Gram-negative, nonspore-forming rods which grow poorly on ordinary culture media. All parasitic on warm-blooded animals; many pathogenic. Some may penetrate intact skin or mucous membranes to cause infection. Heterotrophic.

Tribe I. *Pasteurelleae*

Ellipsoidal to elongated small rods which show bipolar staining. Majority ferment carbohydrates with formation of acid.

Genus   I. *Pasteurella*

> Milk not coagulated. Cause hemorrhagic septicemia, pseudo-tuberculosis, tularemia, or plague. Five species. Type species: *Pasteurella multocida.*

Genus II. *Malleomyces*

> Milk coagulated slowly and sometimes digested. Cause glanders or glanders-like infections. Two species. Type species: *Malleomyces mallei.*

Genus III. *Actinobacillus*

> Milk unchanged to slightly acid. Associated with actino-mycosis in man and animals, but may cause calf pneumonia. Three species. Type species: *Actinobacillus lignieresi.*

Tribe II. *Brucelleae*

> Ellipsoidal or coccoid to short rods which do not show bi-polar staining. Do not ferment carbohydrates.

Genus   I. *Brucella*

> Parasitic and pathogenic. Invade animal tissues producing infections of genital organs, mammary gland, respiratory and intestinal tracts. Pathogenic for domestic animals and man. Four species. Type species: *Brucella melitensis.*

Tribe III. *Bacteroideae*

> Gram-negative, nonspore-forming rods which are obligate anaerobes.

Genus   I. *Bacteroides*

> Cells with rounded ends. All parasitic or pathogenic for warm-blooded animals. Twenty-three species. Type species: *Bacteroides fragilis.*

Genus II. *Fusobacterium*

> Like *Bacteroides*, but cells have pointed ends. Four species. Type species: *Fusobacterium plauti-vincenti.*

Tribe IV. *Hemophileae*

> Minute parasitic organisms which, on first isolation, grow only in presence of hemoglobin, ascitic fluid, or other body fluids, or in presence of sterile, unheated potato extract. Commonly found in respiratory tract or in con-junctiva.

Genus   I. *Hemophilus*

> Minute, Gram-negative rods which are sometimes thread-forming and pleomorphic. Nonmotile, strict parasites. Seven species. Type species: *Hemophilus influenzae.*

Genus II. *Moraxella*

> Short, Gram-negative, aerobic rods which usually occur singly or in pairs. Parasitic and pathogenic. Three species. Type species: *Moraxella lacunata.*

Genus III. *Noguchia*

> Small, slender, Gram-negative rods associated with

diseases of the conjunctiva of man and animals. Three species. Type species: *Noguchia granulosis.*

Genus IV. *Dialister*

Minute, nonmotile, anaerobic, rods which are strict parasites. Two species. Type species: *Dialister pneumosintes.*

Family XII. *Bacteriaceae*

A heterogeneous collection of rod-shaped, nonspore-forming species whose relationship to each other and to other groups are not clear. Heterotrophic.

Genus I. *Bacterium*

Same characteristics as family. No type species.

Family XIII. *Bacillaceae*

Rod-shaped cells capable of producing endospores. Usually Gram-positive. Aerobic, facultative, and anaerobic. Mostly saprophytes, commonly found in soil. Some are animal or insect parasites. A few are pathogenic for animals or insects. Heterotrophic.

Genus I. *Bacillus*

Aerobic, catalase positive. Thirty-three species. Type species: *Bacillus subtilis.*

Genus II. *Clostridium*

Anaerobic or microaerophilic. Catalase negative. Sixty-one species. Type species: *Clostridium butyricum.*

Suborder II. *Caulobacteriineae*

Bacteria which characteristically grow attached to solid surfaces. Nonfilamentous, but may have stalks. Gum, ferric hydroxide, or other material may be secreted from one side of the cell to form the stalk. Cells not having stalks are attached directly to the solid surface in a zoogloeal mass. Cells occur singly, in pairs, or short chains; never in filaments; not sheathed. Nonspore-forming, and typically aquatic in habitat.

Family I. *Nevskiaceae*

Long axis of cell transverse to long axis of stalk; stalks dichotomously branched, lobose, and composed of gum. Form zoogloegal masses. One genus: *Nevskia.*

Family II. *Gallionellaceae*

Long axis of cell transverse to long axis of stalk; stalks dichotomously branched, and composed of bands of ferric hydroxide. Grow in iron-bearing waters. One genus: *Gallionella.*

Family III. *Caulobacteriaceae*

Long axis of cell coincides with long axis of stalk; stalks unbranched. One genus: *Caulobacter.*

Family IV. *Siderocapsaceae*

Cells spheroidal or ovoid, capsulated, and sessile to solid surface. Deposit ferric hydroxide on capsules. Two genera: *Siderocapsa* and *Sideromonas.*

Suborder III. *Rhodobacteriineae*

Spheroidal, cylindrical, or spirillar, nonspore-forming, Gram-negative bacteria which are red, purple, brown, or green in color; contain bacterial chlorophyll or other chlorophyll-like green pigments and carotenoid pigments. Can carry on photosynthesis under suitable conditions. May contain sulfur granules.

Family I. *Thiorhodaceae*

Purple bacteria which contain sulfur granules in the presence of hydrogen sulfide. Thirteen genera.

Family II. *Athiorhodaceae*

Purple and brown bacteria which do not contain granules of sulfur. Two genera.

Family III. *Chlorobacteriaceae*

Green sulfur bacteria which have a pigment system different from the chlorophyll of green plants or the bacterial chlorophyll of the purple bacteria. Six genera.

Order II. *Actinomycetales*

Form elongated cells which may branch to produce a mycelium. Hyphae of mycelium-forming families do not exceed 1.5 microns, and usually are less than 1 micron in diameter. In the *Mycobacteriaceae* no mycelium is formed, the cells are acid-fast, and reproduce only by fission. The *Actinomycetaceae* and *Streptomycetaceae* usually produce a characteristic branching mycelium and produce arthrospores or conidia; these families grow well on ordinary culture media and form colonies which may be covered with aerial mycelium; some species partially acid-fast. Mostly saprophytes, but some are parasitic or pathogenic for plants or animals.

Family I. *Mycobacteriaceae*

No mycelium formed. Cells are acid-fast and reproduce by fission only. Some saprophytes, others parasitic or pathogenic for animals.

Genus I. *Mycobacterium.*

Thirteen species. Type species: *Mycobacterium tuberculosis.*

Family II. *Actinomycetaceae*

True mycelium produced which segments into bacillary or coccoid units. Some species partially acid-fast.

Genus I. *Nocardia*

Obligate aerobes. Usually produce colonies like true bacteria, but somewhat tougher. Mycelium rudimentary. Thirty-three species. Widely distributed in soil as saprophytes, but many are animal parasites and pathogens. Type species: *Nocardia farcinica.*

Genus II. *Actinomyces*

Anaerobic or microaerophilic, parasitic, nonacid-fast. Produce true mycelium which fragments to form ele-

ments of varying size and shape. Pathogenic for man
and animals. Two species. Type species: *Actinomyces
bovis.*

Family III. *Streptomycetaceae*
True mycelium produced on which conidia are formed.
Mainly saprophytes found in soil, but a few are parasitic.

Genus I. *Streptomyces*
Conidia produced on aerial hyphae in chains. Seventy-
three species. Type species: *Streptomyces albus.*

Genus II. *Micromonospora*
Single conidia produced terminally on short conidiophores. Five species. Type species: *Micromonospora
chalcea.*

Order III. *Chlamydobacteriales*
Filamentous, colorless, alga-like bacteria which may or may not
have a sheath. Do not form endospores, but some produce conidia
or motile swarm cells. Cells may branch or show false branching
due to branching of sheaths. Saprophytes which are found in
water.

Family I. *Chlamydobacteriaceae*
Alga-like filaments which do not contain sulfur granules.
Usually free-floating elements; false branching may occur
in sheaths. Three genera.

Family II. *Crenothrichaceae*
Attached filaments which are thin and colorless at tip; thick
and encrusted with iron at the base. One genus.

Family III. *Beggiatoaceae*
Alga-like, unbranching filaments which may contain sulfur
granules when growing in presence of sulfides. Filaments
may be motile by a creeping or sliding movement along a
solid surface. Four genera.

Order IV. *Myxobacteriales*
The slime bacteria. Long, slender, flexible, nonflagellate vegetative cells which may produce a pseudoplasmodium. Cells may be
arranged in groups, lying parallel. Groups move as a unit, de-
positing a layer of slime as they move. Have relatively complex
cycle involving formation of fruiting bodies and cysts. Most species
saprophytic; found in manure, soil, rotten wood, straw, and leaves.
Often found growing in close association with true bacteria and
may be parasitic on them. Five families, including thirty-two
genera.

Order V. *Spirochaetales*
Slender, flexible cells in form of spiral with at least one complete
turn; six to 500 microns in length. Some forms may have an axial
filament, a lateral crista or ridge, or transverse striations. Some
forms may have such low refractive index that they can be seen
only with dark field illumination. Multiply by transverse fission.
All motile by serpentine action or by spinning on the long axis.

Family I. *Spirochaetaceae*
Coarse spiral cells 30 to 500 microns long; have definite protoplasmic structures; found in water or in intestinal tract of molluscs. Three genera.

Family II. *Treponemataceae*
Spirals 4 to 16 microns in length; no protoplasmic structures. Parasitic on vertebrates; many pathogenic.

Genus I. *Borrelia*
Stains easily with aniline dyes. Seventeen species. Type species: *Borrelia anserina*.

Genus II. *Treponema*
Strict anaerobes. Stain with difficulty. Parasitic and pathogenic for man and animals. Eight species. Type species: *Treponema pallidum*.

Genus III. *Leptospira*
Aerobes. Stain with difficulty. Parasitic and pathogenic for man and animals. Four species. Type species: *Leptospira ictero-haemorrhagiae*.

Supplement I

Order *Rickettsiales*
Small, cylindrical, spheroidal, or irregularly-shaped microorganisms which usually are not filterable. Stain lightly with aniline dyes. Gram-negative. Parasitic and pathogenic in man and animals. Intimately associated with tissue cells in animals and in arthropods which serve as vectors. Grow only in living tissue.

Family I. *Rickettsiaceae*
Intracellular parasites, or parasites intimately associated with tissue cells. Do not occur in erythrocytes. Frequently cause diseases of vertebrates; transmitted by arthropod vectors. Three genera; eight species.

Family II. *Bartonellaceae*
Facultative intracellular or extracellular parasites found characteristically in or on the erythrocytes of vertebrates. May be transmitted by arthropod vectors. Four genera; sixteen species.

Family III. *Chlamydozoaceae*
Small, pleomorphic, often coccoid microorganisms which are obligate intracytoplasmic parasites. Not transmitted by arthropod vectors. Three genera; twelve species.

Supplement II

Order *Virales*
The filterable viruses. Usually ultramicroscopic in size; capable of passing through filters that retain bacteria. Multiply or increase in concentration only in presence of susceptible living cells. Parasitic and pathogenic for plants, animals, or microorganisms.

Suborder   I. *Phagineae*
The bacteriophages; parasitic in bacteria. One family; one genus; forty-six species.

Suborder II. *Phytophagineae*
Viruses infecting higher plants. Usually transmitted by insects. Six families.

Suborder III. *Zoophagineae*
Viruses infecting insects and other animals. Six families.

Supplement III

The Pleuropneumonia Group (*Borrelomycetaceae*)

Soft, fragile, pleomorphic cells which appear to have a complicated life-cycle. Smallest forms 0.15 to 0.28 microns in size and may pass through filters that retain bacteria. Can be cultivated on agar, but cultures autolyze after a short period of growth. Cause diseases of man and of animals, the most common of which is bovine pleuropneumonia. One genus recognized at present.

APPENDIX C

A Classification of Yeasts and Yeast-Like Fungi According to Skinner, Emmons, and Tsuchiya, *Henrici's molds, yeasts, and actinomycetes* (2nd ed.). N. Y., Wiley, 1947.

Yeasts and Yeast-Like Fungi Which Form Sexual Spores

Kingdom. *Plant.*
  Phylum. *Thallophyta.*
    Subphylum. *Fungi.*
      Class. *Ascomycetes.* Produce sexual spores in an ascus (ascospores).
        Order. *Endomycetales.* Zygote or single cell transformed into an ascus directly or after proliferation of diploid yeast cells.
          Family. *Endomycetaceae.* Asci with eight ascospores or fewer; gametangia when present, always uninucleate.

Subfamilies and Genera of *Endomycetaceae*
Subfamily A. *Eremascoideae.* Growth form, only mycelium. Ascospores formed by isogamous conjugation, hat-shaped, 4 to 8 per ascus. Entirely oxidative. But one genus, *Eremascus,* description as for the subfamily.
Subfamily B. *Endomycoideae.* Growth form, either mycelium and arthrospores or arthrospores alone. Spores formed by isogamous or heterogamous conjugation, or parthenogenetic. Oxidative or fermentive.
Genus I. *Endomyces.* Both mycelium and arthrospores. Spores by heterogamous conjugation or parthenogenetic; round to hat-shaped, 4 per ascus. Oxidative or fermentive.
Genus II. *Schizosaccharomyces.* No mycelium, only arthrospores. Spores by isogamous conjugation, 4 to 8 per ascus. Dominantly fermentive.
Subfamily C. *Saccharomycoideae.* Either mycelium with blastospores, or only budding yeast cells, the latter often with pseudomycelium. Multiplication by fission, by multipolar budding, or by bipolar budding. Spores by heterogamous or isogamous conjugation or parthenogenesis. All transitions from purely oxidative to purely fermentive forms.
Tribe a. *Endomycopseae.* Mycelium with blastospores, occasionally arthro-

spores. Multiplication by fission or multipolar budding. Spores parthenogenetic or by isogamous conjugation; round, oval, sickle-shaped, or hat-shaped, 1 to 4 per ascus. Dominantly oxidative. But one genus, *Endomycopsis*, description as for the tribe.

Tribe b. *Saccharomyceteae*. Mycelium rare or lacking, budding yeast cells the usual growth forms. Multipolar budding. Spores parthenogenetic or by isogamous or heterogamous conjugation.

Genus   I. *Saccharomyces*. Round, oval, or cylindrical cells. Spores round, kidney-shaped, or hat-shaped, smooth, 1 to 4 per ascus. More or less strongly fermentive in all cases, in addition to oxidative.

Subgenus *Saccharomyces sensu stricto*. Spores parthenogenetic.

Subgenus *Zygosaccharomyces*. Spores by isogamous or heterogamous conjugation.

Genus II. *Torulaspora*. Round cells. Spores formed after unsuccessful attempts to conjugate. Spores round, smooth, 1 to 3 per ascus. Dominantly fermentive.

Genus III. *Pichia*. Cells oval to long cylindrical. Pseudomycelium formed. Spores parthenogenetic, or by isogamous or heterogamous conjugation; angular or hemispherical; 1 to 4 per ascus. Dominantly oxidative, weakly fermentive. Nitrates not reduced.

Subgenus *Pichia sensu stricto*. Spores parthenogenetic.

Subgenus *Zygopichia*. Spores by isogamous or heterogamous conjugation.

Genus IV. *Hansenula*. Cells oval or long cylindrical, seldom round. Pseudomycelium formed. Spores parthenogenetic or by isogamous conjugation, hemispherical or spherical with a band, 2 to 4 per ascus. Oxidative. Nitrates reduced.

Subgenus *Hansenula sensu stricto*. Spores parthenogenetic.

Subgenus *Zygohansenula*. Spores by isogamous conjugation.

Genus   V. *Debaryomyces*. Round, occasionally oval cells, at times pseudomycelium. Spores by isogamous, more frequently heterogamous, conjugation; round, more or less warty; 1 to 2 per ascus. Most species exclusively oxidative, some also fermentive.

Genus VI. *Schwanniomyces*. Cells oval. Spores formed after unsuccessful attempts at conjugation; round, warty, banded; 1, rarely 2, per ascus. Dominantly fermentive.

Tribe c. *Nadsonieae*. Growth forms, yeast cells, occasionally pseudomycelium, no true mycelium. Multiplication by bipolar budding. Buds with a broad base. Spores parthenogenetic or by heterogamous conjugation.

Genus   I. *Saccharomycodes*. Cells lemon-shaped or sausage-shaped. Vegetative reproduction by combination of budding and fission. Spores parthenogenetic, round, smooth, 4 per ascus. Spores conjugate upon germinating. Both oxidative and fermentive.

Genus II. *Hanseniaspora*. Cells lemon-shaped. Spores parthenogenetic, round, or hat-shaped, 2 to 4 per ascus. Both oxidative and fermentive.

Genus III. *Nadsonia*. Cells egg- to lemon-shaped. Vegetative reproduction by a combination of budding and fission. Spores heterogamous. After fusion of nuclei of mother cell and bud, a new bud is formed which becomes the ascus. Spores round, warty, 1 per ascus. Both oxidative and fermentive.

Genus IV. *Zygosaccharomycodes.* Cells oval. Vegetative reproduction by combination of budding and fission. Spores by isogamous conjugation or, rarely, parthenogenetic. Spores round, 1 to 4 per ascus.

Subfamily D. *Nematosporoideae.* Growth forms, both mycelium and yeast cells. Multiplication by multipolar budding. Spores formed by isogamous conjugation or parthenogenetically. Spores needle-shaped or fusiform, with or without flagella. Both oxidative and fermentive.

Genus I. *Monosporella.* Cells oval. Spores parthenogenetic, needle-like, 1 per ascus.

Genus II. *Nematospora.* Cells oval, elongated, irregular, or mycelium-like. Spores parthenogenetic, fusiform, flagellated, 2 to 8 per ascus. Both oxidative and fermentive.

Genus III. *Coccidiascus.* Round to oval cells. Spores by isogamous conjugation, fusiform, 8 per ascus. Entirely oxidative.

Yeasts and Yeast-Like Fungi Which Do Not Form Sexual Spores

Kingdom. *Plant.*
  Phylum. *Thallophyta.*
    Subphylum. *Fungi.*
      Class. *Fungi Imperfecti.* Do not produce sexual spores.
        Order. *Moniliales.* Yeast forms only, or with pseudomycelium or true mycelium. Reproduce by fission, budding, or by formation of asexual spores.

Families, Subfamilies, and Genera of *Moniliales.*

Family I. *Cryptococcaceae.* Yeast forms only or with pseudomycelium and/or true mycelium. Not forming carotinoid pigments.

Subfamily A. *Cryptococcoideae.* Without pseudomycelium, or with only traces. No blastospores budding from mycelium.

  I. Cells lemon-shaped, bipolar budding.
    Genus *Kloeckera*

  II. Cells triangular, budding from angles.
    Genus *Trigonopsis*

  III. Cells flask-shaped, single buds with a broad base.
    Genus *Pityrosporum*

  IV. Cells round, oval, or cylindrical.
    A. No pellicle in liquid media, or a soft moist pellicle after a long time.
      Genus *Cryptococcus*
    B. Pellicle dry, wrinkled, in liquid media.
      1. Cells cylindrical, buds not separated by fission from mother cell.
        Genus *Mycoderma*
      2. Cells polymorphous, buds separated by fission from mother cell.
        Genus *Schizoblastosporion*

Subfamily B. *Candidiodeae.* Yeast forms with pseudomycelium and/or true mycelium, forming blastospores, arthrospores, or both.

 I. Blastospores regularly produced; arthorspores not produced.

   Genus *Candida*

 II. Both blastospores and arthrospores produced.

   Genus *Trichosporon*

 III. Arthrospores regularly, blastospores rarely, if ever, produced.

   Genus *Geotrichum*

Family II. *Nectaromycetaceae.* Forming pseudomycelium, and conidia on the aerial surface of the colonies.

   Genus *Nectaromyces*

Family III. *Rhodotorulaceae.* No conidia. Yeast forms with or without pseudomycelium. Carotinoid pigments formed. Nonfermentive. Not germinating by repetition.

   Genus *Rhodotorula*

Family IV. *Sporobolomycetaceae.* Yeast forms without true mycelium, reproducing by budding and also germinating by repetition; as do the basidiospores of many of the *Tremallales,* of which these forms may be regarded as imperfect species. Nonfermentive.

 A. Vegetative growth with rose, red, or salmon carotinoid pigments. Spores more or less compressed laterally, kidney- or pear-shaped, asymmetric.

   Genus *Sporobolomyces*

  1. No pseudomycelium.

   Subgenus *Sporobolomyces, sensu stricto*

  2. Pseudomycelium produced.

   Subgenus *Blastoderma*

 B. Vegetative growth white, cream, straw, or yellow with no trace of red. Spores round, ovoid, or globular, symmetrical.

   Genus *Bullera*

INDEX

Accessory substances (vitamins), 68–69
Acetic acid, 182–185
Acetobacter, 182–185
Acetone, 198–199
Acetyl-methyl-carbinol, 337
Acid-fast bacteria, 60
Acids: in food preservation, 296–298, 328, 338–343
   in food spoilage, 303, 306–309
   influence on microorganisms, 86–87, 113, 213–214, 228, 231
   produced by fermentation, 182–185, 193–197
   produced in milk, 327–332, 338–343
   produced in soils, 219–223, 228, 234–236
Actinomycetaceae, 61–62, 473–474
Actinomycetales (actinomycetes, or mold-like bacteria), cause of potato scab, 440
   cause of tuberculosis, 392–396, 414–416
   description of, 60–62, 473–474
   in soil, 216–217, 221, 224
Activated sludge, 267–271
Aedes, 376, 406
Aerobacter, 279
   in foods, 307
   in milk, 320, 322–323, 329–330
   in water, 279–280
Aerobes, definition of, 76
   discovery of, 447
Aerosols, 125, 281
Agar, 36, 131–132, 452
Agglutination test, 361, 401, 413, 416–417
Agglutinins, definition of, 361
   in Brucellosis, 401, 413
   in pullorum disease, 416–417
Aggressins, 353
Agitation, effect on microorganisms, 105
Agrobacterium tumefaciens, 439–440
Air, contamination of milk from, 321–322
   microbiology of, 280–281
   transmission of pathogens by, 374–376
AIV silage, 297–298
Alcaligenes viscosus, 329
Alcohol, amylo process of manufacture, 203
   ethyl, effect on microorganisms of, 112
   ethyl, produced by fermentation, 197

Alcohol—(*Continued*)
   butyl, produced by fermentation, 198–199
Aldehydes, effect on microorganisms, 112–113
Ale, 181–182
Algae, description and occurrence of, 35–38
   in soil, 216–217
   in water, 35, 259, 273
   nitrogen fixing, 238–240
   Nostoc, 238, 240
Alkalies, influence on microorganisms, 86–87, 111–112
   treatment of utensils with, 323
Allergies, 369
Ammonification, 223–224
Ammonium salts, bacteria oxidizing, 227–229
   formation in soil, 223–224
   use in soil, 224, 227–229, 231–234
Amebic dysentery, 260, 378
Amoeba, 53, 54, 260
Amphitrichous, 20
Amylase, 71, 73, 169, 181, 202–203, 220
Anaerobes, anaerobic conditions, methods of securing, 144–147
   cause of disease by, 349, 352–353, 381–382, 403–404
   cause of food spoilage by, 306, 314–318
   definition of, 76
   discovery of, 447
   in industrial processes, 186–187, 198–199
   in milk, 320, 322, 329–331
   in soil, 213, 214–215, 238–240
   isolation and cultivation of, 143–147
Anaphylaxis, 368
Ångstrom unit, 104
Anguillula aceti, 185
Anopheles, 376, 409
Anthrax, 417–418
Anthrax bacillus, 417–418
Antibiotics, 121–124, 199–202
Antibodies, 361–362, 390–391
Antigen, 361–362, 365–368, 390
Antiseptic, 96, 449
Antiserum, 361–362, 368–369, 390
Antitoxin, 361, 399, 400, 404, 452
Apple scab, 431, 433